In Praise of *Francesco*

"There are any number of dry saint biographies that are meticulously researched but leave much to be desired as stories. There are still more that are filled with conjecture and assumption, often without even telling a compelling story. *Francesco* takes what's best in both traditions, combining captivating storytelling with many years of research. What a relief to read a novelized hagiography and not second-guess each paragraph, wondering which scenes took place only in the author's imagination. Madeline Nugent includes notes at the end of each chapter, describing which sources provide which material and which details are speculation, leaving the reader with the conviction that she has met the true Francis in these pages. The modern Church needs Saint Francis to call her to holiness—not the bunny-snuggling Francis of our statues and storybooks, but the real, raw, joyful, penitent Francis portrayed in *Francesco*."

—Meg Hunter-Kilmer, author of *Pray for Us: 75 Saints Who Sinned, Suffered, and Struggled on Their Way to Holiness*

"There are countless books written about my seraphic father, Francesco. However, Madeline's wonderful work unleashes the potential to take you places you haven't dared to dream of going. You can feel, as she writes, 'as free as birds, enveloped in God's love.' Hallelujah!"

—Fr. Stan Fortuna, CFR, preacher, musician, and founder of Francesco Productions

"There will always be new books about the saint of Assisi. Eight hundred years after his passing from time to eternity, Francesco di Pietro di Bernardone continues to attract and fascinate. The personality of the Poverello is so rich that studies and publications, as good and deep as they can be, never satiate the interest he generates. With this book, Madeline Nugent gives us an original approach to the life and the spirit of Brother Francis. Basing her work on the primary sources and on the most recent scholarship, she connects the different stages of

Francis' life with major pieces of his sayings and writings. She also literally re-creates events that happened by staging them with a blend of historic and fictional characters. The result is a biography of Francis that is accurate, lively, and deeply spiritual. Enjoy the reading!"

— Jean-François Godet-Calogeras, Franciscan studies professor emeritus,
Saint Bonaventure University

"Get to know Saint Francis of Assisi through the eyes of those whose lives he touched. Each vignette in Madeline Nugent's carefully researched biography shows Francis' impact on others. You'll feel like a participant in every fascinating scene. A wonderful story!"

— Barb Szyszkiewicz, author of *The Handy Little Guide to Prayer*
and editor at CatholicMom.com

FRANCESCO

FRANCESCO

A Story *of* Saint Francis *of* Assisi

By Madeline Pecora Nugent, *cfp*

BOOKS & MEDIA
Boston

Library of Congress Control Number: 2021951754
CIP data is available.

ISBN 10: 0-8198-2754-1
ISBN 13: 978-0-8198-2754-8

Cover design by Ryan McQuade

Published by Pauline Books & Media, 50 Saint Pauls Avenue, Boston, MA 02130-3491

Printed in the U.S.A.

www.pauline.org

Pauline Books & Media is the publishing house of the Daughters of St. Paul, an international congregation of women religious serving the Church with the communications media.

1 2 3 4 5 6 7 8 9 26 25 24 23 22

In gratitude to Fr. Julian Stead, OSB, who was
spiritually part of this book from its conception until completion.
May God grant him the reward of his many years of faith and service
to God's people.

Contents

Part Two

And Every Talent and Power and Knowledge That He Thought He Had Will Be Taken Away from Him

Part Three

Most High, Glorious God, Enlighten the Darkness of My Heart

Part Four

And Afterward I Delayed a Little and Left the World

Part Five

O How Glorious It Is to Have a Holy and Great Father in Heaven!

Part Six

And the Lord Gave Me Such Faith in Churches

Part Seven

The Lord Gave Me Some Brothers

Part Eight

Let Everyone Remain in That Trade and Office in Which He Has Been Called

Part Nine

And I Had This Written Down Simply and in a Few Words and the Lord Pope Confirmed This for Me

Part Ten

To All Christian Religious People: Clergy and Laity, Men and Women, and to All Who Live in the Whole World

Part Eleven

Do Not Look at the Life Without, for That of the Spirit Is Better

Part Twelve

Promises Obedience and Reverence to the Lord Pope Innocent and His Successors

Part Thirteen

Who Desires by Divine Inspiration to Go
Among the Saracens and Other Nonbelievers

Part Fourteen

I Firmly Wish to Obey the General Minister of This Fraternity

Part Fifteen

Let Us Produce Worthy Fruits of Penance

Part Sixteen

A Servant of God Can Be Known to Have the Spirit of the Lord in This Way

Part Seventeen

Brother Francis, a Worthless and Weak Man, Your Very Little Servant

Foreword

Reading the lives of the saints is a devotion going as far back as late antiquity and the early Middle Ages. Meditating on the "legends" helps Christians connect with the saints—and through them, Christ—in a way that is spiritually nourishing. Books on the life of Saint Francis are no exception.

In 1228, Pope Gregory IX declared Francis a saint and commissioned an erudite friar in the Order, Thomas of Celano, to write the first "*Vita*" (Life). Soon after, several close companions of Francis wrote what became known as "The Legend of the Three Companions." Concurrently, Thomas of Celano wrote a second *Vita* of Francis. In the following decades, more accounts of the life of Francis emerged. Some of these, however, presented divergent accounts of the person of Francis, reflecting partisan divisions within the Order. Finally, in 1263, the scholarly minister general of the Order, Saint Bonaventure, composed what he declared to be the "official" biography of Francis and ordered the destruction of all previous *Vitae*.

A century or so later, the "*Fioretti*" ("the Little Flowers of Saint Francis") was written. This popular collection of stories about Francis was written in typical medieval hagiographical fashion. It was less concerned with accuracy and more focused on otherworldly miracles and supernatural phenomena in order to elevate Francis as a model of holiness as conceptualized in that era. And it was largely this "version" of Francis that survived the centuries. From the fourteenth through the late nineteenth century, knowledge of Francis was largely limited to tales from the *Fioretti* and images on dusty icons and fading frescoes.

But this all changed in the late nineteenth century beginning with the French clergyman and historian, Paul Sabatier. During the rational Enlightenment, intellectuals developed the historical method to study medieval subjects, knowledge of which was previously based on faith and tradition. Sabatier's conclusions, however, reflected his biases as an anti-Catholic Huguenot, so the Catholic Church placed his breakthrough work on the life of Saint Francis on the Index of Prohibited Books, where it remained until the dissolution of the Index in 1966.

Shortly after Sabatier's research, Catholic and Franciscan scholars began to use the same historical method to research the life of Francis, both to rebut Sabatier's theses as well as to arrive at a truer understanding of who Francis really was. This began a period of critical research and modern biographies of the life of Saint Francis.

Countless books on Francis followed. However, just as the original medieval *Vitae* had their issues, the twentieth century books also vary wildly. In fact, many of the modern biographies of Saint Francis seem to be written about different people. The Francis who emerges is vastly different from one book to the next, revealing every conceivable bias inside and outside the Church.

Lately, it seems that a fresh new style—a genre, if you will—of writing about Francis is emerging, one that skirts many of the tired controversies and polemics of the contemporary biographies. Francis is not pushed as an early social reformer who bucks institutions and hierarchies; nor is he a humble subordinate who submits himself fully and meekly as an instrument at the service of the Church. Instead, readers are taken back in time and placed squarely in Francis' milieu where they can make up their own minds about who Francis was. This is the approach Madeline Pecora Nugent uses in her captivating new book, *Francesco: A Story of Saint Francis of Assisi.*

Drawing on the early medieval sources—the "histories," as she refers to them—Nugent brings the thirteenth century to life with creativity and sensitivity. Though the word "medieval" is often used pejoratively in contemporary English (synonymous with "cruel, uncivilized, or irrational"), the Middle Ages were a fascinating period, and the High Middle Ages even more so.

Francis lived during the *age of chivalry*: armored knights on horses; swords and shields; castles and damsels; tournaments and hunts; heraldry and banners;

honor, mercy, courtesy, courage, justice. Minstrels meandered through towns, singing of the deeds of greats like Galahad, Arthur, Lancelot, and Tristan.

It was the age of the merchant. Feudalism—the outdated class system that maintained wealth and privilege in the families of the landed nobility—was being forced to reckon with the realities of the markets. Merchants and artisans were moving about, buying and selling their wares in city marketplaces, and making massive amounts of money. Thus, the economy was changing from a land-based system to one based on money.

It was the age of renewed mobility. Migrations and invasions that had plagued the earlier Middle Ages had subsided and people were safer and freer to move about. Thus, the roads were teeming with merchants, pilgrims, crusaders, preachers, and wandering minstrels.

It was the age of communal conflicts. Emboldened by their new wealth and status, the merchants (and other middle-class minors) were rising up everywhere and tearing down the old feudal castles—symbols and sources of their oppression. In place of the fortresses, they established independent city municipalities known as the *comune.*

It was the age of religion. The High Middle Ages were a golden age for Christendom. Soaring cathedrals, abbeys, and monasteries were under construction, and religious communities and movements were flourishing everywhere. City squares were forums for lay preachers and clerics alike who preached penance and salvation. Local pilgrims headed to nearby shrines to ask their saints for intercession, while the courageous set out on the journey of a lifetime to Compostela, Rome, Gargano, or Jerusalem. Conflict often broke out as heterodox and schismatic groups were denounced and excommunicated by the appropriate religious authority. Popes easily launched Crusades, setting off zealous knights and peasants alike to liberate the Holy Land.

In this dynamic world Francis lived and experienced his conversion. Before his conversion—when he was guided by the spirit of the world—he, too, sought the glories of knighthood and crusading. Yet, after a series of transcendent dreams, voices, and visions, he chose another way—that of serving lepers and embracing penance.

Nugent captures all this masterfully in her book. She makes this world accessible to the contemporary English reader who may have little to no familiarity with this period of history. She drops colorful names of people and places, carefully describes dress and trades, and reveals cultural and historical details that only a well-researched writer could do.

With keen insight, she tells the story not as a biographer, but through the narration of people who were present at the scene. This not only makes for delightful reading, but also serves to highlight the communal aspect of Francis' story, as nothing he did was in isolation.

This latest work on Saint Francis could easily enter the Franciscan annals as a classic . . . and I hope it does.

Bret Thoman, OFS
Director of Saint Francis Pilgrimages
(www.stfrancispilgrimages.com)
December 13, 2019

Acknowledgments

Thanks to:

New City Press for allowing me to quote Francis' words from *Francis of Assisi: Early Documents,* edited by Regis J. Armstrong, J. A. Wayne Hellmann, and William J. Short, Hyde Park, New York, 2000.

McKillop Library Staff at Salve Regina University, Newport, Rhode Island, for their patient and diligent help in obtaining a plethora of requested articles and books consulted in the writing of this book.

Dr. Alexander Calenda and Mark Wilson for translating certain words and phrases into Italian.

Jean-François Godet-Calogeras for his many insights, patience, and scholarly help and for reading this manuscript and sharing his excellent insights and knowledge.

Bret Thoman, OFS, for his expertise in knowing the life and places of Saint Francis and for his insights into the Umbrian language used at the time of the saint. Thanks to Bret also for reading this manuscript and offering many insightful suggestions and corrections. This book would be far less accurate without his editing.

Sister Karolyn Grace, PSSC, and Sister Celeste Marie, PSSC, for reading this manuscript and sharing it with the other Poor Sisters of Saint Clare, all of whose prayers, suggestions, and insights have proven invaluable.

Paolo Rossi for his information on Giovanni the Simple, Madonna Jacopa dei Settesoli, and others.

Father Paolo Degasperi for translating several articles into English.

Brother Eunan McMullan, OFM, for his information about the cave at San Damiano.

My husband Jim, who consistently brought home works from McKillop Library that I could use and who—along with our children, whom I also thank—patiently supported the time spent on this work.

Tim Luncsford, who worked overtime to renovate the space where most of this writing took place.

Pauline Books & Media, who patiently waited over ten years for this manuscript.

All those who prayed for this effort.

Above all, thanks to the Lord, without Whom this book would never have been completed.

Madeline Pecora Nugent, CFP,
Queenship of Mary, August 22, 2019

Introductory Material

Early Franciscan Sources

This book attempts to portray, as accurately as possible, how Francis and his followers lived. Since his contemporaries would know this best, primary sources from the decades following the death of Saint Francis were the main documents used for researching this book.

Francis' first biographer, Friar Thomas of Celano, writing within three years of the saint's death, produced a fresh, no-holds-barred story referred to as the *First Life of Saint Francis* (abbreviated 1C). He wrote at the request of Pope Gregory IX, formerly Cardinal Ugolino, who knew Francis well and who canonized him. Thomas of Celano interacted with Saint Francis and held positions of responsibility and leadership in the Order during the later years of Francis' life. Thomas apparently interviewed those who knew Francis, particularly Brother Elias, and used their recollections as well as his own to compose the saint's first biography.

There are some historians who believe that, in his first biography, Celano intended to make Francis' life correspond to that of previous holy men. For example, implying that Francis was a depraved youth compares him to Saint Augustine. Having Francis disrobe before the bishop recalls how, according to Saint John Cassian, new recruits to desert monasticism were stripped of their clothing and then reclothed in monastery dress. However, Francis died on October 3, 1226, and on February 25, 1229, Pope Gregory IX approved 1C as the official biography of the saint. The people of Assisi protested being negatively portrayed in the account, but no one claimed that Francis' disrobing before the bishop or his initial rejection by his father and his native city was fiction. Assisi witnessed and knew the sad facts.

Thomas of Celano condensed his biography into a shorter work, at the request of Minister General Friar Elias, for short readings for the friars to share at mealtimes. This work (abbreviated 1.5C) was lost for centuries. Only recently did Franciscan scholar Jacques Dalarun find and publish it as *The Rediscovered Life of Saint Francis of Assisi.*

This work was followed by a number of other texts, including:

1240–1241: *The Anonymous of Perugia* (abbreviated AP), composed by Friar John of Perugia, who was an acquaintance of Friar Bernard of Assisi, Francis' first follower, and a companion of Friar Giles, Francis' third follower.

1241–1247: *The Legend of the Three Companions* (abbreviated L3C), composed by three of Saint Francis' early followers, Friars Leo, Angelo, and Rufino.

1244–1260: *The Assisi Compilation* (abbreviated AC), seemingly compiled by Friars Leo, Angelo, Rufino, and possibly others.

Some of these were compiled by friars whose years of life with Saint Francis gave them intimate insights into his life. However, political intrigues in the Order, and the allegiances of the tale-tellers, influence the portrayal of certain incidents and personalities.

In 1247, Thomas of Celano wrote another work, *The Remembrance of the Desire of a Soul* (abbreviated 2C), which combines material found in the previously mentioned sources while also adding details.

As time passed, the biographies tended to sanitize the early life of Francis, so that, by the time one reads Bonaventure's *Major Legend of Saint Francis* (abbreviated LMj, written 1260–1263), the early Francis has been transformed from a sinful, arrogant dandy into a happy-go-lucky, innocent youth. Incidents that reflected poorly on the saintly qualities of a holy man were altered or eliminated.

When Bonaventure's *Major Legend* was determined to be the definitive life, Bonaventure, as minister general of the Order, ordered the destruction of all previous biographies. Fortunately, a few manuscripts escaped destruction.

These early biographies, plus Francis' own writings, have been intensely studied by modern Franciscan scholars, and a fuller and more accurate picture of Saint Francis is emerging.

Additional early sources that were used in researching this book include: *Thirteenth Century Chronicles* (abbreviated 13CC), the *Mirror of Perfection* (Lemmens Edition, abbreviated 1MP), *Treatise on the Miracles of Saint Francis* (3C), The *Major Legend* by Saint Bonaventure (abbreviated LMj), *The Little Flowers of Saint Francis* (abbreviated *Fioretti*, its name in Italian), and *Chronicle of the Twenty-Four Generals of the Order of Friars Minor* (abbreviated 24Gen).

Of the many works listed in the bibliography, two secondary sources that were important in researching this book are the following:

Arnaldo Fortini (abbreviated Fortini), Assisi mayor and historian, delved into Assisi archives and shared his research in *Nova Vita di San Francesco* (1926, revised edition 1959), translated by Helen Moak (1980). References to Fortini refer to the English translation.

Raffaele Pazzelli (abbreviated Pazzelli), in his book *Saint Francis and the Third Order*, locates Francis directly within the penitential movement of his time.

This book attempts to help the reader understand Francis as those who knew him may have experienced him. They, like us, had their own preconceived notions, prejudices, and concerns that influenced their perceptions. May one or more of Francis' acquaintances resonate with you personally, and may their experiences assist you in your own spiritual journey.

Notes on the Chronology

Certain dates in the life of Saint Francis, like the dates of the Fourth Lateran Council and the date of Francis' death, are recorded in history, but the exact dates for many other events in his life are uncertain. This book generally follows the chronology in the French edition of *Early Documents* with emendations suggested by Jean-François Godet-Calogeras, professor emeritus, theology and Franciscan studies, at Saint Bonaventure University (Saint Bonaventure, New York) and general editor of *Franciscan Studies*.

Francesco: A Story of Saint Francis of Assisi helps the reader to see Francis through the eyes of his contemporaries, without replicating events covered in *Chiara: A Story of Saint Clare of Assisi* and *Antonio: A Story of Saint Anthony of Padua*. Although *Francesco* can be read on its own, reading all three books will give a more complete picture of Saint Francis' life and influence.

Incidents covered more completely in the other books are:

1200: Civil uprising in Assisi. *Chiara: A Story of Saint Clare of Assisi*, chapters 1 and 2

1205: Francis' recovery after the battle of Colle della Strada. *Chiara*, chapter 4

1206: Francis disrobing before the bishop. *Chiara*, chapter 5

1210: Rufino joins Francis and his brothers. *Chiara*, chapter 7

1210: Clare begins to meet with Francis. *Chiara*, chapter 8

1212: Clare's entering religious life and the bishop's and Francis' role in assisting her. *Chiara*, chapters 10–11

1212: Francis' receiving Clare's sister Catherine (renamed Agnes) into religious life. *Chiara*, chapter 13

1215: The Fourth Lateran Council, as it affected Francis and his brothers and Clare and her sisters. *Chiara*, chapter 17

1216: Porziuncula Indulgence. *Chiara*, chapter 22

1220: New regulations in Francis' Order while he was in the Holy Land. *Chiara*, chapter 25

1220: First Franciscan martyrs and reception of Anthony of Padua into the Order. *Antonio: A Story of Saint Anthony of Padua*, chapter 1

1221: Gathering of friars in Chapter at the Porziuncula. *Antonio*, chapter 4

1221: Francis' referring a potential sister to Clare and Clare's misgivings. *Chiara*, chapter 28

1224: Changes, unapproved by Francis, being made to friars' lifestyle. *Antonio*, chapter 11

1225: Francis' stay at San Damiano while suffering from eye disease and other illnesses. *Chiara*, chapters 31–32

1225: Francis' role in reconciling the bishop and mayor of Assisi. *Chiara*, chapters 33–34

1225: Francis' leaving San Damiano for treatment of his eye disease. *Chiara*, chapter 35

1226?: Friar martyred with Rule in his hand. *Antonio*, chapter 15

1226: Francis' body carried to San Damiano after his death. *Chiara*, chapter 36

Francesco: A Story of Saint Francis of Assisi omits some familiar incidents, such as Francis' being born in a stable, an Assisi simpleton throwing his cloak to the ground in front of the unconverted young merchant, and Francis taming the wolf of Gubbio. These and other stories are found only in later biographies. Historians question their accuracy, feeling that later biographers may have fabricated these incidents to portray Francis as an image of Christ. Due to space constraints, this book also omits hundreds of other incidents recorded in the histories and local traditions as well as hundreds of Francis' recorded words.

Helpful Cultural Information

Biblical Quotations: At the time of Saint Francis, there were no standard verse divisions in the Bible and standardized chapter divisions were just being introduced. In this book, biblical quotes are taken from the *Revised Standard Version, Catholic Edition*, except when they are part of a quotation from the writings of Saint Francis or another early source. The citations are given in the chapter notes found at the end of each chapter.

Canonical Hours: Time was divided into three-hour segments. The friars, like all penitents, clergy, and religious at the time, prayed, at specific "hours," certain set prayers called "offices." The modern name for the "hour" is given in parentheses:

Matins (Office of Readings): First prayer of the morning, usually combined with Lauds

Lauds (Morning Prayer): Prayer at dawn

Prime (This office is no longer prayed): 6 a.m.

Terce (Midmorning Prayer): 9 a.m.

Sext (Midday Prayer): Noon

None (Midafternoon Prayer): 3 p.m.

Vespers (Evening Prayer): between 3 and 6 p.m.

Compline (Night Prayer): 9 p.m. or when darkness was falling

Capitalization: All pronouns referring to God, Christ, and the Holy Spirit are capitalized except those which Francis or his copyists did not capitalize in his quoted writings.

Chapter Notes: Chapter Notes at the end of each chapter provide important and interesting background information. They indicate some of the major references used in that chapter, including the source of the words of Saint Francis, and distinguish material in the historical record from what is supposition. In these notes, the references generally refer to the earliest mention of the incident in the Franciscan historical record. Later histories may also mention and often expand, the incident or information.

Horses: Just as modern society has many different models of cars, so medieval society had many different types of horses. Some types mentioned in this book are:

Courser: Light, fast horse, better for hard battle than a destrier

Destrier: Royalty of medieval horses. They were expensive, strong, agile, used for jousts

Palfrey: Ideal riding horse with comfortable gait

Rouncey: Least expensive war horse, also used as a pack animal

Locations: All places are in Italy unless otherwise mentioned. Some less familiar locations are:

Slavonia: Region in the eastern part of Croatia

Spalatum: Modern day city of Split in Croatia

Names and language: In order to give this book the "flavor" of the places in it, the text uses the current native language for the names of book characters, certain titles and phrases, and churches. (The names of nations, cities, and towns are current English usage.) The "native" names and words used, however, likely do not accurately reflect the language and dialects of the time.

People are named in relation to their ancestors. In Umbrian, Francesco di Pietro di Bernardone means "Francis, son of Peter who is the son of Bernard."

Social Class: Medieval people were honored according to their social class, e.g., emperor, king, queen, lord, lady, baron, count. In the Church, clergy were also ranked: pope, cardinal, bishop, priest, deacon, cleric. The term "prelate" referred to any religious authority. The poor had no titles.

Social Mores: Power rested with the nobles, high religious leaders, and military. The merchants and middle classes were attempting to rise in power. The lower classes were powerless and generally disregarded. Below them were the beggars and then, at the lowest social level, the lepers, robbers, and other outcasts.

Clothing indicated social status and rank. The greatest scandal would be to go without clothing, not because nudity was sexually enticing (people slept in the nude, even in hospices where strangers shared beds) but because it indicated destitution and humiliation.

Stages of becoming a religious order: Francis began his conversion as a voluntary penitent. His first brothers were also lay penitents. However, penitents generally lived in their own homes, not in community. As Francis gained followers who lived a common life with him, their group began to resemble a *religio*.

Religio was the canonical term applied to a group of Christians who lived together a faithful life with certain common practices. The Church monitored a religio closely. Should it become sufficiently organized, a religio could become an approved *ordine* (religious order). The Church required a religio to submit a written rule of life, which the Church had to approve, before designating a religio as an ordine.

Time: In Francis' time, the new year began on March 25, the feast of the Annunciation. However, because that system confuses modern readers, the years in this book reflect current usage.

Titles: The part titles in this book are Francis' own words, taken from his writings.

Translation of Italian Words Used

Castello—Castle and its walled village

Comune—City-states that developed throughout northern and central Italy in the twelfth century

Custos (Latin)—Provincial minister (minister of one of the Franciscan Provinces)

Del, della—"Of" (the Piazza della San Rufino means the Plaza of the Cathedral of Saint Rufinus)

Dom—Title of respect for secular and diocesan priests

Domina—Lady (formal title) used for noble girls and women

Fra (shortened from Fratello, Frate)—Colloquial name for a religious brother

Frater—Latin name given to Benedictine monks who were not priests

Fraternità—Brotherhood

Grazie—Thank you

Locus—A "location." The name the friars used for a place where they lived. These "locations" were not really hermitages, but definitely not convents or monasteries. Plural "loci."

Madonna—Informal term for My Lady (used for noble girls and women)

Mamma—Mommy, Mum

Mercato—Marketplace

Messer—Old Umbrian title of respect for a man: Mister, Sir, Lord

Monte—Mountain

Mostaccioli—Almond cookies

Ordine—Religious Order

Pace e bene—Italian for the Latin greeting "Pax et bonum," which means "Peace and all good." This was the greeting that Saint Francis used.

Palazzo—Palace

Papà—Daddy

Pater—Latin title for Benedictine monks who were priests

Piazza—Wide-open space where several city streets meet, plaza, city square

Podestà—Head of the comune with a council to advise him

Poggio—Knoll

Porta—City gate

Porziuncula—Little portion of land

Religio—An intermediary stage in becoming a religious order

Rivo—Stream, brook

Rivo Torto—Twisted stream

San—Saint

Sì—Yes

Strada—Street

Vescovado—Bishop's residence

Via—Street, road

Zuchetto—Roman Catholic cleric's skullcap, black for a priest, purple for a bishop, red for a cardinal, and white for the pope

Penance—Then and Now

Penance means conversion as well as the sacrificial methods that foster it, such as fasting from food, giving alms, confessing sins, praying, living chastely, having minimal possessions, and doing good works.

Modern minds associate the season of Lent with penance. Lent is a time to see where one has strayed from following God, then do what is necessary to draw closer to Him. However, we are called to conversion and good works, not only during Lent, but always. Penance turns us away from self-indulgence and toward God.

For many people in Francis' time, penance was more than a seasonal practice. Since they saw hell as a very real possibility for those who sinned seriously, penance was appealing as a means of gaining heaven through expiating serious sins. By defeating sinful human desires, penance also kept a person from seriously sinning again.

In medieval times, those who confessed grave sins were enrolled in the Order of Penitents, a recognized order in the Church, until completing the satisfaction given for the forgiveness of these sins. Penitents who had sinned mortally might be told, for example, to make a pilgrimage (or pilgrimages) to holy places, to build a hospital or a church, or to abstain from conjugal relations for a time.

Before Francis was born, a great penitential movement began to sweep Europe. No one knows exactly how it began, but many people began to see the need for a deeper relationship with God and realized that living a penitential life was a means to that end. Because they had not sinned mortally, they were not required to enter the Order of Penitents. Nevertheless, many lay people voluntarily began to live penitential lives because they wished to distance themselves from worldly concerns. Voluntary penitents embraced prayer, fasting, abstinence from food, simplicity of life, and doing good works as disciplines to help them surrender their own wills to God. Francis began his conversion as one of these voluntary penitents.

The Lay Franciscan Charism Today

An Internet search will reveal numerous Franciscan male and female religious orders, some of which evolved from Francis' original foundation and others that are trying to live his original expression today. Lay expressions of the Franciscan charism include not only the largest group, the Secular Franciscan Order (OFS), but also many smaller ones. Those seeking a lifestyle resembling that of Francis' first lay followers, several of whom appear in this book, may wish to consult the Confraternity of Penitents, whose members "live the Rule of 1221 as closely as possible to its original intent." For more information, see www.penitents.org or write to Confraternity of Penitents, 1702 Lumbard Street, Fort Wayne, IN 46803 U.S.A.

Abbreviations for Primary Sources Referenced in the Chapter Notes

1C: *The Life of Saint Francis* by Friar Thomas of Celano.

1.5C: *The Rediscovered Life of Saint Francis of Assisi* (the name given by Franciscan scholar Jacques Dalarun), also by Friar Thomas of Celano.

AP: *The Anonymous of Perugia*, composed by Friar John of Perugia.

L3C: *The Legend of the Three Companions*, composed by three of Saint Francis' early followers, Friars Leo, Angelo, and Rufino.

AC: *The Assisi Compilation*, seemingly compiled by Friars Leo, Angelo, Rufino, and possibly others.

2C: *The Remembrance of the Desire of a Soul* by Thomas of Celano.

13CC: *Thirteenth Century Chronicles.*

1MP: *Mirror of Perfection* (Lemmens Edition).

3C: *Treatise on the Miracles of Saint Francis.*

LMj: The *Major Legend* by Saint Bonaventure.

Fioretti: *The Little Flowers of Saint Francis* (abbreviated by its name in Italian).

24Gen: *Chronicle of the Twenty-Four Generals of the Order of Friars Minor.*

Fortini: Arnaldo Fortini, Assisi mayor and historian, delved into Assisi archives and shared his research in *Nova Vita di San Francesco.*

Pazzelli: Raffaele Pazzelli, in his book *Saint Francis and the Third Order.*

Prologue

"Let Us All Love the Lord God Who Has Given Us . . . Our Whole Body"

Madonna Pica

Bernardone Stable (Assisi, August 1182)

An obviously pregnant Madonna Pica, holding the hand of her four-year-old son, Angelo, stood near a horse-drawn cart outside the doors to the Bernardone stable. They were waiting for Pica's husband Pietro to emerge with a palfrey he'd selected for this journey to the fair of Saint Ayoul of Provins, held on September 14, the feast of the Exaltation of the Cross. Unless this baby was extremely late in coming, Pietro would be away for the birth.

Leading his favorite roan, Pietro strode out of the stable. "Last fair before winter," he proclaimed, taking Pica's hand and kissing it. She knew what he'd say next, what he said before every business trip: "Madonna, I'll bring back the best."

"Of course," she smiled.

"I'll have those fabrics sold before the spring fair at Bar-sur-Abe."

"Certainly," Pica said.

Pietro stroked Angelo's black hair. "Take good care of mamma. When I return, you and mamma will have a surprise for me."

Angelo looked blankly at Pica. Of course, the baby would be a surprise for Angelo as well.

Pietro swung himself into the saddle. Decked out in blue and purple, he reminded Pica of a giant plum. Nodding to his family, Pietro reined his palfrey down the alley while the cart followed, manned by two servants. Outside the city, the threesome would join a caravan of merchants from Orvieto to travel to France. They found safety in numbers on roads frequented by thieves.

"God be with you!" Pica called. She started back toward the house with Angelo scuffling behind.

Every time Pietro left on a business trip, worry needled her. Suppose he died on the journey? Her first husband had been killed in an oxcart accident, leaving her a widow with one-year-old Angelo. God forbid she be widowed again.

With Pietro gone, Pica needed to arrange for Angelo's care. Sending him to help in the shop, she approached Giacomo's house next door and asked to see the mistress, who eagerly agreed to have Angelo play with their son Nicola when the time came for Pica to give birth.

Ten weeks later, Pica was breast-feeding the newborn when she heard Pietro's merry voice at the foot of the stairs that led from the fabric shop to the upstairs living quarters.

"Where's my little Francesco?" She heard a clattering on the steps; Pietro must have been taking them two at a time. Then his short, bulky body burst into the room. Pietro grabbed for the nursling, then, seeming to rethink his intention, knelt on the floor and tenderly stroked the child's cheek.

Gently Pica used her little finger to break the baby's suction on the nipple, then handed the drowsy bundle to Pietro. "Your son, Giovanni di Baptista."

Pietro snatched the child to him with a ferocity more familiar than the tenderness Pica had just seen. "Giovanni! Di Baptista! Your deceased father's name! The name of a saint who dressed in camel's hair! No! My son's name must make people think of fine French fabrics, not camel pelts! He'll be the most renowned cloth merchant in Tuscany!" Pietro's stare bored into Pica. "Never call him Giovanni! Francesco is his name."

NOTES

The quotation on the part page for the prologue is taken from Francis' *Earlier Rule*, chapter XXIII, section 8.

The traditional date given for Francesco's birth is September 26, either 1181 or, more commonly accepted, 1182. The year is extrapolated from 1C (First Book, Chapter I and Second Book, Chapter I). Pietro was away, most likely at a French cloth fair where he'd purchase French fabrics to resell. In Pietro's absence, Pica had the baby baptized Giovanni after John the Baptist (2C, First Book, Chapter I) and possibly after her own father. Angry with the name, Pietro called his son Francesco, "the little Frenchman."

Pica's background is uncertain. Some historians believe that her baptismal name was Jeanne and that she came from the Picardy area of France, which gave her the nickname Pica. Others believe that she was a native of Umbria and that the name "Pica," meaning "magpie," had nothing to do with France.

In his biography of Saint Francis (p. 6), Augustine Thompson notes that, while Francis was always called Francesco di Pietro di Bernardone, Angelo was never called Angelo di Pietro di Bernardone but always Angelo di Pica. This seems to imply that Angelo was Pica's son by a previous marriage and that the citizens of Assisi didn't know Angelo's father. If Angelo's father had died, we don't know how. Nor do we know how Pica met Pietro, nor if Pica's dowry or Pietro's hard work, or both, fostered Pietro's success.

Historians postulate that Pietro was in his early twenties when he fathered Francesco.

If Angelo were Pica's son by an earlier marriage, then he probably was born around 1178. As depicted in the story, it was common practice not to tell children when their mothers were expecting.

Fortini (p. 90, footnote) identifies Nicola di Giacomo as the Bernardones' next-door neighbor. We don't know his age compared to Angelo or Francesco.

Part One

"You Think That You Will Possess This World's Vanities for a Long Time"

1

Messer Pietro di Bernardone

Church of San Nicoló, Assisi (November 1187)

As usual, Mass was endless. If it weren't a mortal sin to miss Mass and work on Sunday, Pietro wouldn't have come. No, he probably would've come because of Francesco who, fidgeting, was clinging to Pietro's leg. Pietro wanted to be the best papà to his son.

A child certainly changes your life, Pietro often thought. Now, besides selling cloth, he had to raise his own flesh and blood to become a man of influence. In twenty years, Francesco would take over and advance Pietro's cloth trade. By then, he might be married and have fathered Pietro's first grandson who, in time, would assume the business from Francesco and continue Pietro's legacy. Time would dim the embarrassing memory of Pietro's father, Bernardone, hacking out a living as a poor *burino* in the Assisi marshes. The young Pietro had toiled on the family property before moving to the city. That land, in addition to many other lands which Pietro's money and Pica's dowry had acquired, would be Francesco's and then his children's after him.

If Francesco lived, of course. Diseases and accidents took many children's lives. Pietro frowned. On his right, the knight Messer Scipione di Offreduccio was standing with his two-year-old son Rufino, alert to the Mass, in front of him. Quiet, well-behaved Rufino! Shy. Prudent. Cautious. He must be easy to rear. Unlike puny, impulsive Francesco. He'd approach stray mongrels, explore anything, and mock sword fight with such determination that Pietro feared he'd be hurt. If disease didn't rob him of his son, Francesco's own impetuousness might.

My God, protect him, Pietro prayed.

The priest Dom Vincenzo's droning burst into a passionate, intense plea. Francesco stirred and stiffened.

What's this? Pietro thought. Hardly six weeks ago, Saladin, leading his Muslim armies, had captured Jerusalem and seized the relic of the true cross. Assisi was still reeling when it heard that grief-stricken Pope Urbano III had died shortly thereafter. Quickly Pope Gregorio VIII had been elected. Now he was calling for a Third Crusade? Crusaders were to wear penitential garb? Dom Vincenzo was hammering out suggestions. Join the Crusade! If that's impossible, do penance for the Crusade's success! Attend Matins! Abstain from meat! Give alms! Pray!

Pietro groaned. He had a family and a business. He wasn't going to join a Crusade! At the time of Matins, he was already working. Let Pica attend! Not eat meat, his favorite food? Give more alms to the poor? They already had enough. Pray? He didn't have time.

When Mass ended, Pietro led his little family out of the church. Around him, his neighbors were muttering about the Crusade. He had about as much time to talk about the Crusade as to be in it. Fumbling in his pouch, he pulled out a few coins, which he handed to Francesco and Angelo.

"Do you remember what Dom Vincenzo said?"

"Sì, papà," Angelo nodded.

"And you, my Franceschino?"

"He said to join the Crusade. Are we going?"

Pietro laughed. "No! We're not going! We're going to help the poor instead."

"Papà, there's a poor person!" Francesco was pointing to a figure clothed in a tattered yellow tunic. Pietro recognized the fabric as one he'd sold to the Dodici family. The tunic must have become so worn that the family gave it to the poor.

"May I give him my coins?" Angelo asked.

"Me, too?" Francesco echoed.

Pietro nodded, then felt his large, rough hand squeezed by a softer one. He looked into Pica's smiling face.

"Grazie, Messer."

As the boys dropped Pietro's few coins into the beggar's grimy palms, Pietro grinned with satisfaction.

NOTES

The quotation for Part One is taken from Francis' *Earlier Exhortation to the Brothers and Sisters of Penance (First Version of the Letter to the Faithful)*, 14.

The pope requested that all priests recruit Crusaders and spiritual and financial aid from their congregations. We don't know Pietro's response to this appeal.

According to Fortini, the Offreduccio (p. 329) and Dodici (p. 154) were two noble Assisi families. Rufino was Scipione di Offreduccio's son (Fortini, p. 329), but his birth year is unknown. Several stories about him in the early Franciscan sources indicate that he, when older, was quiet and shy.

History did not record the name of the priest of San Nicoló, nor does it mention any of Francesco's childhood escapades.

2

Messer Giovanni di Sasso

Scuola di San Giorgio, Assisi (September 1195)

Although standing made him appear shorter, Giovanni di Sasso rose from his stool in front of his class and straightened his shoulders. Too diminutive to intimidate his students by height, he relied on sharp, quick gestures. With his slender arms free to gesticulate, he paced in front of his class. "Now we'll see who's learned Psalm 57. Who wrote this psalm?" Several hands shot up. "Morico?"

"Davide, when he was fleeing from King Saul."

"Excellent! Now, who can recite this psalm?"

Few hands were raised this time. "Sabbatino?"

"I know part of it."

"Recite what you know."

Twelve-year-old Sabbatino began in hesitant, awkward Latin. "*Miserere mei, Deus, miserere mei, quoniam in te confidat anima mea.*" Giovanni let the mistake pass. *Confidat* for *confidit* was, for Sabbatino, close enough. After a few more lines and a few more errors, Sabbatino stopped. "I'm not sure of the rest."

"Francesco, can you complete it?" Giovanni asked. Of course, he could. Francesco had achieved the goal of recitation, to commit every psalm to memory. For Sabbatino, that goal was impossible.

In his strong, melodious voice, Francesco began the recitation. Too bad Giovanni wouldn't hear him recite again. Nor would he be able to help Francesco improve his written Latin and master certain math skills. Francesco had just turned fourteen, and his father, wanting him to learn the cloth trade, was taking him out of school. "He's learned enough from you," Pietro declared. "Now he must learn from me."

NOTES

According to legal records discovered by Arnaldo Fortini (p. 95), Giovanni di Sasso was Francesco's instructor at the school at Saint George's Church. We don't know Giovanni's age or physical description or the names of Francesco's classmates.

Learning the Psalter was a primary means of education in a typical lower primary school, such as the one at San Giorgio (Oktavian Schmucki, "Saint Francis's Level of Education").

Francesco's scholastic achievements are postulated according to what we know of his abilities from his writings. Fourteen was the normal age for a young man to leave school and begin his occupation (Pazzelli, p. 75).

3

Grullo

Assisi (Spring 1196)

In this unrelenting famine, Grullo survived better than most. Today Nicola di Giacomo had asked Grullo to mend and polish his boots, a difficult task for an old peasant whose strength had left his arms. But Grullo was clever. He could use the heel of one boot to push the needle through the leather of the other.

Grullo's growling stomach provided incentive, because Nicola, Assisi's prominent young notary, would feed Grullo well when the job was completed. *Ah*, Grullo thought, *God timed this weakness well. The fields will not produce again for some time.*

Grullo didn't know how he knew. But he knew. He knew more than the Assisiani who, ignoring his baptismal name of Bartolo, had dubbed him "Grullo" or "Crazy Man." Crazy, was he? Crazy enough to know that, with his weakened arms, he could no longer plow the soil, hard as steel, nor plant the weakened grain in the dry furrows. He could not haul water from the trickles that used to be streams, nor could he root up tenacious weeds, shrunken and tough, that rivaled grain for dew. Unlike the starving landowners, Grullo owned no property to sell to rich lords or merchants or to wealthy abbeys, monasteries, and churches. He was almost glad that he had no money to spend on food, for even half a turnip cost an outrageous sum.

Grullo was crazy, all right. Crazy enough to find work here or there, repairing a lock, mending pottery, altering clothing, polishing shields. He was his own master, sleeping in churches at night, tinkering by day, and eating what he was given. And because he was deemed crazy, people talked to him and around him of things no one thought he would remember. They were wrong, even though Grullo shared little of what he heard. Sharing could be dangerous.

Here, on the street outside Nicola di Giacomo's house, one could hear tales. Now he was overhearing Rufino and his father Scipione di Offreduccio, and Francesco and his father Pietro di Bernardone, arguing in Pietro's cloth shop across the piazza. Did lords have the right to levy taxes on roads which merchants took to France to obtain their wares? Why did lords have power over a city made prosperous with merchants' money? Didn't people have a right to govern themselves?

The deep voices of the fathers were pitted against one another. But the more tremulous voices of their sons, both just coming into their manhood, didn't always side with them. People had argued their positions in countless places around the city. They would be argued again. Someday, Grullo knew, more than words would be exchanged. Someday, weapons would be drawn, grappling hooks unleashed, and torches lit. The streets of Assisi, so often conquered and overrun by enemies, would run yet again with blood.

Grullo shoved the needle through the leather of Nicola's boot, but he was thinking of the voices in the cloth shop instead of his mending. Scipione and his six brothers were great in power, all of them knights who lived in the *contrada* near the Cathedral of San Rufino. Each lord among them was strong, cunning, fearless, even cruel. Although Scipione was passionate about city affairs, all the knights took part, for they held vast possessions and lands in Assisi. Francesco's father held lands, too. As the wealthiest city merchant, he wielded considerable influence. Rumor had it that Pietro wanted his sons to be lords. One social class buying its way into another! A new social order that would, Grullo knew, reshape Assisi and all of Umbria.

Ah, the arguing had died. The door of Pietro's cloth shop swung open, and Rufino and Francesco, talking excitedly together, strode out.

"Good morning, my lords!" Grullo called as they walked past.

"Lords!" Rufino punched Francesco's shoulder. "He calls you a lord!"

Francesco laughed. "I will be a lord some day! Papà and mamma wish it and so do I!" He made a flourishing bow to Grullo. "Messer Francesco thanks you, Grullo!" Then he laughed again.

"So, Francesco," Rufino chided, "Someday you will be a lord, yet you decry what the lords claim as their rightful due? Shame, Messer Francesco." The young nobleman bowed low to the merchant.

Grullo watched the exchange. He had no idea if Francesco would become a lord or not. He had called the young man what he wanted to hear. Giving people what they wanted led them to give Grullo what he wanted.

"I'll be a lord since Grullo says so!" Francesco grinned. "And a better one than *Mosca-in-cervello*, 'Fly-in-the-brain.'" Francesco gestured in the direction of the count's fortress, Rocca Maggiore, clinging like a hawk's nest to the heights of Monte Subasio.

"Count Conrad may not be as mad as you say," Rufino countered. "Could a madman destroy Monte Rodone? Could he win fame in defense of Perugia?"

"Perugia! You defend our rival city? Grullo, Messer Rufino is defending Perugia!"

Grullo shrugged. The young men really didn't want his opinion.

"I defend nothing," Rufino protested. "I only point out the count's prowess."

"And I point out his capriciousness. What kind of man would kill everyone in Monte Rodone, women and infants alike? You feel safe with him perched up there? Suppose he turns on us?"

"He's not as cruel as you say. When Empress Constance went into labor on her way to join the emperor in Sicilia, Count Conrad opened the Rocca so that she could give birth there!"

"Why not? He's the emperor's kinsman."

"Not every kinsman welcomes his kin," Rufino said. "Think of how many have killed, abused, or rejected relatives, even their own children, for honor or power."

"You're too gentle for a knight, Messer Rufino."

"Perhaps you're right," Rufino admitted. "I don't aspire to greatness as you do. I only aspire to enjoy my dinner."

"Ah, now we agree! What delicacies will be for sale in the mercato? Capicola? Asiago? Mortaroli? Race you!" The young men sprinted forward, leaving Grullo behind.

NOTES

Fortini (pp. 82–83, and 112–113) has found evidence of an unrelenting fifteen-year famine in Umbria, beginning with severe windstorms in 1182.

According to Fortini (p. 90, footnote), Nicola di Giacomo was a notary whose family house adjoined Francesco's.

The seven Offreduccio knights (Fortini names five of them, pp. 328–329), well known in Assisi, likely bought Pietro's cloth. Even though nobles and merchants were in different social classes, Francesco was a leader among his peers, and those peers likely included noblemen his age. Francesco's friends dined with him, laughed with him, and went through the streets of Assisi singing and dancing with him as leader (1C, first book, chapter I, and 2C, first book, chapter III).

The history of wars, taxation, and occupation by the emperor and Count Conrad, nicknamed "Fly-in-the-brain," is in the historical record.

Francesco's skeletal remains in the Basilica of San Francesco indicate that he was about five feet two inches tall. Rufino's remains, also buried in the Basilica, are those of a short, delicate-boned man.

4

Madonna Latuza Sugulla

San Lazzaro d'Arce, Assisi (June 1197)

Dodging questions, Madonna Latuza Sugulla darted into the forest surrounding San Lazzaro d'Arce. Today when the sun was grinning, she wanted to be alone with the poppies.

Latuza pushed her way in the direction of Assisi in which rose her opulent house. There she had entertained her friends and raised her children until being forced into the leper hospital four years ago. Her husband, abandoned like a widower, had given their oldest daughter in marriage two years ago. Their second child would wed in a few weeks. In time, the other three would follow. Latuza could not attend the ceremonies because Assisi statutes forbade lepers to enter the city. Should they try, they would be beaten and driven out. She could see her family only when they visited her. That wasn't often enough.

Tears welled in her eyes. Leaning against an oak's sturdy trunk, Latuza let the tears dribble down her hollow cheeks. Strands of her graying, once luxurious hair danced about her face in the gentle breeze, but she noticed them only when they impeded her vision. Pushing her hair over her shoulders, she remembered that she had come to find the poppies. She kept walking until the woods abruptly ended at a broad field, red with blooms. Ah, she knew she would find such a field. Countless such fields bloomed in June.

Latuza waded out into the poppies, then plopped herself down to sit on their softness. Squirming about, she slid her legs out from under her rough gray tunic and swept them over the poppies and the new grass. She had done this every year since her childhood, always delighting in the softness and scratchiness.

Now she felt hardly anything.

Years into this illness Latuza had stumbled upon its one mixed blessing: the loss of a sense of touch. All that had previously felt prickly seemed now as silken as the French fabrics she used to wear. As a noblewoman from Assisi, she used to feel faint at the sight of blood. But now she could look disinterestedly at the scabs covering her arms and marvel how they neither itched nor ached. Leprosy destroyed physical pain. Why couldn't it also obliterate emotional pain?

It grieved Latuza that leprosy, a punishment for sin, had sullied her reputation. Admittedly, she'd had a wandering eye toward good-looking men. Oh, she'd never done more than greet them politely, but God knew her heart. She must have secretly lusted after those men. That's why God was punishing her. Some male lepers seemed to sense her vulnerability, for more than once she'd had to repel them when they sought to take her honor.

Constant fearfulness and guilt, coupled with isolation from her family, had almost destroyed her faith. Almost, but not quite, for every time she left her cell, she looked at the wooden cross on the door and realized that she was nailed to it along with Jesus. He had given her the same unsought vocation that a priest made clear to each new leper, namely, to live with leprosy and to die on its cross. Like everyone else here, she was required to say when she first entered, "Here is my perpetual resting place. Here I shall live. This is my vow."

Upon entering the hospital, she had been given a leper's tunic, crudely sewn of *gattinello*. How it had irritated her delicate skin as she plodded in dismal procession from the chapel to her cell! Then everything had felt rough—the low bed, small table and chair, wooden bowl, clay pot. The sandals she had to accept in place of her soft shoes were like boar's hair to her tender feet. Now she felt them not at all.

She was pitying herself! *You won't rob me of joy!* Latuza asserted to the disease. She would delight in sunshine on broad fields of red and green. She would warble with birds whose discordant harmonies surrounded her. Her memory would hold everything because, God knew, this disease might yet steal her eyesight.

The sun was dipping toward the horizon when Latuza meandered back to San Lazzaro d'Arce. She took the long way by the road that wound in front of the men's hermitages and then forked off down a narrow path to the women's hospital far in the rear. As she drew near the men's hospital, she spied a horseman quickly approaching. Backing off the road into the scrub, she pulled out of her pouch her *tentennella* which, as was legally required, she began to clap rapidly. The crisp clacking warned passersby that a leper was near.

The dappled palfrey's ears twisted forward at the clacking. A short distance away, the rider reined his mount to a halt. This was no Crucifer Knight, carrying a cross in his left hand and coming from the hospital San Salvatore delle Pareti to tend the lepers at San Lazzaro. Latuza recognized the dandy in red breeches and blue blouse. Only one short young man in Assisi sported such a head of thick black curls that, nevertheless, could not hide his protruding ears.

Francesco di Bernardone had frequently waited on her in his father's fabric shop on the Via Portica. Now he gave no indication of recognizing her. Plunging his hand into a pouch on his saddle, he pulled out a lumpy cloth bag that he flung at Latuza. It landed to her left, splaying open, its coins bouncing into the road. At the same moment, Francesco, holding his nose, reined the palfrey around and headed back toward Assisi.

If leprosy had not robbed her of pride, Madonna Latuza would have reacted to such rudeness by kicking the alms into the scrub. However, she and the other lepers needed this offering. She bent down to gather the coins to bring to the hospital.

NOTES

Poppies are prolific bloomers around Assisi in June. Fortini (p. 206) mentions a leper by the name of Madonna Latuza Sugulla who lived in Assisi during Francesco's early years. We know nothing more about her.

The Crucifer Knights were an order whose members cared for the ill and offered hospitality to pilgrims. Fortini (p. 255) mentions that they were attached to the Hospital of San Salvatore delle Pareti, one of the leper hospitals in the vicinity of Assisi.

Leprosy was considered a punishment for serious sin and not a contagious disease (Richards, 1977, chapter 1). Thus, the Crucifer Knights, penitents, and others could work among the lepers and then return to city life without other people fearing that they were bringing disease with them.

Fortini details how a leper received his or her "vocation," was clothed in *gattinello*, and assigned living quarters (pp. 206–210). Even though citizens were encouraged to give lepers alms, Assisi statutes forbade lepers to enter the city and allowed citizens to beat and run off those who did (Fortini, p. 211).

1C (first book, chapter VII) recounts Francesco's aversion to lepers and that "when he saw their houses even two miles away, he would cover his nose with his hands."

5

Messer Elia di Bonbarone

Tavern, Assisi (June 1197)

Grinning widely, Messer Elia di Bonbarone sat in the approximate center of a cluster of young men in Scolante's tavern. All of them were chatting in ten or more animated conversations. Elia was a head taller than the others. Most of that height was in his long, lean torso and his long, lean face, so he felt part of the din, but also above it.

A man shorter than all the others leaped onto a chair and raised his mug. "To Elia," Francesco called out, "and to his new son, Guiduccio! May he prosper as much and even more so than his papà!"

"Sì! Sì! Congratulations, Elia!" The young men shouted and downed their wine.

Elia could not believe how God had blessed him. Assisi knew Elia's father as Bonbarone, the good baron. He cared well for the simple people who lived and worked in the protective shadow of the family's castle, Beviglie, a few miles north of Assisi. Since Bonbarone wanted his son to learn a trade, Elia was taught carpentry and mattress-making before being sent at age fourteen to study law in Bologna. He so quickly and thoroughly mastered the material that he earned his degree in three years. Now he was back in Assisi, teaching youngsters the arithmetic, geometry, logic, rhetoric, and astrology that he had learned. On the side, he made mattresses and was becoming increasingly involved in city politics. After each busy day, he would enjoy a simple meal with his lovely wife. Now his newborn son added to his joy. Could life get much better?

Ah, the food was coming, paid for by Francesco, who ingeniously found reasons to host parties. Guiduccio's baptism was certainly a legitimate occasion to celebrate. But how about Mattiolo's new fox-fur lined cape that occasioned last week's feast, or Adamo's winning ten dice games in a row, a feat that the youths celebrated last month? No matter, Elia thought. Francesco could celebrate whenever he wanted with his parents' money. They seemed quite willing to let him spend it.

The discordant chatter faded as the celebrants ladled a pottage of mutton, carrots, garlic, cucumber, and parsley onto large, thick squares of bread. Then they pulled their own knives from pouches and dug into the meal. Tavern wenches refilled pitchers of wine and water as quickly as they emptied. Laughter and jesting competed with chomping and burping until appetites were sated, the broth-soaked breads were collected to give to beggars, and someone called for dice. Nobody won ten rounds in a row this time. Elia didn't win even one round.

When the men had enough of dice and drinking, Francesco, as usual, snatched the baton from its corner in the tavern. Then he strutted into the street where his sonorous voice sang out a French troubadour song to which he danced and cavorted, the youths joining in. Elia suspected that Francesco misremembered some words, or perhaps never understood French grammar, but who cared?

Elia had never seen Francesco anywhere but at the head of the crowd. He was so like his father: taking charge and taking over were part of his nature. Yet Francesco treated everyone like an equal. With him, you could conquer the world!

Right now, his rowdy band was conquering Assisi. Like everyone else, Elia was singing and prancing when Francesco impulsively snatched a pot of rosemary and placed it on a neighbor's step. Whooping, the other youths began to switch pots from one place to another. Some urns were so heavy that two men together had to hoist them. Imagine the consternation when Assisians found their parsley and geraniums on someone else's stoop!

From somewhere, a shutter creaked open, and a masculine voice boomed, "Shut up!"

"Good night!" Francesco cheerfully called.

"Good night!" the youths echoed.

Leaping and prancing, they followed Francesco until each reached his home where he chortled "Good night" and stumbled inside.

When Elia reached his house, his wife was asleep on her side with Guiduccio dozing beside her breast, his little mouth next to the nipple. Elia undressed quietly, then blew out the candle that his wife had kept lit for him. Sliding into bed at her back, he snuggled close and slipped his right arm across her shoulders. She stirred contentedly but did not awake.

NOTES

Elia's background is sketchy. Some local Italian historians believe that his father, Bonbarone, could have been the "good baron" of the castle of Beviglie, and that he had Elia trained and educated as this chapter states. Franciscan historians generally agree that Elia was born in the territory of Assisi but are not sure where. Fortini (p. 121) postulates that Elia may have married and fathered a son, named Guiduccio, who is recorded in 1246 as a witness in an Assisi legal proceeding.

6

Messer Angelo di Pica

Provins, France (Early Morning, September 16, 1197)

Messer Angelo di Pica threw back the sheet that covered him on this portable cot inside the portable tent on the Bernardone campsite close by the Fair of Saint Ayoul of Provins. He ran his hands through his thick auburn hair, smoothing it down to his shoulders and hoping he would be presentable once he dressed. Angelo had been to this fair previously, but always with his father. Last month, for the first time, Pietro had decided to remain in Assisi while sending Angelo and Francesco to purchase new fabrics in France. So here they were, Angelo awake, Francesco snoring.

What time had his brother gotten in? He and a few other young Umbrian merchants had made plans last night to try the fare in the taverns. Angelo had declined to join them and had gone to bed.

"Get up!" He shook Francesco.

Two days ago, on the feast of the Exaltation of the Cross, the fair had begun with monks from the priory processing through Provins with a relic of their patron, Saint Ayoul. Over five hundred years before, he had been murdered by the monks of the monastery that he was trying to reform. The festivities invoked his blessing on the fair, held here yearly in his honor where major north-south and east-west roads met. Judging by the quantity of coins and merchandise, the martyr was commending the event.

"Francesco, get up!"

Angelo groaned. Francesco was difficult to awaken, especially after a night of carousing. One thing generally worked. Angelo, who was bigger all around than Francesco, grabbed his brother's ankles and dragged him out of bed. Semi-awake, Francesco moaned as Angelo dumped a tunic and hose into his lap.

Angelo pulled his olive-green tunic over his head and then adjusted his coif. "Francesco, you'd better be dressed when I get back." Better be? What could Angelo do if he weren't? He might use the dousing-with-water treatment.

Angelo pushed aside the tent flap and searched for a fig vendor. Figs were always good, especially at dawn.

"How do I look?" Francesco asked when Angelo returned with a napkin of figs. Francesco was wide-eyed and clothed in a tunic, the left of which was lemon yellow and the right azure blue. His coif was the same two colors, stitched together at the middle to line up perfectly with the tunic.

"You look like *un idiota*! Where did you get that outfit?"

Francesco grinned. "So, you like it? I made it myself."

"Don't walk with me dressed like that."

"Why not? You told me you saw this style at the May fair. It's elegant!"

"It's ridiculous!"

"Nonsense. I'm promoting a new fashion trend."

"You're so vain!"

Francesco smiled smugly, did a little jig, and bowed to Angelo. "Shall we go peruse the cloths, my dear brother?"

"Ridiculous," Angelo muttered under his breath.

Francesco attracted stares as soon as the brothers, munching the figs, left their tent. Angelo hated being stared at. Francesco seemed to revel in it.

"Where to today?" Francesco sang in French.

Angelo's quiet reply was in stark contrast to Francesco's volume. "Silks today. Papà wants several."

"Silks!" Francesco called out the word in French. "Silks!"

"Be quiet! Why do you always have to call attention to yourself? You're embarrassing."

Francesco was, indeed, garnering attention. Why did he turn everything into a party? Trying to ignore him, Angelo pushed ahead, leading the way to the silk merchants' stalls. He had gone a short distance when he checked to see if Francesco was following. No.

A French troubadour song rang out above the din.

"*Lo rossinhols s'esbaudeya . . .*"

Angelo groaned. Following the lilting melody, he found Francesco singing and surrounded by rapt listeners. Angelo grabbed his azure-covered arm.

"The silks," Angelo snarled.

"Silks!" Francesco called out gaily in French. "Silks!"

NOTES

This chapter accurately describes the Fair of Saint Ayoul, as well as the saint's martyrdom. As was the custom elsewhere, the monks of the monastery probably processed with his relics to open the fair. Francesco was known to wear garments of two different colors and fabrics sewn together (L3C, chapter I), considered eccentric in his time. Employed by their father, Francesco and Angelo must have attended several cloth fairs. The personalities of the two brothers reflect those deduced from the historical record.

Part Two

"And Every Talent and Power and Knowledge That He Thought He Had Will Be Taken Away from Him"

7

Madonna Bella

Parlascio, Assisi (Early Morning, Spring 1198)

Bella awoke with a start, her old heart tense. Beside her, the bed was empty. Dawn's faint light glowed outside.

Why hadn't Tancredi come home? He'd been gone all day. Last night she'd waited up for him. Two candles had burned down before she'd realized that her body could stay awake no longer.

She pushed back the feather coverlet and pulled her chemise over her head. Then she snatched the coverlet from the bed and wrapped herself in it. When she was younger, she was never this cold in the morning.

Stretching morning pains out of her hips and legs, Bella hobbled toward the window on this topmost floor of their family home. Here in the northwest Parlascio section of Assisi, a tepid morning breeze was carrying the faint smell of burning wood. In the distant west, Bella could see the Rocca Maggiore clinging to the side of Monte Subasio. The towering fortress, built to protect the city, was sputtering flames and smoke like a giant hearth fire burning down.

She started at the bedroom door's creaking and whirled around to see her husband's grizzled, rugged face smudged with soot. The stench of smoke, mingled with Tancredi's sweat, wafted toward her.

"Messer, you're safe!"

"Of course, I'm safe!" he bellowed. "What did you think, *la mia Bella*? This was a burning, not a battle!"

"Don't be mad at me. I worry." Then she smiled at the familiar gruffness. "You're still one handsome knight, Messer."

"Bah." He brushed off the compliment even as he removed his coif and shook out his damp gray curls. "I'm an old man, la mia Bella."

"An old woman still loves you."

He grinned at her. Then, taking her by the hand, he led her back to bed. "I told you not to wait up for me. You need your sleep."

"I did sleep. But I woke up."

He sat her on the bed and plopped himself beside her. "La mia Bella, there was no danger."

"Hours after you had gone, I heard the galloping of many hooves."

Tancredi laughed. "The pope's forces. And the emperor's troops." His voice was merry. "Together, la mia Bella. Can you imagine?"

"Together?" Now she was laughing. Two mortal enemies joining forces?

"They tried to stop you?"

"*Naturalmente*. But they could not. How could they stop so many of us?" Tancredi peeled off his hose. The smell of his grimy feet had always been an annoyance.

"Would you mind . . . ?"

"Sì, sì! Wash before coming to bed." As Bella removed her chemise and slipped under the coverlet, she watched Tancredi stride over to the side table and splash some water on his face and neck. As she snuggled down under the blankets, she heard water pouring into the basin, then a familiar sloshing followed by Tancredi stamping his feet. He would replace the basin on the table, then come to bed, his sweaty body and damp feet nestling against hers.

Twenty-four hours ago, the emperor's underling, Messer Conrad of Lutzenfeld, Count of Assisi and Duke of Spoleto, had taken with him a large retinue and left his fortress, the Rocca Maggiore, to go to Narni at the summons of the pope. Even as Conrad was leaving, Tancredi di Ugone and other leaders were rallying the people, who needed little encouragement to rid themselves of the hated count. The Rocca had been deserted not an hour when the men of Assisi, armed with clubs, grappling hooks, chains, ladders, and torches, began to ascend Monte Subasio. From the bedroom window, Bella had watched this giant herd of ants scurrying up the slope. "Down with the Rocca! Up with the people!" The cry was so loud that Conrad, it seemed, could have heard it on his journey.

"Did you have any resistance?" Bella asked as she snuggled against her husband's chest.

"What resistance? From old Fly-brain's cooks? Stable hands? Servants? They were as eager as we were to replace Conrad with a government of the people."

"It will be good to have our servants back at work today."

"Not today, la mia Bella. They worked like donkeys yesterday. All day and through the night. I told them to take today to rest."

A spontaneous moan slipped past Bella's lips.

"What do you think, woman? Pulling down a fortress is child's play?"

"No, I didn't think . . ."

"No, you didn't think." Tancredi was peevish again. He must be exhausted. "Every servant and serf in Assisi will be resting today. And every lord and merchant who was there."

"Not all were there?"

"La mia Bella, you know that some think we instigate the people. Fools! Discontented people need no instigation." His voice was firm with fire and conviction. "Organization is what it takes. Organization."

Bella understood. Why didn't every lord see that times were changing, that people wanted self-government, that the iron wills of the pope and emperor were equally wrong?

Bella lightly kissed Tancredi's stubbly cheek. "You're a good organizer, Messer."

"Bah!"

Bella thought of something. "Messer, you wanted those cloth hangings for the armaments room. I went today, but Madonna Pica said I would have to wait until Pietro could help me."

"Pietro was at the Rocca. Angelo and Francesco, too. Like all the merchants. Let Pietro sleep today. You can order the cloths tomorrow."

"I can do that. And about . . ."

Tancredi cut her off. "La mia Bella, your husband doesn't care about cloths or servants or whatever you want to tell me. I'm exhausted. Let an old man sleep."

Bella kissed him again, snuggled down, and said not another word.

Some months later, Bella stood beside her husband in a throng of Assisi citizens who had elected Elia di Bonbarone as the first consul of their comune. The government of the people had begun.

NOTES

The opening quotation for Part Two is from Saint Francis' *Later Admonition and Exhortation to the Brothers and Sisters of Penance (Second Version of the Letter to the Faithful)*, 83.

According to Fortini (p. 287), Tancredi di Ugone was instrumental in the revolt of the people against imperial rule in Assisi, which climaxed in the pillage and burning of the Rocca Maggiore. History doesn't record how many days it took to accomplish the feat. Apparently, all able-bodied men, excluding the dissenting nobles, took part in the destruction (Fortini, pp. 120, 129). It is almost certain that Pietro di Bernardone, Angelo, and Francesco would have participated.

Following the Rocca's fall, the people established their own government. Assisi records show that Bonbarone, who Fortini (p. 288) believes was Elia, was its first consul, an office which was held for one year.

Fortini (p. 288) postulates that Tancredi was about sixty years old at the time of the uprising. We have no record of or name for Tancredi's wife.

8

Dom Pietro

San Damiano, Assisi (June 1199)

With his gaze fixed on the attentive face of Christ, painted on the large crucifix icon suspended above him in the chapel of San Damiano, Dom Pietro chanted the psalms for the hour of None. He had barely begun the second psalm when Francesco's familiar, sonorous chanting joined Pietro's weak, high-pitched voice. The thin, gray-haired priest smiled and kept praying.

Was Francesco heading down to see his father's lands that bordered Rivo Torto? The road that led there went right past San Damiano. Or was he going to prepare the Bernardone summer homestead at the Stradette Farm? Or had the seventeen-year-old come just to visit?

Dom Pietro forced his wandering mind to focus on the Latin words he was chanting. He'd not quicken his pace just because he had a visitor.

When, about a year before, Francesco had first stopped to say hello, Pietro had been working in his garden, visible from the road. Francesco had asked if he might have some parsley to settle his queasy stomach. *Probably too much wine and too little sleep*, Pietro surmised, but he didn't lecture the youth. Not then, anyway. Better to advocate virtue when your listener is sober.

How had he gotten to the reading? Dom Pietro couldn't remember the psalms he'd just prayed. He'd study the reading. Now. Intently.

Since that day of the parsley, Francesco generally stopped in for a visit when passing by. He made Pietro smile, for he brought life to this abandoned house of God.

Pietro shook the distraction out of his head and ended his meditation with a short prayer. Only then did he turn to see the teen kneeling in the chapel's dust behind him.

"I don't know how you can pray so long. All day, too."

"When you get old like me, prayer means much more than the things that you youngsters do."

Francesco stood up and brushed the wrinkles out of his tunic. "How do you know what I'm doing?" His eyes were twinkling.

"What would a young man do if he has rowdy friends and money to spend?"

"I haven't killed anyone." Francesco always pointed that out when Dom Pietro tried to talk to him about virtue.

"Murder is not the only mortal sin, you know."

"I didn't come here to receive a lecture about my morals," Francesco said with mock indignation. "I came to bring you biscotti. Freshly baked today." He handed the priest a parcel wrapped in green silk and tied with a pink ribbon.

"Did Madonna Pica make this?"

Francesco laughed. "Papà doesn't want mamma to bake now that we have Alonza to cook."

Oh, yes. Alonza. Occasionally Pica sent her to bring a loaf or two to Pietro. Pretty servant girl. Big lips. Big eyes. Big bosom. Big all over.

"Did Alonza give you these?"

"Anything in my house belongs to me," Francesco said, "so I took what was mine."

Dom Pietro sighed. "Does that also apply to Alonza?"

Francesco's eyes widened. "You know that I wish to become a knight. Why would you ask me that question?"

Because, even though knights are to remain pure, many don't, Pietro thought. Best to say nothing more. Let the youth retain his idealism.

"So, you came down here to bring me cookies?"

Francesco did a little dance out the door of the chapel and, with a grand flourish, produced a bouquet of daisies and poppies that he must have plucked.

"For you, cookies. For Him, these," Francesco smiled, dancing toward the crucifix and laying the flowers down below it. "And . . ." He danced outside again and twirled back in, wearing a helmet. "For myself, this! I'm going to be a knight!"

"Really? Now? Knighthood isn't all glamour the way those French songs make it sound."

"Aren't you happy for me? Papà says I will bring glory to our family!" The voice echoed behind the visor.

Papà. Always Francesco tried to please his father. However, Pietro di Bernardone was difficult to please. He expected much of his single blood-child, but Francesco seemed always to fall short. Pietro wanted a sharp-witted merchant, but Francesco was not good with figures. Pietro wanted a learned son, but Francesco's Latin was mediocre. Pietro wanted a serious businessman whose main goal was making money, but Francesco was too fun-loving and capricious to be shackled to a shop. Now Pietro wanted a knight? Knights were born to knights, not to merchants. However, wealthy merchants could buy the trappings for knighthood. Should Francesco prove his prowess in battle, he could earn the rank of knighthood. Although he could never attain to the rank of knights nobly born, he could become a knight of great esteem.

But could he really? He would have to train, try his mettle in skirmishes, grow physically stronger.

"Who's training you to be this knight?"

"Messer Tancredi di Ugone."

Ah! Unlike many nobles who had switched allegiance to Perugia last year, Tancredi di Ugone had remained in Assisi and sided with the populace. He had been invested with the top governing role and his name was recently affixed over a new city gate requested by the merchants.

"You don't look very happy," Francesco noted. He had removed the helmet and was polishing it against his chest.

"Francesco, knighthood isn't the only way to bring glory to your family."

"Nonsense!" Francesco laughed. "Knighthood is the best way! I can become a knight in Assisi and then go elsewhere. I might fight for the emperor. Or for Lord Pope. All the world will know me. My bride will be the loveliest of all. Our castle will be towering and strong."

Pietro groaned. Francesco had recounted to him countless tales of King Arthur and the Knights of the Round Table. He had sung for him French troubadour songs of knightly prowess and honor. "Francesco, you're living a fantasy. You're not Sir Galahad."

Francesco slipped the helmet over his head. "I'll be Sir Francesco!"

Pietro shook his head.

"You haven't heard? We're at war with Perugia, and everyone who can bear arms in Assisi must do so. This is God's path to greatness for me. My brother Angelo is also training."

War again? In war, merchants became archers, marching on foot against the enemy or, at best, cavaliers equipped with shield and sword. Only knights were protected with armor, shield, sword, and lance. Pietro di Bernardone was buying his sons the best way to survive the war.

NOTES

AP (chapter 1) records Dom Pietro as the old priest at San Damiano. Since Francesco used to wander about the woods and visit his father's properties in the vicinity of San Damiano (listed by Fortini, pp. 114–115), he likely developed a friendship with Dom Pietro.

While it is generally assumed that Francesco wanted to become a knight, Fortini points out that all able-bodied men in Assisi would have been required to defend their city or be severely punished (p. 152, footnote). Both Francesco and Angelo would have been conscripted to serve. History doesn't record who trained them for battle.

The histories mention nothing about Pietro di Bernardone's concern for his sons' safety, but any good father would do what he could to preserve the lives of his children.

9

Cucciolo

Assisi (November 1201)

Cucciolo emerged from the Church of San Paolo. He had slept the night near the warmth of flickering candles lit by worshippers seeking God's favor. Clouds cloaked the sun, whose paleness radiated more chill than heat. Hungry, Cucciolo drew his tattered cloak around his ribs and grimly thought of winter. He'd have to beg more cast-off clothing to survive. Not for nothing had the town nicknamed him "Cucciolo"—"Puppy." Although his hair was graying like this morning sky, his puffy, drooping eyelids and pinched jowls gave his face a perennial doleful look. His helpless expression earned him alms denied to other beggars.

Cucciolo understood begging—whom to ask, what to request, how often to plead. He knew the most effective postures, the right words, and the perfect facial expressions. Today he would work the Via Portica, the street of the merchants. The first stop was next door to San Paolo, Pietro di Bernardone's cloth shop.

Cucciolo grimaced. He had one chance in four of meeting Pietro. He could not count on Pietro for alms. The heavyset, muscled merchant was as unpredictable as most wealthy Assisiani. What whims inspired them to give alms some days but not others? Angelo di Pica was only a tad more generous. At least he turned down beggars with a sad smile instead of an impatient "Not today."

Now if he met Pica or Francesco! They never refused. Their alms might be small, but they would be given.

Cucciolo whispered to the leaden sky, "Let it be Madonna Pica or Messer Francesco."

Working his face into its most doleful demeanor, Cucciolo took the few steps over and down into the cloth merchant's shop. Brightly colored, expensive fabrics, folded neatly on the shelves that lined the walls, made the otherwise drab shop glow with gaiety. Ah, here was Francesco, jauntily dressed and waiting patiently while Messer Rufino di Scipione was comparing bolts of saffron-dyed wool.

"Excuse me," Cucciolo interrupted, opening his cloak to expose his ribcage. "Alms for the love of God." The phrase every beggar used.

"Not today," Francesco said, shaking his head.

Cucciolo was dumbfounded. This was not how a young man who aspired to knighthood, who embraced the ideas of chivalry, would act. "Please. For the love of God."

Francesco's eyes narrowed; his face hardened. Like Pietro. "Not today. Go!"

It was a no. How could it be "no"? Francesco spent enough money on himself and his friends. Couldn't he spare a coin for Cucciolo?

Cucciolo plodded out of the shop. Could Pietro have beaten Francesco for being generous? Was he turning out just like his father?

Looking up at the sky, Cucciolo spoke through gritted teeth. "You answered."

He moved on down the Via Portica, past the Church of San Paolo.

NOTES

L3C (chapter 1) records the undated incident of Francesco refusing alms to a nameless beggar who asked them "in the name of God."

10

Messer Rufino di Scipione

Bernardone Cloth Shop, Assisi (November 1201)

In Rufino's delicate hands, the smooth saffron cloth suddenly felt as rough as *gattinello*. Never had he heard Francesco respond so rudely.

Taller than Francesco, Rufino idolized the young man three years his senior. Longing to possess Francesco's self-assurance and courtesy, Rufino always felt more confident and powerful with Francesco nearby.

Often Francesco jousted with Rufino, sometimes besting him. Both had ridden side-by-side in raids and parlays with Perugia. In one skirmish, they had routed Rufino's uncles and cousins who had switched their allegiance to the enemy city.

"Isn't this soft cloth?" Francesco asked. "If not soft enough for your mother, I have this one." He lifted a roll of emerald silk from one of the shelves and placed it before Rufino.

What had happened to Francesco? Endlessly he and Rufino had discussed the exploits of the legendary King Arthur and his knights. Both strove to cultivate Arthur's gentility and courtesy. Francesco may be foolish, idealistic, and impulsive, but he was never cruel. Yet what had just occurred with Cucciolo was cruelty.

"Either would make a beautiful Christmas gift, eh?"

Rufino threw up his arms. "Why do women worry about these things? Saffron? Emerald? Who cares? What do you think?"

"I think you don't know how to choose cloth that women like. Now, for my mamma, I would select this one." Francesco pointed to the emerald.

"All right. Fine."

"Is something bothering you?"

"You are! I would have given him alms myself if I had any!"

Francesco nodded dolefully. "I'm bothering me, too. Knights don't turn away anyone begging in the name of God. It's like refusing Jesus. I swear to you, Messer Rufino, I will never again turn away anyone who asks for alms in the name of God."

NOTES

In 1244, Crescentius of Iesi, minister general of the friars, "directed all the brothers to send him in writing whatever they could truly recall about the life, miracles, and prodigies of blessed Francis." In L3C, three friars wrote their own memories and those of four others whom they consulted. Of these, Rufino is the most likely to have witnessed this incident.

When the common people rose against the Assisi lords, Rufino's family, according to Fortini (p. 171), remained in Assisi, although some of his uncles and their families switched allegiance to Perugia. While raids and skirmishes between the two cities happened, we have no proof that Francesco and Rufino ever met relatives in battle.

11

Messer Monaldo di Offreduccio

Offreduccio House, Perugia (November 1202)

Monaldo di Offreduccio was scrutinizing yesterday's accounts with his steward. His right hand's index finger, thick as a sausage, pointed at a figure on the parchment. "Six chickens yesterday? For what?"

"Messer, your lady hosted the Offreduccio women for dinner while the knights were hunting."

Monaldo nodded. She had mentioned something about that. "Six seems like a large number of hens."

"Messer, there are many Offreduccio women and children."

"Hmm." Monaldo supposed so. The excessive number of loaves must have been also used for dinner. Why couldn't his wife understand that they had less income here than in Assisi? Monaldo no longer had access to his properties under Assisi's jurisdiction. Did his wife think he could still obtain revenues from them? His lectures about spending did little good. Unlike everyone else, his lady refused to cower to him.

A nearby church bell began clanging madly. Almost immediately another bell picked up the sound, and then another and another.

"Damn!" Monaldo cursed. This was no ringing to call the faithful to Mass or prayers.

"A fire, Messer?"

"Or an attack. They don't ring the bells like that because a juggler has come to town."

Before his steward could comment, Monaldo was out the door and into the street teeming with people pushing their way toward the main piazza.

The cry was coming from all directions. "The Assisiani have invaded Colle della Strada!"

So that was it. According to Perugini spies, this invasion had been developing for weeks. So today was the day. The Assisiani might be able to occupy Colle della Strada, but what made them think they could hold it?

Monaldo had been born in Assisi and had lived there all his life. He and his family had helped build the Cathedral of San Rufino, maintained order in the city, and fought for it against Perugia. Two years ago, Monaldo's loyalties had shifted when upstart city merchants had incited a civil war by tearing down castles and burning houses of Assisi nobles. The Offreduccio knights, like other noble families of Assisi, had seen the tide turning. Monaldo and most of his brothers had taken their wives, children, and as many goods as they could muster and switched allegiance to Perugia. Thus, they deprived Assisi not only of their protection but also of their patronage and taxes. When Perugia demanded that Assisi rebuild the ruined castles and pay the nobles for damages, Assisi refused, and war erupted. For the past two years, Monaldo and his brothers, who had defected to Perugia, had participated in intermittent raids, skirmishes, ambushes, burning of fields, and destruction of towers. In all that time, he had not met with his pig-headed brother Scipione who, at the last moment, had refused to defect.

Monaldo remembered that shouting match in the great hall of the Offreduccio house. "It's time the people of Assisi had a voice in its government!" Scipione had thundered. "Trust, and you will keep your castles, Monaldo."

Monaldo trusted no one but himself.

Until now in this war, neither Assisi nor Perugia had won a decisive victory. Both cities had made alliances with other cities. Both had been training their citizens and mercenary cavaliers for the combat now upon them.

The main piazza was clogged with Perugini rushing into it from all directions. Standing on the fountain's rim, the *podestà*, clad in his greaves, was gesturing for quiet. "Assisi has invaded Colle della Strada! But we'll mount the attack! You have your orders! Show no mercy! Let these stupid hens see what happens when they dare to attack the *gryphon*! To arms!"

"To arms!" the crowd whooped and then, as if one voice, the terrifying war cry of Perugia burst over the city.

NOTES

In 1200, the Offreduccio brothers, all knights who switched allegiance from Assisi to Perugia, would have fought for Perugia in the battle of Colle della Strada. As the oldest, Monaldo would have had authority over the others in his clan.

The gryphon is the symbol of Perugia.

12

Messer Tancredi di Ugone

Colle della Strada, Assisi/Perugia (November 1202)

In the pale, early morning light of a crisp November day, Messer Tancredi di Ugone was one commander in an army of knights, archers, and foot warriors moving in a vast, determined wave toward Perugia. He was riding close by the young knights he'd trained, watching over them with fatherly pride and concern. Protected in the finest armor, their coursers festooned with red and blue ribbons, the colors of Assisi, Francesco rode to his left, Rufino to his right. The others he'd trained rode on either side of them. Having seen skirmishes, these young knights would now see war.

The cleared field was tranquil, the dried grasses and flowers bobbing gently in a light breeze. Above, on a knoll surrounded by leafless trees, stood the grim leper hospital of Perugia, from which wafted a barely perceptible, putrid scent of death and decay.

Bad omen, Tancredi thought grimly.

Despite Tancredi's heightened senses, the attack surprised him. The terrifying war cry of the Perugini coincided with their massive frontal attack. Tancredi was surrounded by battle almost before he could draw his sword. The armies clashed and, in the furious, bloody onslaught, Tancredi could no longer see the young men he'd trained. He was fighting for his life, and his only thought was to stay alive. And stay alive he did until he realized that the battle had turned against Assisi and that, if he were to save any men under his command, they had to retreat.

Slashing left and right, guiding his courser through bodies, he shouted to his men, "Retreat! Retreat!" Those who were able followed him as he spurred his mount back toward Assisi.

NOTES

Without giving details, L3C mentions that Francesco fought in a war between Assisi and Perugia. Later histories, particularly the Eulistea, flesh out the details of this bloody confrontation.

The histories do not note if Tancredi di Ugone fought in the battle of Colle della Strada, although, as an Assisi knight, he must have.

Fortini (p. 153) mentions the leper hospital in the battle area.

Part Three

“Most High, Glorious God, Enlighten the Darkness of My Heart”

13

Messer Rufino di Scipione

Ponte San Giovanni, Perugia (November 1202)

Chained about his naked waist to the men before and behind him, Rufino shuffled across the Ponte San Giovanni in a long line of other naked, captured knights. Rufino could see, in advance of the column, Perugini knights clearing the bridge by heaving over the side the bodies strewn across it. With each sickening splat, the dismal, shivering column advanced a few feet.

Stunned by images of carnage and plodding through this nightmare of defeat, the seventeen-year-old's mind seemed frozen, unable to respond to the unthinkable. With the Tiber and the slaughter behind them, the wavering column of exhausted men attracted city dwellers like carrion attracting flies. Along with mud and stones aimed at them came jeers and imprecations. Gradually, Rufino realized that the conquerors were parading their hostages up one street and down the next so that as many Perugini as possible could mock them. Finally, with a crazy sense of relief, Rufino saw his sad column disappearing through a narrow doorway carved into a cliff.

In semi-darkness, Rufino half-stumbled down rough stone steps into a coarsely hewn underground vault. At the bottom of the stairs, a Perugini knight unlocked each man's chains, then pushed him into a mass of bodies. Armored

Perugini, wielding swords and clubs, lined the dungeon's perimeter. Rufino surmised that they'd mercilessly cut down any prisoner who attempted escape.

The large vault grew crowded as more men collapsed into it. Rufino recognized some as compatriots from Assisi. Others must be knights from Nocera, Spello, Bevagna, and Rosciano, Assisi's ally cities.

After the last prisoner had been unshackled, three Perugini knights threw piles of rank tunics down the stairs. Not a garment was left after the prisoners scrambled and jostled for them. Some men must have snatched two, to ward off the chill. Eyeing the men, the Perugini guards backed up the stairs and bolted the door behind them.

Only then did Rufino feel safe enough to move. Where was Francesco? He had heard Messer Tancredi call for retreat, but the Perugini had already encircled him and Francesco. He had thought they would be killed until he'd heard the shouted order. "Only knights as prisoners! Kill everyone else!" How could he erase from his mind the systematic slaughter of Assisi archers and foot soldiers who also had been cut off from retreat?

After the bloodbath, he and Francesco had been pulled from their mounts and stripped. A Perugino with blood on his breastplate had slapped Rufino on the behind, then bellowed with laughter. "You, skinny one, your papà will pay good money to have you back."

Through the vault's distant high window, evening twilight was fading when Rufino found Francesco huddled against the back wall. He was still naked, a rumpled rank tunic beside him.

Rufino squatted next to his friend. "Francesco," he said, touching the elder's shoulder. Francesco lifted his head and opened his glazed eyes. "Francesco, I'll help you dress." Rufino gently tugged Francesco to his feet and slipped the tunic over his head. He eased Francesco down again, then sat across from him and threw his arms about his friend. The two of them clung to each other, each heaving with silent sobs as the dim light turned to darkness.

The following morning, the door opened, and two peasants descended the stairs. They carried out buckets of filth and brought them back empty. They also lugged in sacks of moldy bread and jugs of water. The prisoners who had quarreled about using the makeshift latrines now quarreled over food and drink. There was not enough for all. They had to share.

The days varied little, with one dragging into the next. Rufino was dumbstruck by what had happened, but Francesco seemed shattered. He ate and drank what Rufino brought him but spoke and moved little. Often, he seemed asleep or half-dead, but sometimes he would tremble and, other times, cry out in terror. Rufino's father had told him about this sickness which sometimes follows war. It would go away, most of the time. Rufino was patient. Instead of quarreling, or speculating, or engaging in foolish games of chance with the other knights, he tended Francesco, keeping him comfortable, speaking with him, encouraging him to walk.

As the days wore on, the memory of the battle faded as did memories of his palazzo and family. Rufino stopped considering how his mamma must feel. He stopped speculating about whether his father or brother had survived. He could do nothing about these unknowns. He could only pray for his family. What became real were these rugged gray walls; the drip, drip of water; the fetid smell; and the rats that overran the dungeon at night.

"Four things can happen in war," Scipione had frequently lectured his sons. "You are victorious. Then you must curb your pride because success is God's, not yours. Or you are injured. Then you must heed to healing, which comes from God, not from you. Or you are taken prisoner. Then you must survive because your release is up to God, not up to you. Or you are killed. For that, you must have prepared beforehand so that your soul is always ready to meet the Lord."

Rufino focused on survival. He would eat. Drink. Pace to strengthen his muscles. Pray to strengthen his spirit.

On a wall, one of the knights recorded the days by scratching lines. One month passed. Two. Three. No one left unless he died or became very ill. Rumor had it that the Perugini did not kill captured knights because their wealthy families would pay good ransom for them. However, Perugia was dallying in honoring the ransoms. Only when a ransomed knight became deathly ill would the Perugini cart him home. The arrival of each nearly dead prisoner reinforced the message in the Colle's carnage: unless you wish to repeat this experience, don't attack Perugia again.

Five months had passed by the time Rufino realized that, although physically thinner and weaker, he was surviving. Francesco, however, seemed to be merely existing. Even though Francesco had gradually emerged from his lethargy, his gaiety was now a façade. He had become simply another *braggadocio* knight whose silly songs and dances amused the other prisoners. If criticized, his familiar answer, proclaimed with gusto in Assisi, was now a stock response: "Why shouldn't I be happy? One day all the world will honor me!"

The knights' constant quarreling and complaining seemed to physically accost him. Francesco would plead for peace as if his own depended on it. Once, after two knights scuffled, the other knights ostracized the aggressor. Francesco alone spoke with him and cajoled the other knights to give him another chance.

For Rufino, Francesco, and some others, the suffering of the ill knights beckoned for compassion. With moist rags, they cooled the fevers of the ill. With their own hands, they fed them.

The months dragged on, the gray of winter yielding to the earlier morning light of spring. Sometimes at dawn, when the men about him were snoring, Rufino could hear the twittering and cheeping of sparrows and the eerie cries of swallows. The rats grew fat with pregnancy.

Summer came. Mosquitos infested the dungeon. More knights fell ill. Francesco, Rufino, and some others continued to comfort the sick. However, they were ill themselves. Francesco developed a cough. Every other day, it seemed, fever prostrated him. Then he became the one needing care.

The days grew shorter. Francesco could no longer stand, much less sing and dance. He could barely eat or drink. Hardly conscious, the fastidious Francesco could no longer care for himself. Rufino had to pick the lice from his tunic and clean his feverish body to keep him from wallowing in his filth. Francesco was dying.

The latrine brigade must have told the Perugini guards about Francesco because, one morning when the slash marks on the wall had just passed the twelve-month mark, two guards clomped down into the prison and dragged the half-conscious Francesco up the stairs into the light.

Five months later, Rufino was alternately cold and hot with fever. His body constantly trembled, and his legs no longer supported him. To move about the vault, he had to crawl. Then he could no longer do that, and other knights had to care for him. He no longer wished for survival. He wished for death.

One day, when the spring sun was pouring through the high, distant window, the latrine brigade hauled him out of the vault and dumped him into another where every one of the few occupants was prostrate with disease. Falling in and out of consciousness, Rufino knew that a doctor sometimes poked and turned him and bathed his burning body. Some days later, when the sparrows were singing and the swallows crying, limp Rufino was carried up the stairs. He was stripped of his tunic and placed in a rough cart that bumped along the roads until he was dumped on the side of one of them. The next thing he remembered was a frantically ringing bell and a high-pitched woman's voice calling, "Messer Scipione! Messer Rufino is moving!" When he struggled to open his eyes, he saw that he was lying in his bed in his father's house and his father, dressed in his workday tunic, was sitting beside him, weeping.

NOTES

The opening quotation for Part Three is from Saint Francis' *The Prayer before the Crucifix*, lines 1–3.

Fortini (pp. 158–159) notes that Perugia took only knights as prisoners while slaughtering all other Assisi survivors.

L3C (chapter II) mentions Francesco's capture, imprisonment, and the incidents specific to him. Among the *Legend*'s authors, Rufino is the only possible eyewitness to these events.

Historians believe that the prison was an underground Etruscan vault, the "Campo di Battaglia" that was "beneath the spot where the Palace of the Captain of the People now stands in the Piazza del Sopramuro" (*History of Perugia* by William Heywood, 1910). While Franciscan histories describe neither the trek to the prison nor prison conditions, this chapter reflects descriptions of other prisons and prisoners of the time.

Fortini (p. 169) notes that "According to the ancient rule in Perugia that governed the treatment of prisoners of war, those who fell seriously ill could be returned to their city."

14

Messer Elia di Bonbarone

Bernardone House, Assisi (September 1204)

With a light heart and a spring in his step, Messer Elia di Bonbarone ascended the stone stairs that led to Francesco's bedroom in his parents' house. Francesco was sitting on the bed, his hose-covered legs dangling over the side. Elia strode up to him and flung his arms around his friend. How skinny he still felt!

"Can we go now? I can't wait to get out of this room!"

Elia nodded. "We can go now. Take my arm. Your legs are still weak."

Obediently Francesco grabbed a cane with one hand while clinging with the other to his taller, sturdier friend. Francesco's stride had a hint of its former bounce as the two descended the stairs into the late morning sunlight. In the street, Francesco paused and, eyes closed, lifted his face to the sun. After a few moments, he said with exuberance, "Today, Elia! Today we go to the fields!"

For the past several weeks, Francesco, supported by Elia, had been taking ever longer strolls about the city to strengthen his legs, but his goal had been to reach the countryside.

Francesco's step developed a resolute firmness as he led the way through the Porta Moiano and outside the city walls. Vineyards lined the road, the vines drooping with plump grapes nearing harvest. Pale stalks of ripe wheat swayed in the light breeze, awaiting the swinging sickles of serfs who had already leveled some of the meadows. Birdsongs surrounded them. Now and then, an orange or purple or white butterfly flitted by. The men came across a boulder by the roadside and sat on it, each lost in thought.

Francesco had always loved such walks. Elia, on the other hand, preferred work. Francesco was a dreamer, a thinker, a strange mixture of a lighthearted, congenial comrade and a man of silent introspection. In contrast, Elia was always a man of action. Sitting here beside a thoughtful Francesco, with time ticking on, was tiresome, so Elia began to think.

Two years ago, Elia had gone to Bologna for additional study. Six months ago, with his wife and seven-year-old son, he had returned to Assisi to find his ill friend as well as an ill comune. With the noble and merchant factions unable to cooperate, the city had chosen Girardo di Giliberto as podestà to guard the peace. However, objecting to the election of an excommunicate, the papacy had placed Assisi under interdict. Elia was frequently consulted about how to persuade Pope Innocenzo III to lift the interdict so that Assisi could resume celebration of Holy Mass, Matins, and Christian burials. Maybe the comune should request a papal representative to assess the situation?

"Let's go back."

The soft voice startled Elia. Go back? Already? Francesco must be tired.

Wordlessly they walked back to Francesco's house. Francesco sat on his bed. "Grazie." His face was expressionless.

"Did you enjoy it?"

"It meant nothing to me."

The response unnerved Elia. Such walks used to exhilarate him.

"What's wrong with me? I must have been a fool to enjoy that. My friend, grazie. I'm tired. I must sleep." Without removing his shoes or hose, Francesco lay down and turned his back to Elia.

Sleep? Francesco slept constantly. Would this illness never relent? Elia quietly left the room, breathing the prayer he'd been praying for six months, "My Lord, heal him."

NOTES

In 1.5C, Celano mentions that Elia gave him all the information for 1C. As an able-bodied Assisi man, Elia would have been conscripted to fight in the Colle della Strada battle. However, 1C skips from Francesco's youth to his "long illness." Perhaps Elia was away from Assisi during the battle, returning only after Francesco was home and recuperating.

1C (first book, chapter II) records that a recuperating Francesco received no joy from visiting the countryside that once delighted him. He thought it foolish to have once liked these things.

Fortini (pp. 173–174) notes the election of the excommunicate podestà and the subsequent interdict.

Elia's being consulted about civic matters is speculation.

15

Ghita

Tavern, Assisi (February 1205)

Ghita's heart and feet were skipping! Tonight, Francesco had come to the tavern! It must have been over two years since he'd been here. Tonight, his thick black hair and protruding ears made him more appealing than ever to Ghita who, like him, was short and wiry. She was also rather startling with her nose that bent to the right, the result of papà punching her face when she was three. What had she done to deserve that or any of his other abuses?

No matter. Papà was dead. Francesco was here! She could wait on him and his friends and lose herself in his lilting laughter and raucous jokes. She didn't expect him to pay her any more attention than usual, but just being near him was good.

How exhilarating to scurry back and forth from the kitchen with wine and mutton! Now and then one of the men would grab her. Occasionally one planted a kiss on her cheek. She resisted these advances, but not too strongly. She was waiting for Francesco's turn, but he had not yet responded to her playful bottom-bumps or her bending over him a little too closely when she served the turnips.

However, when she scampered to the table with the fourth flagon of wine, her hand accidentally bumped into his and the wine sloshed over the rim and onto both her and Francesco. Mortified, she grabbed the corner of her apron and impulsively dabbed at the purple stain spreading across the shoulder of Francesco's saffron tunic. His hand grabbed hers and she froze, expecting him to cuff her. "Let it be, Ghita." Francesco's voice was flat. "It's merely cloth." Then he drew her close and planted a gentle kiss on her cheek. She returned to the kitchen, puzzled by his lack of gusto.

NOTES

When Francesco was well enough, he returned to his former lifestyle but without his former enthusiasm (1C, first book, chapter II). In an attempt to show this, the author has imagined this scene with Francesco, his companions, and the fictitious Ghita.

16

Bishop Guido

Bernardone Cloth Shop, Assisi (March 1205)

Bishop Guido stood before the shelves of fine fabrics in Pietro di Bernardone's cloth shop. Which would be suitable for a bishop? Last week, he'd been in a hurry to visit the outlying monastery of Santa Maria di Valfabbrica. As he had spurred his steed through the dense forest on that blustery day, his flowing cape had tangled in brambles. The ruined cape had been a deep vermilion, but he was now favoring pine green. Of course, lemon would also be nice. Or violet.

Francesco came out from the back storeroom. Guido would ask to see all three colors.

"Messer Bishop." Francesco bowed courteously.

The youth's thin face and hollow eyes startled him. Gone were the sparkle, the grin. Rumors that Francesco had changed must be true.

"Francesco, how are you feeling?"

Francesco shook his head.

"Have you seen a doctor?"

"Sì. Many times."

"What does he say?"

Francesco shrugged. "He says sickness is no longer in my body but in my heart. Messer Bishop, I left for war, thinking to return in glory, not shame."

"There's no shame in being taken prisoner. You fought bravely. Manfully. Gloriously. Where's the shame?"

"I killed. I think. I tried to." His voice was weak, his face impassive.

"Killing is what one does in war, Francesco."

"The war was unjust. It was about money and power."

Isn't that what all wars are about? Guido thought.

"You've preached that it's a sin to kill unjustly."

Yes, he'd preached that. "Francesco, you were defending yourself. You were defending others. You had to fight. Assisi demanded it."

"I wanted to fight. I wanted glory. Admiration. Power. Messer Bishop, people died. But not me. I wish I'd been killed. I've tried to do penance. Eating less. Giving to the poor."

Guido could feel the young man's pain. In the crusty old bishop's heart, the spirit of compassion was still vibrant.

"Is someone else working with you today?"

"Sì. Angelo."

"Can he tend the shop? I'd like to speak with you."

"If you wish, Messer Bishop."

"Angelo!" Guido boomed. Angelo came hurrying out of the back room. "I need to speak to Francesco. Would you tend the shop until he returns?"

"Sì, Messer Bishop."

Sì, of course. Who would argue with the bishop?

Guido had one of his servants kindle a fire in the hearth of a small sitting room in the bishop's palace. As the leaping flames dispelled the chill, Guido listened intently to Francesco's disjointed ramblings.

He's afraid, but he doesn't know it. Intense battles could ruin inexperienced knights. To combat fear, fight again! Guido found an opportunity to speak.

"Francesco, you keep saying that you need to do penance. Do you know that Messer Gautier de Brienne is gathering forces in Apulia to fight for Lord Pope, who has granted the same indulgence to knights who defend this cause as to Crusaders to the Holy Land? The complete cancellation of all punishment you'd justly deserve for sinning."

Francesco was listening intently.

"Battle has proven your bravery and skill. Why not join de Brienne? You'll be fighting to defend pilgrims who wish to journey to holy places held by the emperor. You'll help to increase the landholdings of the Church and make them places where the faith may be proclaimed freely. And any punishment for your sins will be remitted."

Francesco was nodding.

"You'll come to know when it's just to take an enemy's life. Perhaps, after fighting for Lord Pope, you'll join Crusaders going to the Holy Land. There you may free captive Christians and defend those in danger. There you may regain Jerusalem, making it safe for pilgrims. How glorious to return to Assisi as a knight with your sins forgiven! Should you die in battle instead, your cleansed soul will enter eternal glory. What better way for a knight to do penance?"

Francesco's eyes had grown wide, and a grin had spread across his face. "I'll do this, Messer Bishop! Grazie!"

NOTES

Paul Moses (*The Saint and the Sultan*, pp. 28–29) gives an excellent summary of the background of Gautier de Brienne and the pope's granting an indulgence (complete remission of all temporal punishment due to sins) to his knights. 1C (first book, chapter II) mentions Francesco's plans to join Gautier's forces.

Francesco developed a trusting relationship with Bishop Guido, but we don't know if Guido was instrumental in Francesco's decision to go to Apulia.

17

Messer Enea

Bernardone Cloth Shop, Assisi (Early April 1205)

Standing tall in his pea green tunic, Messer Enea rubbed his stubble-lined chin. How did unemployed knights provide for their families?

He pushed aside the violet fabric. "Have you anything more economical?"

"Sì." Francesco folded the violet damask and replaced it with a large swath of honey-colored wool.

Enea nodded. This he could afford.

"How's your family, Messer?" Francesco asked as he folded the wool.

"My wife is still sick." Her nausea and abdominal pain had lasted over a year. "And the children. They are . . . children!"

Francesco grinned. "Has a baron or a count employed you?"

"Here and there someone will hire me." Life had been comfortable when Count Conrad had employed him. However, ever since Conrad abandoned Assisi after the fall of the Rocca, Enea had been struggling. Since he had worked for the emperor, no lords in Assisi trusted him. Occasional pay could not match his former salary. Poverty had forced Enea to abandon the estate given him by Conrad and move into a small house in the city. If only one Assisi landowner could realize that Enea would defend his lands as readily as he had defended Conrad's!

Francesco took Enea's coins and handed him the wool. "Could you wait a moment? I have something for you."

Enea was in no hurry. After several moments, Francesco returned with a neatly folded heap of extravagant cloth. "I'm going to Apulia to fight for Lord Pope."

"Sì. Everyone has heard this."

"I had these clothes prepared for me, but how can I wear them in battle? When a grand lord knights me and hires me, I'll get more clothes as fine as these. These will fit you, Messer. We're about the same size."

Enea recognized Francesco's generosity as concordant with the code of chivalry. Knights were to give gifts freely, at a sacrifice to themselves, and they were to accept freely and humbly gifts given. The clothes were more lavish than any Enea possessed. Maybe they would fit his oldest son.

"Grazie, Messer Francesco. May God help you realize your ambition."

NOTES

L3C (Chapter II) states that Francesco was so enamored with chivalry that he gave away to an unnamed poor knight all the expensive clothing that he had made for his trip to Apulia.

18

Messer Orsino

Via Portica, Assisi (April 1205)

Messer Orsino sat erect in his saddle, his polished armor glittering in the early morning sun. If he had left his palazzo earlier, fewer people would have been in the streets to see him.

Ahead was the Bernardone stable, and there were Francesco, his parents, his squire, and his mounts. Like Orsino, Francesco had fought bravely at Colle della Strada. Like Orsino, he wished to gain greater glory in Apulia.

Orsino waited indulgently while the Bernardones embraced one another. Then, his foot supported by a squire, Francesco swung himself into the saddle of a chestnut courser. *Fine steed!* Orsino thought. *Where had Pietro bought him?*

Then they were off. Orsino glanced sideways at Francesco's armor, brand-new and more extravagant than his own. *Pietro always has to outdo everyone else.*

Each followed by his pack horse and squire, the two knights rode along majestically, nodding to the citizens of Assisi who parted to let them pass. "They're going to fight for Lord Pope," an old woman shouted to an even older one.

"God be with you!" the older woman hailed.

He certainly has been, Orsino thought. As they rode through the Porta Moiano, Orsino was grateful to God for the good fortune of his past thirty years. A page, then squire, and now knight, Orsino had learned courtly etiquette, music, and dancing. He knew the code of chivalry and the rules of heraldry. His body could become one with his courser, and he was skilled with bow and sword. Although only of medium build, he was strong, swift, and dexterous. His body amazed him. Orsino could climb and swim with ease, skills needed for a castle siege. Any fear, he had overcome. He had withstood cold and heat, exhaustion and hunger. Those were the penances of knights! Glory comes through suffering!

Like the day, the horses plodded on. Sunshine faded behind darkening clouds and a light drizzle had begun when, at eventide, the group reached the outskirts of Spoleto. They came upon a small, abandoned hovel, the wind whistling eerily through its open doorway. Tethering the horses so they could graze, Orsino intuitively sought for a nearby water source. Sure enough, downhill from the hovel bubbled a small stream. The men refilled their waterskins and then ducked indoors to kindle a fire. They could easily avoid the one leaky corner and sleep elsewhere on the packed earth floor. In the cozy ruin, safe from wolves, the knights ate their bread and bedded down. Orsino fell asleep, dreaming of glory in Apulia.

When Orsino awoke, Francesco was dressed and his courser saddled. "Grazie, Messer Orsino, for agreeing to have me accompany you," he said, "but I must return to Assisi. God be with you!" Then his squire supported Francesco's foot while he mounted. Turning toward Assisi, the two rode off.

Dumbstruck, Orsino watched them.

He's lost his nerve, he thought. Undoubtedly humiliation awaited Francesco in Assisi. Glory would greet Orsino in Apulia.

NOTES

Sometime in the spring of 1205, Francesco, extravagantly outfitted, started for Apulia with an unnamed Assisi knight. The histories mention no squire, but a knight generally had a squire to assist him. After spending the first night in Spoleto, Francesco abandoned the goal and returned to Assisi (1C, first book, chapter II, and 2C, first book, chapter II).

19

Messer Rufino di Scipione

Tavern, Assisi (Late April 1205)

Rufino di Scipione sat at a long table in the candlelit tavern. Along with a dozen or more of Francesco's other friends, he stuffed himself with salted pork, dried peas, and pears preserved in honey. The brown bread was ample and the wine flowing. Ghita was scurrying, trying to keep the trenchers stocked and the jugs filled. To Rufino's knowledge, Francesco had never hosted such a lavish banquet. It had turned his humiliating return into a celebration. "I'm going to achieve glory at home!" he boasted. One could almost believe it because Francesco was so assured.

When the men were bloated with food and wine, they called for dice and played several rounds before spilling out into the street to dance and sing their way home. As usual, Francesco took the baton and led the group with his leaping and foolishness.

On the Via dell'Abbazia, Saverio called out in his booming voice, "Where's Francesco?"

Where, indeed? How could they lose Francesco?

The group danced and cavorted back the way they had come. Sure enough, there was Francesco. Standing. Near the Torre della Catena. Looking. At nothing.

"Francesco!" Rufino called.

No response.

"He's drunk," Saverio announced.

"Francesco," Vitale asked, "are you all right?"

"He's dreaming of Ghita!" Saverio tittered. "Or Alonza."

Zenzo guffawed. "Are you thinking of taking a wife, Francesco?"

"You're right," Francesco quipped. "I was thinking about taking a wife more noble, wealthier, and more beautiful than you have ever seen."

The group burst into laughter at the outlandish comeback.

From somewhere a deep voice commanded, "Quiet!" The youths bellowed. The voice came again, louder. "Quiet!"

"Sì, Messer!" Francesco called. Waving the baton, he called out, "Let's go!" and danced down the Via dell'Abbazia, the group weaving along behind.

NOTES

The early histories, most completely L3C (chapter III), describe this incident that occurred a few days after Francesco returned from Spoleto. A trencher was a thick slice of bread that served as a plate. When the meal was finished, trenchers were given to beggars.

20

Messer Elia di Bonbarone

Elia's Home, Beviglie, Assisi (Late April 1205)

Flinging open the door from his home's second floor living quarters, Elia found Francesco, just as his servant Beppe had told him, waiting for him by the hearth in the anteroom. "Francesco!" Exuberantly, Elia embraced his unexpected guest, hugging him from one shoulder and then the other. Francesco heartily embraced him. Elia could feel his joy.

"You've ridden here on a Sunday afternoon. No mattress-making or teaching today. We can visit in peace."

"Sì. I need to speak with you, my friend."

After sending Beppe to tell his wife that he was leaving, Elia had his palfrey saddled. Then he and Francesco rode through the village streets, smattered with adults but thronged with children.

In the piazza, eight-year-old Guiduccio broke away from a knot of others fighting with wooden swords. Racing toward the two horsemen, he called out, "Papà, I'm getting good!"

Elia chuckled at the child's mock sword-thrusts. "Sì, Guiduccio. Very good!"

"Good morning, Messer Francesco." Guiduccio bowed.

"Messer Francesco and I have some things to talk about," Elia said. "Bye!"

"Bye!" Guiduccio ran back to his playmates.

"The cave?" Elia asked.

"Sì."

"It must be serious."

"Sì."

Obviously, Francesco was reticent to speak. When they got to the cave, he would unburden himself. The men rode on, leaving Beviglie and climbing through fields of waving yellow mustard, making their way to a hill halfway between Beviglie and Assisi.

On a long-ago summer day, while roving and exploring, they had pushed through tangles of vines, brambles, and weeds on this hillside and stumbled upon a crumbling arch that opened into a dark cavern. Giddy with excitement, they had entered a delightfully cooler and deliciously dark cave. Maybe a wolves' lair? Near the entrance, Elia had kindled a fire, then, making a torch of a thick fallen limb, they had lit their way through what turned out to be a rather disappointing tunnel. Without any twists or side branches, the rough-hewn passage went straight through the hill and opened out under a second arch into another jumble of tough foliage. They had met no wolves, not that first day, not ever. The only excitement about the cave was that they alone seemed to know it existed.

Elia kindled a fire today, too. Just in case. With their palfreys tethered outside, the two men hunkered down on the rock-strewn earth where they could feel the flames' warmth. Francesco was gazing beyond the fire to whatever caught his attention in the brush at the entrance. Elia was gazing at Francesco.

"My friend, you must help me think something through."

"Sì, Francesco."

"You remember the dream about the castle of armor?"

"Sì." How could he forget? A few weeks ago, Francesco had been elated about a dream of his house—or was it a palace?—filled, not with cloth but with armor, swords, and shields. He had seen a shadowy figure in the house. A beautiful bride, perhaps. A princess? A guide appeared and told him, "Francesco, all of this is for you and your knights." In his exuberance, Francesco had proclaimed this dream not only to Elia but to many other friends as well, saying that it proved that he would become a great prince.

"I was sure that the dream confirmed what Messer Bishop suggested—that I go to Apulia and fight for Lord Pope. This is what I said at first. But later I wasn't sure."

Elia remembered his confidence and then his vacillation.

"I went because I'd told my friends. They expected it."

Your boasting made them expect it, Elia thought.

"Elia, I had another dream. That's why I came back."

This Elia had not known.

"That first night when Messer Orsino and I stopped in Spoleto. I started to feel unwell. I thought I'd feel better in the morning, but when I was half asleep, I heard a voice say to me, 'Francesco, where are you going?' So, I told him. Then he said to me, 'Who can do more good for you? The master or the servant?' 'The master,' I answered."

Elia nodded.

"Then he said to me, 'Then why are you abandoning the Master for the servant, the patron for the client?'"

Francesco paused.

"'My Lord,' I said, 'what do you want me to do?' He answered, 'Go back to your land, and what you are to do will be told to you. You must understand in another way the vision which you saw.'"

Francesco hesitated, then added, "And there is something else."

Elia cocked his head, attentive. "The other night, after a banquet, when we were dancing in the streets, suddenly it was like I was seeing everything from outside myself. I couldn't move. If someone had cut me to pieces, I wouldn't have felt a thing. It was as if I had died. As if I were looking on Assisi and my life from eternity, and everything was nothing. Nothing, Elia."

"You were drunk."

"My life is worthless. Why am I here? What value are my possessions? If I died, which of them would I have? Only my sins, Elia. They come with me. Nothing else. What was my Lord trying to show me?"

Elia had no idea. He touched his index finger to his mouth in a familiar gesture that meant he was thinking.

"What did the first dream mean, if not to go to Apulia?"

Elia again put his finger to his lips. *Quiet, Francesco. Let me think.*

"Does it mean I will become a knight at home?"

Elia drew his legs up to his chest and rested his head on his knees, his eyes closed. Francesco would get the hint that Elia was thinking, praying.

"Everyone thinks I came back because I'm a coward."

"Are you?" Elia lifted his head.

"I don't know."

Elia gazed at his friend. In the firelight, Francesco's face looked clouded. Questions had replaced the joy and vanity he had when planning to join Messer Orsino. Elia had no answers. But Someone did.

"The voice told you to come home, where you would be told what to do?"

"Sì."

"Then, my friend, you must pray about what to do. Maybe what happened in the street is part of the answer. God will show you. Pray. I'll wait outside."

Elia walked around the fire and found a boulder near the grazing palfreys. Climbing onto it, he relished the thin April sunlight warming his chestnut-colored mantle. He pulled his knees up to his chest and wrapped his arms about them. *My Lord,* he prayed, *show him what to do.*

The Lord might not answer for many days. Until he did, Francesco would want to come here again and again, and Elia would accompany him. Then they would both pray where they liked best to pray—Francesco in quiet, close darkness and Elia in open spaces of light.

NOTES

1C (first book, chapter II) records Francesco's dream of his house filled with armor. 2C (first book, chapter II) records the dream in Spoleto.

According to 1C (first book, chapter III) and L3C (chapter IV), at this time, Francesco often prayed within a cave. According to 1.5C, Elia was Celano's primary source of information for 1C. Therefore, since an eyewitness seems to have relayed the account of Francesco's prayer in the cave, historians believe that Elia was the friend who waited outside the cave while Francesco prayed within.

Some believe the cave was the crypt at San Damiano. Others locate it at the Carceri above Assisi where the friars later built hermitages. Recent research indicates a third location called the Cave of Cinnicihio from which one can now see the Basilica of Saint Francis (https://www.youtube.com/watch?v=bokXy5Td_xU&feature=youtu.be). This book, following the hypothesis of Italian archeologists who explored this cave on June 9, 2012, postulates that the Cave of Cinnichio is where Francesco prayed, and that cave is accurately described in this chapter.

21

Dom Pietro

Woods around San Damiano, Assisi (May 1205)

Dom Pietro was snoozing with his back against a huge oak whose boughs overshadowed the decrepit Church of San Damiano. During warm weather, he napped here daily. The moss was soft under his behind and the tree sturdy against his stooped and achy back. Lying prostrate was getting too painful with every bone poking and every muscle pinching his withered frame.

As he often did, he was daydreaming of when he had come to this church as a young cleric. Then the walls were sturdy, and the sanctuary swept, and the building where he lived was a hospice for pilgrims. After housing visitors for a night in his spare bedroom, he'd send them on their way to Rome and other destinations. Seeing a way to make money, astute Assisi citizens then built inns to entice pilgrims. Those staying with Pietro decreased. The consortium of Lombard lords who held this chapel then gave it to the bishop, and it had fallen into disuse. *Just like me*, he thought wryly. The bishop tended to prestigious churches, not derelict country chapels. Likely, the bishop and nearly all of Assisi had forgotten San Damiano, and that suited Pietro just fine. He liked solitude, prayer, reflection, unhurried work in his garden, gleaning in nearby fields and olive groves. In winter, he ate nuts and turnips he'd stored in the fall. His was a poor but simple life, answerable to God alone.

"Dom Pietro! Wake up! It's me! Francesco!"

Pietro groaned. Wake up? He was comfortable. Asleep.

"Dom Pietro!" The voice insisted. "You told me to wake you whenever I came. I'm here. Wake up!" Francesco was shaking him.

Pietro groaned.

Francesco. Francesco. "Francesco!" he shouted, waking. He threw his arms around Francesco, who threw his arms around the priest.

Pietro shrieked. "You're squeezing me to death!"

Francesco broke his grip as they both laughed.

"I heard that you were home. Let me look at you!"

Francesco looked well. But not quite. Was this the young man who used to prance down here with alms and poppies? Pietro was looking at the face of a somber man.

Francesco plopped onto the ground, his back to the oak. "I wish I could sleep that soundly."

Pietro caught the discouragement. "What's wrong?"

"I don't know." Francesco's voice was weary. "I should be dead. I should have died in the war or in prison, or at home with fever. Why am I still alive? I would be happier dead, I think."

"Would you like to talk, Francesco?"

"If I were dead, I would be in hell for all my sins. But hell cannot be worse than, than," he waved his arms aimlessly about, "this."

His dimmed priesthood glimmered in Pietro's mind. "Do you wish to confess? Maybe if you confess, the Francesco I knew will return."

Francesco looked doubtful. "Perhaps the Francesco you knew is dead. I'm just walking around in his body."

"What's troubling you?"

"Have you ever been in battle?"

Pietro was about to answer "no," but Francesco had not stopped talking. "I have. I've been in prison. What does war do to people? Men I trusted, men I admired . . . . They became wolves." Francesco's eyes widened. "I saw slaughter. Of defenseless men. Boys. I thought these woods would soothe me, but no. I see invisible corpses everywhere. I tried parties, but my friends' faces remind me of the faces of men I saw murdered. I led the Tripudianti dancing through the streets, but the streets seem red with blood. My sins are so many! I must do penance for them. The bishop told me to join the forces of Lord Pope, and I would gain complete forgiveness of my sins. But my Lord God sent me home. I cannot live like this, Dom Pietro. I don't know what to do."

Pietro whispered a quick prayer. *Where do I begin to help him, my Lord?*

The answer seemed imperative. FORGIVE HIM HIS SINS.

"Francesco, do you want to be forgiven your sins?"

"Can God forgive me? I may have sent men to hell. Men who had no time to repent before I killed them. Why should God forgive me? So that I can go to heaven while they are forever banned from it?"

"Francesco, are you sure you killed anyone?"

"I struck them. They fell . . . ." His voice trailed off.

"Do you think you are God to know the state of a dying man's soul? God will have extended His mercy to those men. Now He extends it to you. Do you want forgiveness for all your unforgiven sins?"

Francesco looked at Pietro with eyes red with tears. "I want it, but I'm unworthy."

"Who's worthy? God doesn't expect worthiness. He wants remorse."

Francesco groaned. "That I have."

"Then I give you absolution." Dom Pietro placed his hands on the young man's head and blessed him. "Now for restitution."

What penance should he give him? Pietro thought of Church-appointed penances to make restitution for sins.

Like the numerous penitents in this region, Francesco could repair churches and other holy places—he knew how to do it, for he had helped as a mason to build the city walls. No, doing manual labor was below his station in life unless it were to help the comune and the merchants. Francesco's parents would never approve.

He could give alms, but his father had not emancipated him. What money did Francesco have that belonged to himself and not to his father?

He could put on sackcloth and tend the poor and the lepers, but his family would never tolerate such indignity.

Francesco needed a respectable, Church-approved penance for grave sins. There was one. "For your penance, you must make a pilgrimage to Rome."

Francesco frowned. "Papà would never permit it. He says work will cure me. He doesn't believe I've sinned."

Pietro sighed. "Does your papà ever send you to Rome for business?"

"Sì. I will be going at summer's end."

"Turn it into a pilgrimage. Conduct whatever business he asks but also pray in the holy places. Find an extra, difficult sacrifice to make while there. That's your penance."

Pietro thought he caught a glimpse of hope in Francesco's eyes. "I'll do it. Grazie!"

NOTES

While the histories don't record any confession of Francesco, he was remorseful for his sins and so would have sought forgiveness. Pazzelli (chapters 2 and 3) lists the penances mentioned in this chapter as being common for demonstrating repentance for serious sins. 1.5C (section 61) records Francesco's trip to Rome as a business trip while 2C (first book, chapter IV) calls it a pilgrimage.

22

Grandenaso

La Basilica di San Pietro, Rome (September 1205)

Grandenaso shifted his weight from one foot to the other as he stood between the Porta Sancta and the Porta Guidonea leading into la Basilica di San Pietro. Near the middle doors, where most pilgrims entered, most beggars clustered. There he had never received as many alms as he did here, off to the right, where fewer beggars awaited the fewer pilgrims who entered.

In a repetitive gesture, Grandenaso smoothed his black beard, flecked with gray, then rubbed his drippy nose with his sleeve. He had come to like his prodigious nose; pilgrims might overlook others, but they almost always gawked at Grandenaso. Confidently, he held his small begging bowl a bit farther out into the pilgrims' pathway and held out his dirty palm, smiling his gap-toothed smile into each new face. The several coins he had already collected he had tucked into the nape of his green hood. No point in letting pilgrims think he had already received some revenue.

How many mornings had he stood in this spot, begging from pilgrims piously intent on venerating the tomb of Christ's chief apostle and the first pope? Long ago, his parents had exploited this spot. He was their youngest son, the only one of his family still alive, as far as he knew. His own children and wife were begging elsewhere. As usual, they would meet him here tonight. Maybe there would be enough scraps for a meal or enough coins to buy one.

What was it like to work for a living? Or to have enough money to hire others to work for you? It was easier to beg.

Ah, someone was stopping. A dandily dressed fellow with big ears. Did people call him Grandiorecchie? Grandenaso stifled a laugh. No, this dandy would be called Messer.

Coins clattered into the begging bowl. Grandenaso wheezed in amazement. Generous. Excessively generous.

"Good beggar, I would like to pay you to exchange your clothes with me."

What? Did the dandy really say that?

"Will you exchange your clothes with me? For today?"

Was he mad? Once an insane man had throttled Grandenaso. Another time a raving woman had knifed him. He now refused to deal with anyone whose brain was broken. What to do? Leave? How? If he tried to escape, the man might knife him. He had better agree. "Sì, Messer."

"Grazie!" Grandiorecchie exclaimed and began removing his shoes. "These clothes will fit you. I made them myself."

A noble who sews his own clothes? Crazy!

The man was undressing. Right here. At the Porta Sancta. At the basilica's entrance. People stared as they filed past.

The exchange was quick. Grandiorecchie stood clothed in the grime-splotched, ragged beggar's tunic while Grandenaso was decked in a red ermine cape, azure tights, sapphire smock, and scarlet cap. Some of the finest clothes he had ever seen. Now what to do? He couldn't beg in this garb.

"Wait," Grandiorecchie said. He spit a few times on the hem of Grandenaso's tunic and then scrubbed the beggar's face and hands. "You look a little better. Wash in the fountain and you can pass for me today." Grandiorecchie was beaming. "If anyone asks your name, tell him Francesco di Assisi. What shall I tell them if they ask me?"

"They won't ask you." No one asked beggars their names.

"May I eat with you this evening? Whatever I collect? I'll pay you well," Francesco said. Grandenaso felt a coin pressed into his hand. "Give this to me when I beg from you. It'll be yours at the day's end."

What if I don't come back? Grandenaso thought. But he'd come back. In this garb, he could never beg.

"Grazie for doing this for me. It's a penance."

A penance? His penance was Grandenaso's life.

As Grandenaso backed away, Francesco pressed into Grandenaso's niche and held out his hand. "*Pour l'amour de Dieu*," he said, smiling at Grandenaso. The beggar-turned-Francesco dropped the coin into the beggar's bowl. How odd to be giving alms! But he would receive them in the end, eh? Francesco had promised that. Grandenaso would find his family and show them his finery. Dressed like this, he might be good-looking. The still water at the edge of the fountain would show him his reflection. "*Pour l'amour de Dieu*," he heard, and then the clatter of the pilgrims swallowed up the French words.

NOTES

L3C (chapter III) and 2C (first book, chapter IV) describe Francesco's clothing exchange with an unnamed beggar at Saint Peter's Basilica in Rome. Grandenaso translates as Big Nose, Grandiorecchie as Big Ears.

23

Palfrey

Colle della Strada, Assisi/Perugia (November 1205)

In the warm autumn sunlight, the chestnut palfrey plodded along at a lazy pace. With determination and without stopping, its youthful master had guided the horse to certain fields and forested areas. Twice they had circled the only house they'd approached.

A while ago, the master had turned the animal about and, by the scent the horse was following, they were returning the way they'd come. This meant that eventually they'd reach home where grain, fodder, and water awaited.

Suddenly the palfrey's ears twitched and turned back and forth. He raised his head, alert. The palfrey saw nothing, heard nothing. But he knew. The Great Master, always present but usually silent, was speaking.

Obedient to the tug on the reins, the palfrey slowed its gait. Another tug. The horse halted. His young master sat quietly, the palfrey awaiting direction. Then more tugs. His master was circling the horse. Strange. After circling a few times, the master guided the palfrey down the road, then up again. Down and up.

More tugs at the reins and the palfrey stepped off the road into the forest. Following the guidance of the reins and the master's knees, the palfrey began climbing a gentle knoll. A faint stench of decaying flesh wafted from the slightly higher knoll to the right. It was the stink of certain ragged people to whom the master occasionally threw pouches of something heavy that clattered when they hit the ground. When this first happened, the palfrey had started at the noise, but the master threw the heavy pouches so frequently that the horse had conquered his skittishness.

Today the master didn't guide the palfrey toward the smell. Instead, he slowly rode through the forest into a cleared area of tangled grass and dried wildflowers. Following the gentle guidance of the reins, the palfrey leisurely stepped throughout the field until the master reined it to a halt with nothing nearby except more grass and dead flower heads. Slowly the master dismounted and led the horse behind him as he walked. Suddenly he dropped the reins. The presence of the Great Master was strong, soothing. The palfrey felt complete peace. He began to nibble grass.

A short distance away, the master had sunk to his knees and buried his head in his hands. The palfrey could hear his frightening, swelling and subsiding gasps and cries. Perhaps this was how humans communicated with the Great Master.

The nibbling palfrey had wandered slightly when his master, his face wet with the rain that sometimes appeared on human faces, patted the steed's neck and mounted.

The palfrey lifted his head and swiveled his ears. As always, the Great Master was here. But now He was silent.

The horse followed the master's lead and some long time later was standing before a familiar building of colorful cloths. His master's master filled the doorway.

"Papà, as you requested, I have visited your lands in the Campagna near Colle della Strada. All is well."

"The Perugini have not disturbed our country house?"

"No."

"May this peace last so that we can visit there again."

"I hope so."

"Tomorrow, visit the properties in Fontanelle and Bassano. I'll give you a list."

"Sì, Papà."

"Good, Francesco. Now go water your horse."

His master bowed, and soon the palfrey was taking a long drink of water in its stall while a groomsman wiped down its back.

NOTES

Pietro di Bernardone owned land in the Campagna, the area near the hill of Colle della Strada and the leper hospital (Fortini, pp. 114–115). Assisi and Perugia established a fragile peace agreement on August 31, 1205 (Fortini, p. 196). Only thereafter could Pietro safely send Francesco to Colle della Strada to examine his properties.

Following battle and imprisonment, Francesco displayed the symptoms of post-traumatic stress disorder common to veterans. We don't know how he was healed of this. However, a veteran's revisiting the places of battle after the war can be a major step in healing. See, for example, *War and the Soul* (Tick, 2005).

24

Palfrey

Fontanelle, Assisi (November 1205)

Under a thick, gray sky, the palfrey plodded through the forests of Fontanelle. His master was kind, allowing the horse to drink freely of the occasional springs that bubbled up from the forest floor. They were resting beside one spring, the palfrey's head lowered, his back leg cocked, almost asleep when his eyes shot open, his ears pricked.

The Great Master was here.

The young master was sitting on a fallen log, his eyes closed, his head resting on his hands.

The palfrey heard nothing except the breeze, heavy with moisture, sifting through the trees and the soft bubbling of the spring.

In His silent voice, the Great Master was speaking.

After some time, the palfrey's young master rose and mounted. For a while he sat in the saddle. Unmoving. The palfrey switched his tail and waited.

Slowly the young master turned the palfrey's head, gently kicked his sides, and set him walking through the woods. After some distance, the horse's nostrils flared at the stench growing stronger as he plodded toward it. Anytime now his master would throw a small, heavy pouch at a ragged, smelly human and then bolt away.

The stench was strong. The palfrey turned to look to the right. There, among the trees, was one of those decaying humans.

The palfrey's ears pricked.

The Great Master was speaking again. Wordlessly. The palfrey sensed a great warmth flooding him.

He stopped at the light tug on the reins.

The palfrey felt his young master slowly dismount and fumble through the pouch slung over the palfrey's back. Then he patted the palfrey on the rump.

"My Lord, help me." The horse's ears flicked at the soft whisper.

His master began slowly to approach the ragged man who began to shake some object that clacked loudly. The palfrey had heard it often, but the noise still made him skittish.

His master was walking toward the man with the clacker. The man had no nose. One eye drooped. His face was swollen with many bumps.

"Leper, Messer. Stay back."

His master kept walking.

The palfrey twitched his tail. This had never before happened.

Warmth flooded the animal. The Great Master. Here. Speaking. Wordlessly.

Clacking wildly.

"Leper, Messer! Stay back." The man with no nose began to back away.

"Stop!" his master ordered. "I mean you no harm. I wish to do mercy to you."

The ragged man did not move. The palfrey's young master took the ragged man's fingerless hand in his own and kissed it.

Then his master placed the small, heavy bag into the other man's palm.

"What's your name?"

"Ambrogio, Messer."

"I am Francesco. May I . . . may I . . . ?" Slowly his master reached out.

"Messer, don't touch me. I'm a leper."

"No. I'm the leper. You are Jesus to me. Let me touch you so that I may be healed."

The young master slowly placed his hands on the noseless face. With great gentleness, he drew the man's face toward his own and touched his lips to each bumpy cheek the way humans sometimes did. Then he bowed to the ragged man. "Grazie, Ambrogio. I'll be back. I wish to do mercy to you."

NOTES

Most people during Francesco's time believed that lepers were moral degenerates who were being justly punished by God (Richards, 1977, chapter 1). At some point, Francesco began to see things differently. He begins his *Testament*, written in 1226, in these words: "The Lord gave me, Brother Francis, thus to begin doing penance in this way: for when I was in sin, it seemed too bitter for me to see lepers. And the Lord Himself led me among them and I showed mercy to them. And when I left them, what had seemed bitter to me was turned into sweetness of soul and body. And afterward I delayed a little and left the world."

1C (first book, chapter VII) records Francesco kissing a leper. L3C (chapter IV) adds that he gave the leper alms, kissed his hand, and accepted a kiss of peace from him. No history names the leper or tells where this happened, or what led Francesco at that moment of time to this particular action. Many historians believe that Francesco's encounter with the leper happened at San Lazzaro d'Arce. According to Fortini (pp. 114-15), Pietro di Bernardone owned land in the vicinity of this hospital.

Part Four

"And Afterward I Delayed a Little and Left the World"

25

Ambrogio

San Lazzaro d'Arce, Assisi (November 1205)

Ambrogio straddled a long row of huge turnips growing in a cleared patch of ground outside the leper hospital of San Lazzaro d'Arce. With his fingerless hands, he'd been no help in planting, but he had been able to hoe out the weeds. His efforts and those of others paid off. The turnips would serve the lepers well this winter. In fact, Tiberio, the cook, had sent him to fetch a big one for dinner. Since the bulbous roots grew half above ground, they were easy to pull, even without fingers.

He was just about to tug the biggest turnip when the pounding of hooves stopped him. He heard only a single steed. Since women did not ride alone, and the poor did not ride at all, Ambrogio guessed the rider to be a man of wealth. Maybe he brought provisions, and Tiberio would not have to cook.

The rider was a young fellow wearing a finely tailored tunic of blue brocade sewn together with coarse sackcloth. Ambrogio had seen troubadours sporting similar, fashionable garments of cheap and expensive cloth. But this was no troubadour. This was that strange Francesco who had embraced him yesterday in the forest.

"Ambrogio!"

The grinning youth slipped off his steed and, in a gesture so quick that Ambrogio could not stop it, threw his arms around Ambrogio and heartily embraced him as if meeting a good friend. Then, just as quickly, Francesco reached into his leather shoulder bag and pulled out a bulging red silk pouch. This he pressed into Ambrogio's palm. It was heavy with coin.

Ambrogio sputtered at the spontaneous familiarity and the weight of the gift. "Grazie."

"Now show me what to do. I wish to do mercy to you."

Ambrogio's mind was spinning. Among holy Christians, especially penitents, doing mercy meant showing compassion and providing assistance.

"I came to help," Francesco said again. "Can you show me what to do?"

Ambrogio smiled. The youth's grin was irresistible.

"You want to do mercy. Come on!"

After introducing Francesco to the other lepers, Ambrogio led him to a hut where the roof leaked. Then he showed him the inefficiently patched hole in the garden wall where wild boars pushed through at night.

"I'll come back in workman's clothes to fix these. I'll bring clothing for you, too. I can make warm winter garments for everyone." Francesco waved his hand toward a cleared patch near the garden. "Can you call everyone here so I can measure them?"

Francesco used his palms to measure each of the seven most poorly clad lepers. Then, with a short stylus, he jotted some figures on a small wax tablet pulled from his leather shoulder bag.

With aloof curiosity, the men and women submitted to Francesco's ministrations.

"I think he's sincere," Ambrogio whispered to old, feeble Silvio, who rolled his eyes in disbelief.

"Messer!" Domina Stefania called. She had been sitting on a stump off to the side, watching. When anyone came to tend the lepers, Stefania made sure that she got her share of attention. Francesco jotted Silvio's measurements onto the tablet and looked up.

"I don't need garments. Mine are fine enough." Yearly Stefania's wealthy family brought her new clothing. Then she would give her castoffs to other women in the hospital. "But Zappolo here."

Scowling Zappolo, a tattered mantle pulled tightly about him, was pressed against the trunk of a huge beech. He had not even bothered to stand when

Francesco measured him. He was, Ambrogio knew, the angriest leper in the hospital, totally unwilling or unable to accept his condition as God's mysterious way of cleansing the soul. Not a year ago, Zappolo had been taken away from his wife and small children and put here. As a tanner, he had hardly made enough to support his family. Now his wife had to keep his business going.

"Zappolo, show him your feet," Stefania commanded.

Zappolo pulled the mantle closer about himself.

"You know he's not going to do that," Tiberio offered.

"He has to," Stefania decreed. She nodded to Tiberio and Ambrogio. "Make him."

The two men were not about to cross Domina Stefania. They lunged at Zappolo and pulled him to the ground. Ambrogio held his head and arms in a tight grip. Tiberio stretched out his legs until the filthy soles of his feet were clearly visible, as were the gaping, foul sores in the center of each. Ambrogio could not see the wounds, but he remembered what they looked like. Raw, nasty, and round, they deeply penetrated skin and muscle. Francesco put the wax tablet and the stylus back into the pouch. Gazing at the wounds, he asked gently, "Could I have some water, please?"

Stefania rose and soon returned with a bowl.

"Zappolo, may I will cleanse these wounds and bandage them for you?" Francesco asked.

Zappolo scowled, but he did not pull his feet away. Nor could he. Tiberio had a good grip on them.

Francesco removed the jaunty blue cap that covered the coif over his head. Then he untied the coif, dipped it into the water, and used it to wipe the grime from Zappolo's sores.

"Am I hurting you?" Francesco asked.

Zappolo shrugged.

Of course, he wasn't hurting him. Leprosy removed the sense of pain.

"These are like the wounds of Christ on the cross," Francesco noted.

Ambrogio had never thought of that.

With his blue brocade cap, Francesco dried Zappolo's feet. Then, sitting flat on the ground, he pulled off his boots and hose and slipped the hose over Zappolo's feet. He tried to work the boots over the feet as well, but Francesco's feet were small. So he gave up, measured Zappolo's feet, and, taking the tablet and stylus from the leather pouch, wrote something.

"You can let him go now," Francesco said.

Ambrogio and Tiberio released their grip. Zappolo gathered himself under his mantle again.

"I'll bring you shoes," Francesco said.

"Why?" Zappolo shot back. "Why do you care?"

Francesco sat back on his heels. "It was bitter for me to see lepers," he said, looking from face to face. "But yesterday, God led me among you." He smiled at Ambrogio. "By His mercy, what was bitter has become sweet. I have much to make up for in your regard. Will you permit me to begin?"

He handed the wet coif and cap to Stefania. "Perhaps someone can use these." Then he looked down at his boots. "Will these fit anyone? I have others."

They fit Sansone, a teen who had grown up in the hospital.

NOTES

The opening quotation for Part Four is from Saint Francis' *Testament*, 3.

At this time (L3C, chapter IV), Francesco was visiting leper hospitals around Assisi to minister to lepers by bathing them and tending their sores. Most historians believe that he began this ministry at San Lazzaro d'Arce. Fortini (p. 206) mentions that one of the lepers at San Lazzaro was named Domina Stefania. The other names in this chapter are fictitious and the ministrations of Francesco postulated.

26

Bishop Guido

Bishop's Palace, Assisi (Late November 1205)

On a hearth in the bishop's palace, a crackling fire threw its heat into the chill room. Firelight, added to that of strategically placed oil lamps, lent a cozy radiance to the study. Guido was hunched over a wide table, his thick fingers tracing columns of figures regarding his Semetone vineyards. His notary had done an exemplary job.

Although grapes had been harvested two months ago, Guido was just now perusing the profit and loss evidenced in these important but tedious records. These would help him, in consultation with his overseer, to plan for next year.

He heard a crisp knock at the door.

"Sì?" Guido boomed.

The door cracked open. "Messer Francesco would like to see you, Messer Bishop."

"Show him in."

Guido took one last glance at the ledgers and looked up to see Francesco standing before him. Guido embraced the young man, first one shoulder and then the other. He felt and smelled the dampness of Francesco's azure, fur-lined cape.

"So, today it rains again," Guido stated. "Sit down," he offered, seating himself on a wide, cushion-covered seat pushed to the side of the table. Francesco sat on an intricately carved four-legged stool facing him.

"How's your work going with the lepers?"

"Not work. Joy."

Guido nodded. "Excellent. Are you still staying with them at San Lazzaro d'Arce?"

"Sometimes. Sometimes with Dom Pietro. Sometimes at home."

"How are things at home, Francesco?"

Francesco shrugged. "Papà is edgy. He wants me home at night."

"Does he know where you're staying?"

"He thinks I'm with a friend."

Guido nodded.

"You're still working at your father's shop?"

"Sì."

"Good." Working for his father would keep Pietro's anger at bay. "Did you want to see me about something?"

Francesco nodded. "It's difficult to explain. You know the old woman Speranza?"

Guido tried to place the name. He shook his head.

"Very poor, from the countryside. She hobbles through the piazza with a cane and a basket. Hunchbacked. Several bumps on her face."

Ah, her! "Her name is Speranza?"

"Will I come to look like her? Because I'm doing penance?"

"What makes you think that?"

"Last week I saw her when I was in the *mercato* to purchase some cheese. On my way home, a thought came. 'If you keep doing penance, you're going to end up looking like her.' The thought torments me."

"It's a thought, Francesco."

"But is it true?"

"Why are you doing what you're doing?"

"Because it brings me peace."

"If you did, in time, come to resemble Speranza, would you then not have peace?"

Francesco paused.

"I think I'd still have peace."

"Then that's your answer. Whether these thoughts are true or not doesn't matter, does it? You'd keep doing what you're doing whether they're true or not."

Hesitantly, Francesco nodded.

"Don't let the devil frighten you with these thoughts, Francesco. He wants to keep you from this good path you've chosen."

"Are these thoughts from the devil?"

"They're not from God. God made Speranza. He's permitted her deformities for reasons He alone knows. Deformities of the body mean nothing to God. He loves Speranza the way she is. If He gives you similar deformities, that's part of His plan for you. He'll continue to love you. God detests deformities of the spirit. He's healing you of those."

Francesco nodded again.

"If those thoughts come again, pray, 'God bless Speranza. And God bless me.' The thoughts will stop. Satan doesn't want God to bless anyone. He'll find another way to tempt you from where God has led you."

"Another way? What will that be?"

"I don't know. Probably something you've never considered. It's likely to come suddenly." Guido slung about for a comparison. "Like a punch to the head from behind."

Francesco's eyes widened.

"You'll find out when it happens." Guido hoped it would be as easy a temptation to overcome as this one. But he doubted it. He knew how Satan worked.

NOTES

L3C (chapter IV) mentions Francesco's temptation involving the hunchbacked woman. L3C (chapter III) also states that "he did [not] seek counsel from anyone except from God alone, and, periodically, from the bishop of Assisi." Francesco was dividing his time between staying in three places: with the lepers at San Lazzaro d'Arce, with Dom Pietro at San Damiano, and with his parents. Initially, Pietro and Pica probably had no idea of his activities.

27

Messer Elia di Bonbarone

Cave between Assisi and Beviglie (Early December 1205)

Elia liked to wait outside the cave while Francesco prayed. But today a chill breeze, laced with light snow, made the outdoors uncomfortable for a man praying on a boulder. "Elia, sit by the fire today. I'll seek treasure deeper in the cave," Francesco had told him.

Obediently, Elia had sat down near the dancing flames while Francesco disappeared into the recesses of the tunnel. Weeks ago, Francesco had begun using the "seeking treasure" expression. Why would he seek treasure when he seemed increasingly unconcerned with what treasure could buy? Unlike his previous habit of sporting new, exquisite garments weekly, lately he'd been wearing only garments Elia had already seen. Francesco had always been fastidious about his clothing. But now, when he emerged from the cave, his hasty brushing at the dust clinging to him sent him home looking unkempt. Captivation with food delicacies had disappeared from his conversation.

Elia stretched out his cold hands toward the cavorting flames. What delicious warmth! On drier days, while Francesco sought his treasure, Elia had scoured the area for kindling, which he had piled neatly in the cave. Today's fire was a direct result of Elia's foresight.

What was God showing Francesco? Although Francesco was sharing little with Elia, he still preferred being with a friend to being alone. Elia smiled at the irony. Francesco had never been happy alone, but now he was alone in his thoughts although a friend was nearby. Could he be getting accustomed to solitude?

Accompanying Francesco to pray complicated Elia's life. While keeping his promise to be with his friend, Elia found it difficult to reclaim time lost from his business. How could he speed up mattress-making? If he rearranged his storage rooms, he might be able to store more skins to cover the mattresses and more straw with which to stuff them. Traveling less often to the vendors would save time. Now that night fell earlier, he was often working in shadowy lamplight. Suppose he hung his lamps in different places. Or got more lamps. With better light, he could work faster. Mentally he paced his workroom. This could go here. That there. He could build bigger bins. *My Lord*, he prayed, *show me what to do*.

DO NOT STORE UP FOR YOURSELVES TREASURE ON EARTH. The Gospel verse startled him. Where did that come from? WHERE RUST AND MOTH CONSUME. And fire? For an instant, his mind conjured up fire enveloping his mattresses. BUT STORE UP FOR YOURSELVES TREASURE IN HEAVEN WHERE NEITHER RUST NOR MOTH CONSUME. Nor fire. FOR WHERE YOUR TREASURE IS, THERE WILL YOUR HEART BE ALSO.

Elia's thoughts unnerved him. Whatever treasure Francesco was seeking was irrelevant to Elia. What treasure was Elia seeking? He tried to pray, but then he began to think about his livelihood. He would return to reorganizing his work area, and he would begin to pray, *My Lord, show me what to do*. This unfamiliar, confused mix of prayer and planning disoriented him. If he gave himself wholeheartedly to prayer, where would that lead? Yet this meticulous planning was making his work into a ravenous wolf swallowing him like a nursling rabbit.

As daylight faded, Francesco emerged from the darkness, his face smudged and his azure mantle dusty. "My friend, you've been good to come with me all these months. Now it's getting chilly, and the distance between our homes seems longer as the days shorten. I know another place to pray, close to the city. From now on, I'll go there."

"Who will accompany you?"

Francesco smiled. "I won't be alone."

Elia understood. The Lord was always with them.

"Elia, I've found the treasure I sought." The firelight lit Francesco's gentle smile. The pain that had distorted his face for so long had slowly been fading. Now it seemed entirely gone. In Francesco's features, Elia saw only peace. Was peace the treasure?

Elia placed his hands on Francesco's shoulders. "I'm happy for you, my friend." Then he drew Francesco close and they embraced, first one shoulder and then the other. They kicked dirt over the fire until the flames sizzled out, then dusted off their clothing. Untethering their snow-dappled palfreys from a scrubby bush, they headed home, Elia to Beviglie and Francesco to Assisi.

NOTES

At some point, Francesco ceased praying in the cave and moved his preferred prayer spot to San Damiano, perhaps because this was closer to the lepers whom he was tending.

28

Mouse

Church of San Damiano, Assisi (Early December 1205)

The yearling mouse twitched her nose. The scent told the creature that the kindly human was in the church again, kneeling before the large, painted man with stretched out arms. The large, painted man, and all the other painted people around him, never moved from their big cross, so the mouse paid them no attention. But this human would come with crumbs or cheese shavings or slivers of meat in his palm. The mouse had learned to approach warily and nibble at them. She could smell food on him today. Warily she crept out of the shadows and looked up imploringly at the young face.

He didn't see her. He was looking at that painted cross. The scent of the meat in the man's purse was tantalizing. It emboldened the little creature to scurry closer. She was at the man's knee now. No response. He was looking at the painted cross. Most of the time, he talked to the cross when he was here. Words like, "My Lord, I give you my life. What do you want me to do? Show me what to do, my Lord." He had said those words so many times that the mouse recognized the cadence of them, although she didn't understand what they meant.

The man wasn't talking today. But Someone Else was. Someone Else was always here, gentle and welcoming, and the mouse felt safe in the continual Presence. The mouse had never heard Someone Else speak. Now she sensed sounds that she didn't hear and couldn't understand. Someone Else was speaking. Maybe the man, kneeling so still, could hear and understand. The mouse put her paws on his knee. No response. She pulled herself up onto his leg. Maybe she could wiggle into the purse and get the meat. She had no reason to fear. The man and Someone Else were kind.

Suddenly the man laughed a little, startling laugh. Frightened, the mouse leapt off his knee and fled into the crack under the altar.

"Oh, little mouse! I'm sorry. Come out from there, little sister, and I'll feed you. Come on. Don't be afraid. I'm your big brother. Come." The young man's hand was stretched toward the mouse, who could smell the slivers of meat on it.

"Come on," the gentle voice coaxed. "You must get used to me. I'll be staying here. If Dom Pietro lets me. But he'll let me, don't you think? Even though I'm such a sinner?" The man was talking, but was it to her? He was looking at the cross again. The creature scampered forward and climbed onto the open palm. The hand didn't flinch. She began to nibble the pork.

"'Repair my house which, as you can see, is falling into ruin.' That's what You said, my Lord. He just told me that, little sister. I can't repair it if I'm not here. And I'll have nowhere else to go. Little mouse, my sister, you're sinless, and you live in God's house and you're happy. And I . . ." The man's voice snagged.

A salty drop of water splashed onto the pork. Then another. The mouse had seen rain come from this man's eyes before. How odd that people could make rain, but not rain like the sky made. Salt rain. It made the pork tastier.

NOTES

2C (first book, chapter VI) records Francesco's prayer and the words spoken from the crucifix. It mentions nothing about Francesco's interaction with mice. This imagined encounter is consistent, however, with Francesco's treatment of animals.

29

Dom Pietro

Church of San Damiano, Assisi (Early December 1205)

After praying the Office of Sext at noon, Dom Pietro's new daily routine was to sweep the Church of San Damiano. Previously he hadn't been so concerned about cleanliness, but lately Francesco had been coming here to pray. A few days ago, Dom Pietro had caught him sweeping. "Too much dust and mouse droppings," he had complained. Dom Pietro would give him no more reason to complain. He would sweep first.

He had accumulated a small pile of debris when the door of the church swung open. An unfamiliar man stood there and pushed a pale-blue woolen hood away from his long, angular face. Bowing, the man stepped inside. "Excuse me," he apologized. "Is Francesco here? His father is looking for him."

"No."

"Grazie." The man bowed and was gone. Pietro shrugged and went on sweeping.

That evening, wrapped in his old mantle lined with thinning gray fox fur, Dom Pietro stood before the life-sized crucifix and slowly intoned the Office of

Vespers. Since he prayed it daily just before sunset, he was praying it as early as ever during the year. He was gazing at the benevolent image of Jesus when he heard the door to the church creak open and shut quietly. A traveler needing lodging?

Dom Pietro prayed through the Office, reverently crossed himself, and turned to greet his guest.

"Francesco! Your father was looking for you. Did you see him?"

"No." Ignoring the question, the young man took the priest's hands and kissed them, then pressed into them a bulging purse. "A few days ago, I gave you money to repair the church."

Dom Pietro nodded. A generous sum. Almsgiving was a suitable penance for a spendthrift, rebuilding a church appropriate restitution for laxity in the faith.

"Here's more."

The purse was heavy with coins.

"Please let me stay with you as an oblate, and I'll repair the church."

Oblates were penitents who assisted a specific church with its upkeep. Francesco had discussed this with Pietro, but the idea seemed too fantastic. Why would God ask him, as Francesco believed, to repair this run-down place? Why not send him to a wealthy, well-attended church like San Giorgio, San Rufino, or San Nicolo?

The priest was suspicious. "Where did you get this much money?"

"I took cloth to Foligno and sold it. And my destrier, too."

His destrier? Penitents didn't ride horses.

"You walked back here from Foligno?"

"Sì."

Francesco's nonchalant manner was disconcerting.

"Francesco, the money you gave me earlier was money your father had given you to spend as you wish, wasn't it?"

"Sì."

"Then that was your money. But selling the cloth and the horse? Did your father permit this?"

"I didn't ask him."

Pietro groaned. No wonder his father was looking for him. "Francesco, that's stealing. This is his money, not yours."

"I sold the part of the business that belongs to me."

"None of the business belongs to you until your father gives it to you. He hasn't done that, has he?"

"He will."

"But not yet. This money is his, not yours. I can't take it." Pietro handed the purse back to Francesco. "Give it to your father."

"No! The money is to repair the church." Francesco flung the purse onto a windowsill. "I'll repair the church without it. Let me stay here with you."

What to do? Send Francesco home to a likely beating? He deserved discipline, but not like that. Pietro thought quickly. His house had two small rooms. One he slept in. The other he ate in. "You can sleep on the kitchen floor. Tonight." *While I think what to do about tomorrow.*

Through the thin walls, Dom Pietro could hear Francesco snoring gently in the kitchen. How could he have no worries? Pietro was beset with them. If he sent Francesco home, his father would thrash him. Or worse. If Francesco stayed in the house, his father would eventually find him. Could Francesco stay hidden until his father's fury died down? That could take months.

All night such thoughts tormented him. *My God, show me what to do!* The answer came at dawn.

The cave under the kitchen.

Dom Pietro had discovered it shortly after coming here. That spring day, the always damp floor to the right of the door had cracked when he set two full pails of water on it. Removing the tipsy buckets, he'd examined the damage. The floor needed replacement. When he had torn off the rotted wood, he discovered beneath it—not packed earth, but a deep pit. Mystified, he had grabbed a torch and, squatting on the floor, had peered into the damp cavern. The wooden steps descending into it were crumbled and rotted far below. What had he found? A wine cellar? A crypt? A storage vault? No matter. He had needed none of these, so he'd replaced the rotted floor with new wood and thought no more about it. Until now.

Even before praying, the priest woke Francesco and the two of them pulled back the newer floor, now as weathered as the old. "If you jump down there, can you get out?" Pietro asked.

"I could make a ladder from some of that old lumber." Francesco pointed to the heap of stairs. "Have you got an ax? And rope?"

Pietro nodded. "By the woodpile."

Francesco bounded off. When he returned, Pietro advised, "Work quickly before your father returns. I will work on the floor so that you can easily push it open. Do not come out except for necessity. I will lower food and water to you. When your father's anger cools, you can safely go home."

Francesco grabbed Pietro's hand and kissed it. "Grazie. Molte grazie." He dropped the ax and rope into the pit, then jumped down. Pietro lowered a lighted lamp to him so that he could work.

NOTES

Francesco's selling the horse and cloth and wanting to stay at San Damiano as an oblate to rebuild the church (1C, first book, chapter IV) are consistent with penitential practices of the times (Pazzelli, chapters 2 and 3). The priest at San Damiano refused the money, which Francesco threw on a windowsill. To avoid his father's wrath, Francesco went into hiding in a "pit" or cave "in the house" known "to only one person" (1C, first book, chapter V). Most historians believe that this "pit" was at San Damiano and only Dom Pietro knew its location.

Excavations at San Damiano in the 1990s and early 2000s uncovered a cave located meters below what became the refectory. According to Marino Bigaroni, OFM ("San Damiano—Assisi," 45-97), the refectory is the original structure, predating the church, and may have been built as a Romanesque home. This book postulates that Dom Pietro was living in what is now the refectory and that he hid Francesco in the cave.

30

Dom Pietro

Church of San Damiano (Mid-December 1205)

The days passed, moving methodically toward Christmas. In preparation for the Christ Child's coming, everyone was fasting, so benefactors brought Dom Pietro less food, but he shared what he had with Francesco.

After several days of Francesco calling up from the pit, "Don't bring me any food. I have enough," Pietro realized that Francesco was fasting excessively.

"I'll bring you food every three days," Pietro called down into the darkness. "Don't starve yourself."

"The stomach that glutted itself needs to feel want." The thickness of the voice startled him. Was Francesco weeping down there?

"Eat what I lower to you," Pietro commanded. "It won't be much."

No response.

"Francesco!"

"Would you hear my confession before Christmas?"

Pietro tried to contain his surprise. "Certainly."

In the days that followed, Pietro pondered how to administer the sacrament. The rubrics asked that confessions be heard before the altar, but that was risky. Churches were kept open for travelers and those wishing to pray. Even if Pietro bolted the door from inside the church, he would have to open it if anyone came, and Francesco would have no place to hide. God would have to forgive Francesco's sins in a safer place.

In the morning, two days before Christmas, Pietro di Bernardone came, searching everywhere, including Pietro's house. He found only the priest. He'd return, but not today.

After his noon meal of bread and water, Dom Pietro stirred into flame the fire in his bedroom hearth, bolted the house door, then fetched Francesco from the pit. The young man's face was gaunt, his beard straggly, his eyes swollen. Obviously, as required before receiving God's forgiveness, he had been weeping for his sins.

Pietro led Francesco into the sparsely furnished room. The two men sat on the floor near the hearth where they could gaze at a crucifix hanging on the opposite wall.

Pietro began to pray the customary prayers and the seven penitential psalms. After more prayers, as required by the rite, he reviewed the truths of the faith, then admonished Francesco to be well disposed to confess. Following that, he began a detailed interrogation, with Francesco responding affirmatively or negatively to each question.

"Have you prayed, Francesco?"

"Sì."

"Have you been distracted while praying?"

Francesco's gaze was on the crucifix.

"Sì. Pardon me, my Lord."

Dom Pietro worked his way through the long list of questions and answers. The sins came, jumbled, tearfully admitted. Then suddenly another penitent called out to Pietro who, being careful to close the bedroom door, hurried out to meet him. The penitent had brought a small fowl for Pietro's Christmas feast, the first meat he'd eat since beginning the fast of Saint Martin. After thanking the penitent, Pietro returned to Francesco. With tears trickling down his cheeks, Francesco was kneeling, gazing at the crucifix.

The hearth fire was low. Pietro added more kindling. Francesco returned to sitting near Pietro. The questions and answers continued until Pietro had covered the entire list. Next came a detailed examination of the seven capital sins. Lust. Anger. Envy. Pride. Greed. Gluttony. Sloth. Francesco's tears became profuse. Several times Pietro had to remind him, "Only the sins committed since your pilgrimage. The pilgrimage has forgiven the ones you committed before that."

Once, Francesco asked, "Does the pilgrimage remit sins committed on the pilgrimage?"

Surprised, Pietro replied, "What sins did you commit on the pilgrimage?"

Francesco's head was bowed. Pietro could recognize shame. "First of all, papà thinks I was on a business trip."

"He sent you, didn't he?"

"Sì."

"Did you conduct your father's business?"

"Sì."

"Then you fulfilled his request. He doesn't need to know what else you did."

"Dom Pietro, I made something holy into something sinful." Francesco raised his head so that his gaze met Pietro's. "Before returning home, I threw all my coins as alms into Saint Peter's tomb. I thought myself better than others who were giving small amounts. That was forming judgments. That was pride. I flung the money hard enough to call attention to myself. I wanted people to see how much I gave. That was vanity. When I returned home, papà assumed I had spent all the money he had given me. I never told him the truth."

"If the pilgrimage didn't forgive these sins committed during it, God has forgiven them now, as you have sincerely confessed them."

"There's more. You asked me to do an additional penance."

"The almsgiving at Saint Peter's tomb."

"No. I would have given the money anyway. I exchanged clothes with a beggar for a day."

"You did what?"

"I thought dressing like a beggar would conquer my vanity and pride. Instead, I felt vanity and pride in doing it. Then I ate with the beggars. I thought this would oppose my gluttony. It didn't. The begged leftovers tasted sumptuous. Dom Pietro, I can't even do penance without sinning."

Pietro placed his hands on the young man's slumped shoulders. "Francesco, the Book of Proverbs states that even the just man falls seven times a day. You were hardly just when you went to Rome. However, you recognize your sins and are sorry. Do you think you're better than most people?"

Francesco's head hung lower. "I am far worse."

Dom Pietro disagreed but didn't contradict. "Francesco, most people need a lifetime to conquer pride, vanity, and gluttony." Pietro interrupted the anguished moan. "Don't be discouraged! Rejoice! These persistent sins remind us that we're sinners. Only sinners look for a savior. Fight your sins manfully, and don't let Satan discourage you. He can't win victory in souls that continually turn to God. Ask God's grace to preserve you from committing these sins again."

"My Lord, help me!"

"He will. Now continue."

Pietro had to add more kindling to the hearth before Francesco finished confessing. Pointing to the fire, Pietro said softly, "God's fiery love has consumed your sins, Francesco. Prostrate yourself and request absolution."

As his part in the ritual, Francesco stretched facedown on the floor. "Pardon me, my Lord."

Pietro prayed the formula over Francesco. "May almighty God have mercy on you and forgive you all your sins, past, present, and future, visible and invisible, which you have committed before Him and His saints, which you have confessed, or which you have hidden by some negligence or forgetfulness or bad will; may He free you from all evil here and in the future, may He preserve you in every good and lead you to life without end, Who lives and is glorified forever." Then Dom Pietro knelt, prayed the Our Father, and sang the required psalms and versicles, again asking God to forgive Francesco.

"Francesco, rise," Pietro gently commanded.

Francesco pulled himself into a sitting position.

"You have memorized the Psalter?"

"Sì."

"For thirty days, you must pray it once daily in full. That will be your penance."

"Grazie." Francesco kissed Pietro's hand.

"There's one penance more," Pietro smiled. "On Christmas, you must help me eat the fowl I've received."

Francesco burst into laughter. "To celebrate the birth of our Lord, even the walls should eat meat!"

NOTES

Francesco considered himself a great sinner. The histories give no record of the confession detailed in this chapter. However, the rite of confession and formula of absolution as described follow the process enumerated by Lawrence D. Isabell, OFM (Lawrence, chapter 1).

All the faithful observed the fast of Saint Martin, which began on November 12, the day after the feast of Saint Martin of Tours. The fast lasted until Christmas. The faithful ate no meat, dairy products, or eggs during this fast (Habig, *English Omnibus*, "First Rule of the Third Order," chapters II and III).

31

Dom Pietro

Church of San Damiano (January 1206)

With the Christmas feasts, ending with Epiphany, come and gone, Pietro had been happy to resume his daily routine of prayer, meals, mending, and cleaning. Today, however, when he returned from his daily walk before praying the noon Office of Sext, he found Francesco sitting cross-legged on the floor of the church, gazing at the crucifix.

Francesco turned to him nonchalantly. "Oh, it's you." He sounded disappointed. "I thought it might be papà."

"You've been hiding for a month so that your papà would not find you. And now you're waiting for him?"

"Sì."

"He's been here several times. He's infuriated. Do you know what he'll do to you if he finds you? It won't be nice."

"I know." The voice was calm, resolved. Francesco again turned his gaze toward the crucifix. "The Lord gave me knowledge about my dreams."

The change of subject caught Pietro off guard. "The two you told me?"

"Sì. Remember how, when I was going to Apulia, the voice asked me if it were wiser to serve the servant or the Master? And I said, 'The Master.' The voice told me that I had to interpret the dream about the armor in another way. I've been interpreting it wrongly. Somewhere Scripture talks about the armor of God. Can you read me the passage?"

Pietro knew where this interpretation was going. "Francesco, be reasonable."

"Please."

The gentle courtesy was difficult to resist. Reluctantly Pietro opened the Scriptures on the altar and paged to Saint Paul's Epistle to the Ephesians. It was in here someplace. His eyes scanned the text. Here. Right near the end. In a flat voice, he began to read:

> "Finally, be strong in the Lord and in the strength of his might. Put on the whole armor of God, that you may be able to stand against the wiles of the devil. For we are not contending against flesh and blood, but against the principalities, against the powers, against the world rulers of this present darkness, against the spiritual hosts of wickedness in the heavenly places."

Despite his misgivings, the words were rousing the old priest's spirit, recalling the forgotten fervor he'd had as a young cleric. "Therefore, take up the whole armor of God, that you may be able to withstand in the evil day, and having done all, to stand."

Frightening. Idealistic. Powerful. Pietro looked up.

"There is more, I think. Helmets. Shields. Breastplates."

"Sì. There is more." The embers of the old fire of Pietro's faith were crackling into flame.

> "Stand therefore, having girded your waist with truth, having put on the breastplate of righteousness and having shod your feet with the preparation of the gospel of peace; above all, taking the shield of faith with which you will be able to quench all the fiery darts of the wicked one."

Inadvertently, Pietro was mentally clothing himself in this spiritual armor.

> "And take the helmet of salvation, and the sword of the Spirit, which is the word of God; praying always with all prayer and supplication in the Spirit, being watchful to this end with all perseverance and supplication for all the saints—and for me, that utterance may be given to me, that I may open my mouth boldly to make known the mystery of the Gospel, for which I am an ambassador in chains; that in it I may speak boldly, as I ought to speak."

"Grazie. This is the armor of my dream. The Master's armor in His palace. 'All this is for you and your knights,' the voice said. Who the other knights are, I don't know. But I know who I am. I'm His knight. I'll serve my Master. Now I understand."

Francesco pointed to the crucifix. "Dom Pietro, look at Him." Pietro left the Scripture on the altar and sat down beside Francesco. "Do you see? He's been beaten. Mocked. Spat upon. Nailed. Pierced. But how triumphant! How noble! The crown of thorns has become a halo of glory. He was obedient to death. Powerless before His enemies. He didn't fight back. 'Love your enemies,' He said. 'Do good to those who hate you. If someone takes your cloak, give him your tunic also. Don't be afraid of those who kill the body. Be afraid of the one who can kill the soul in hell. If someone strikes you on one cheek, turn to him the other also.' This meekness is His glory. His nobility. 'My power is made perfect in weakness.' He has called me to follow Him. To do as He did. And what have I been doing? Hiding in the crypt while you feed me. This isn't what He did."

"You're safe there. Your father won't find you."

Francesco jumped up. "Then I'll go into Assisi. There he'll find me." He bowed courteously to the priest. "I've always sought glory. Now I'll find it. Like He did. In shame."

Pietro was unnerved by this bravado. "Francesco, think about this."

"Don't look so worried! This is the meaning of my dreams." He grabbed Pietro's hands and hoisted him to his feet. "Be my squire! Help me dress! My shoes!"

Pietro felt disoriented. Francesco was wearing shoes. Very dusty, pointed, red ones.

"Here they are." With a deft and exaggerated motion, Francesco plucked air from the empty space near Dom Pietro's feet. "Let me support myself on your shoulder, please." With quick, sharp motions, he mimed pulling on one shoe and then the other.

"Now. The belt. There!" He pointed to the air on Pietro's right. Feeling self-conscious at this pretend game, Pietro took the invisible belt and handed its nothingness to Francesco, who swiftly mimicked fastening it around his waist.

"Breastplate!"

Despite himself, Pietro smiled. He picked up the imaginary breastplate. "Oh, this is heavy, Francesco! How can you knights wear such armor?"

Francesco smiled. "That is why we have squires to help clothe us in it."

Pietro grinned. Francesco bent at the waist, and Pietro slipped the invisible breastplate over his head. Francesco adjusted it into place, then nodded at Pietro, who pretended to buckle it.

"Helmet!"

With two hands, Pietro handed nothing to Francesco, who took it and slipped it over his head.

"Sword!"

Pietro handed the sharpest weapon in creation to him. Francesco hoisted it aloft, its invisible blade pointing to the ceiling. Thrusting it into an invisible scabbard, Francesco bowed.

"What do you think?"

Francesco had had no change of clothing nor any bath since hiding here a month ago. His olive green surcote and mustard-tinted leggings were smudged with grime. Beneath his limp green cap, his usually perfect hair was grown out and shaggy. A month's growth of beard left a straggly stubble on his thin cheeks. He looked anything but the dandy he had been. Appearing like this, he would fare ill in Assisi.

"I think you're the most noble knight in all the world."

"Grazie! You've been too good to me. Better than any father! Grazie!" Exuberantly Francesco threw his arms around Pietro and kissed him on both cheeks. Then, with a swift flourish of his invisible sword, he bounded up the few steps and exited the church.

Dom Pietro called after him, "May the armor of God protect you!"

NOTES

After a month of hiding, Francesco emerged to face his father (1C, first book, chapter V). The histories give no reason for this sudden decision, nor do they explain the meaning of Francesco's dreams. This chapter postulates that Francesco finally understood the meaning of his dreams and that God gave him the grace to act on them.

The passage Dom Pietro reads is Ephesians 6:14–20.

Part Five

"O How Glorious It Is to Have a Holy and Great Father in Heaven!"

32

Sabbatino

Hospital of San Rufino, Assisi (Early January 1206)

Sabbatino was strong, sturdy, and tall enough to support Scontroso as he slowly guided the lame beggar around the perimeter of the large room. It housed ten poor patients at the Hospital of San Rufino. Baptized Felice, "Happy," Scrontoso's nickname "Grumpy" fit him better.

"Slow down." To Sabbatino.

"Out of my way." To Palmiro, another patient.

"Who cleans this place?" To no one in particular.

Sabbatino had eased Scontroso onto his bed when he heard the commotion.

"Quiet!" Scontroso shouted, as if the mob outside could hear him.

The yelling and jeering swelled. The crowd must have found a poor unfortunate. Sabbatino had been such a person after his gentle mother died. Then a child, he had not understood why she hadn't risen as usual following his father's beating. After that, his father's anger had turned to his son. "Trash!" papà would scream at him. He'd heard himself called "Trash" so often that he found it increasingly difficult to remember that Mother had called him "my little treasure." As the boy aged, the abuse escalated. Two springs after his mother's death, he fled from home, wherever that was. For days he hid in fields and forests, not knowing if papà was looking for him. Hunger drove him into towns for food until he had come to Assisi. There Giovanni di Sasso, cleric of the cathedral and rector of this hospital, took him in to help care for the patients. As he did not know his name, Giovanni called him Sabbatino, since he had come begging on a Sabbath. Giovanni had been so good to him, even inviting him to sit in his classroom with boys from noble families. What he had learned in the classroom strengthened his mind, but what the hospital taught him enlarged his heart.

Now his heart pitied whoever was being reviled in the street.

Tucking a wool blanket around Scontroso, Sabbatino hurried toward the door.

"Where you going?" Scontroso demanded.

"To keep someone from being killed!" Sabbatino pulled the door closed behind him and ran toward the Trivio di San Giorgio. If he could not break up the shouting mob, he could at least bring the victim into the hospital and bar the door.

Bulky and strong, he pushed his way into the crowd. The rabble was catcalling, throwing mud and rocks at a grimy figure who was responding cheerfully to them. "Many thanks! Pace e bene!"

A lunatic. How can people harm someone whose mind is broken?

Sabbatino summoned his deepest, most authoritative voice. "This man belongs in the hospital!" Gently he put his hand on the man's mud-spattered shoulder. "Come," he said tenderly.

The man turned toward Sabbatino.

"Francesco?"

With startling swiftness, the two friends flung their arms around each other. A rock crashed into Sabbatino's back. Anger overrode the joy of his surprise. He was no longer a hospital nurse shielding a poor soul from attack. Instead he was again the battered, abused, mocked child who fought his tormentors in the streets, only to go home and succumb dumbly to his father. Like a beast, Sabbatino pulled away from Francesco and lunged at the crowd. Strong arms clamped onto him and pulled him back.

"No, Sabbatino!" Francesco ordered. Twirling away from Sabbatino, Francesco sang, "One blessing for one stone. Two blessings for two!" Flung stones and mud followed him. "Many thanks! Pace e bene!" over and over as he was being pelted.

Francesco had lost his mind. The mood could easily shift from derision to death. Sabbatino grabbed Francesco and threw him over his shoulder like a sack of flour. Like a sack of flour, Francesco did not resist. The chaos of jeers and projectiles followed them and muffled Francesco's blessings.

"Put him down!"

Sabbatino ignored the deep male voice and kept walking toward the hospital.

"Put him down, or you'll be a patient in that hospital, not a nurse!"

Sabbatino attempted to sidestep around Pietro di Bernardone, who moved to block his way.

"Sabbatino, put me down."

"He'll kill you, Francesco!"

"No. He won't kill me. Will you, papà?"

In a swift motion, Pietro ripped off Francesco's coif and grabbed his hair. He pulled Francesco's head up and slapped his son's face.

"Put me down, Sabbatino. Before you're hurt."

Sabbatino tried to push past the older man, but one of Pietro's servants blocked the way.

"For the love of God, Sabbatino, put me down. Please." Francesco's struggle to escape Sabbatino's grasp ended when Sabbatino, filled with fury, dumped him to the ground.

"You're *un idiota*!" he shouted. Then his pity returned.

To Pietro, he pleaded, "Don't you see that he's lost his mind?"

"Get inside your hospital or you'll lose more than that," Pietro threatened. He hoisted Francesco to his feet, slapped him again, and kicked him. As Sabbatino retreated to the hospital, he saw three of Pietro's servants surround Francesco and push him up the street. *They're going home*, Sabbatino knew. *God help you, my friend.*

NOTES

The opening quotation for Part Five is from Saint Francis' *Earlier Exhortation to the Brothers and Sisters of Penance (The First Version of the Letter to the Faithful)*, 11.

Upon emerging from hiding, Francesco was treated with mockery and brutality by the crowd. Finding him, his enraged father took him to the Bernardone house (1C, first book, chapter V).

Sabbatino's presence in this affair is the author's imagination. L3C (chapter IX) states that Sabbatino was from Assisi, but the histories tell us nothing more about him.

33

Madonna Pica

Bernardone Cloth Shop, Assisi (Late January 1206)

In the faint, early morning light, Madonna Pica and Angelo were pulling cloth from the shelves for today's display. Pietro, well bundled against the cold, strode downstairs from their living quarters and announced, "I'm off to Spoleto. I'll see you in three days." Dutifully Pica walked around the counter and kissed him, first on one cheek and then on the other.

Grazie, my Lord, Pica mentally prayed. To Pietro, she said, "Go with God, my husband."

Angelo embraced his father, first one shoulder and then the other. "May the Spoleto nobility give us many orders to take with us to the Lenten fair."

"This year, only one of us will go to the fair. The other will stay here with your mother. Farewell."

"Farewell," Angelo and Pica simultaneously replied.

Methodically, Pica arranged the wares and chatted with customers, repressing her bubbling joy. The never-ending day dragged toward evening. Finally, Angelo locked the shop and extinguished the lamps. They plodded upstairs to dinner, which tasted better than any Pica had eaten in the past weeks. As she had been doing each night, she arranged a trencher of meat and herbs and took it, along with two loaves and a small jug of wine, down to the house prison.

"Francesco," she called softly.

"Mamma! Pace e bene!" Always the same greeting. Was he ill in the mind? She couldn't tell.

Through the bars, Pica handed Francesco the food and drink. He was getting deft at eating with his hands chained. Pica watched him, her lips silent, her mind teeming. Almost three weeks ago, Pietro had thrown Francesco into this cell and locked the door. That night she had come down after Pietro was asleep and, despite Francesco's objections, insisted that she bathe his cuts with warm water and soothe his bruises with oil. She had tried to hide her dismay at his emaciated and battered condition. It was more evident when he obediently removed his filthy clothing and dressed himself in the clean surcote, leggings, and shoes she had brought. Like a child, when commanded, he had pressed his head against the prison bars and she had trimmed his hair, then his straggly beard. He looked better, but for whom? Pietro continued to beat him daily, swearing he would not release his son until he gave up this madness.

Last week, Pietro had reached his limit. After beating Francesco with a strap, he had chained him hands and feet. When Pica pleaded, he had struck her. "He'll come to his senses or rot!"

Yes, Pietro was within his rights as father of a wayward son. Yes, he could legally beat and imprison him for stealing that cloth and that horse. But is what's legal always moral, always just? Whether he was insane or just willful, Francesco didn't deserve this. No matter what happened to her, Pica would release him tonight. She took the keys to the prison and to his chains from the nook in the wall where Pietro kept them and unlocked the prison door. Then she unlocked the chains. She allowed him no protest. "Take your mantle and go with God," she said.

NOTES

Francesco's father locked him in a cell in the Bernardone house. When beatings didn't deter his son from his resolutions, Pietro had him chained. When Pietro left on a business trip, Pica released Francesco (1C, first book, chapters V and VI).

34

Messer Pietro di Bernardone

Piazza Santa Maria Maggiore, Assisi (Late January 1206)

Clinging to the wad of cast-off clothes and a money pouch heavy with coins, Messer Pietro di Bernardone strode through the fringe of the crowd that filled the Piazza Santa Maria Maggiore. In the gently falling snow, in the stunned silence of his neighbors, Pietro's ears were ringing with the stinging words just directed at him by his own son. Directed to him, but flung out in Francesco's clear and sonorous voice across the whole mob of Assisi citizens gathered in the courtyard of the bishop's palace. "Up to now, I have called Pietro di Bernardone my father, but from now on, I shall say, 'Our Father, Who art in heaven.'"

Impudence! Imagine Francesco selling his father's cloth and steed and wanting to rebuild a crumbling country chapel with his father's money.

Impudence! Francesco declaring that he was under the jurisdiction of the Church, not the comune, because he was living as an oblate at San Damiano.

Impudence! That old priest must have been hiding him. But where?

Impudence! Francesco deciding to end his hiding game and prancing into Assisi like a fool.

Impudence! Pietro's wife defying him by releasing Francesco! She deserved the beating that threw her, whimpering, to the floor.

Impudence! Francesco just now stripping off his clothes and tossing them and the pouch of money from his thievery at Pietro's feet.

Impudence! The bishop, gathering Francesco into his mantle. He had to be part of this.

Pietro's anger boiled. If he hadn't been trying desperately to remain dignified, he would have thrashed the bishop. That would have earned Pietro excommunication. No matter. God had already abandoned him.

Pietro scurried through the deserted streets. He had heard Guido dismiss the crowd, but only Pietro had moved. If he hurried, he would get home before the mob shook itself out of its stupor and dispersed. He wanted to hide from his neighbors just like Francesco had hidden from him.

Up to now, I have called Pietro di Bernardone my father . . .

If Francesco wanted to give his life to God, why didn't he do it nobly in a monastery like San Pietro near the Porta San Pietro, or San Benedetto on Monte Subasio? Respectable religious institutions for respectable men.

The streets were going by quickly. Pietro's thoughts swirled like snowflakes. His son. The son for whom he had worked and sacrificed and bought the best of everything. The son he had educated and trained to become a partner in the region's most respected cloth business. This son, who could sell fine fabric to a dolt while making him feel like a prince.

All right. Francesco had rather be a knight than a merchant. So much the better! Pietro's money had backed his son's dreams. The best armor. The best weapons. The best destrier. Francesco possessed a knight's valor, courage, and courtesy. Sì, he was a prankster, but he honored civic life. Sì, he was impetuous, but so was Pietro when he was young. Francesco was everything Pietro could have hoped for. His only fault was squandering money. "Do you think I'm a prince?" Pietro would ask with a smile. Francesco would only shrug. "You want me to have a good time, eh?"

Pietro pulled open the door of his cloth shop and entered the inviting warmth. He, Pietro. Son of a small businessman in Assisi. Grandson of a peasant eking out a meager living down on the plain. Pietro's father had wanted to escape his family's poverty. He had worked hard and saved his money until he could buy a small house in the city. Pietro had his father's spirit. Work invigorated him. Money delighted him. Honor beckoned him. He, Pietro, had become one of the comune's wealthiest merchants. He had bought houses in the city. Properties below the city. Land investments. All for the son of his loins, raised like a French nobleman's son. Francesco. His "little Frenchman."

Pietro hurried upstairs. The Bernardone house wouldn't be deserted for long. Pica, weeping, would be back. Angelo, humiliated, would return.

There was the table where they ate and laughed and argued over what was important. Francesco had embraced all of Pietro's ideas until he returned from that prison. He had left for war, confident of victory. When he had not returned, the comune had searched for his body. God, the anguish of those long days! The battlefield had yielded many bodies. But not Francesco's. Was he alive?

Then Pietro had learned that Francesco was a prisoner. He'd bartered a hefty sum for his son's ransom. However, the Perugini took so long that Francesco had been nearly dead when he arrived.

Bitterly Pietro strode into Francesco's room. Why wasn't he slain? Why didn't he die in prison? Pica's nursing and the best doctoring had healed his body but not his mind. Francesco had spun completely into madness. He had dishonored his family.

If he wanted to give his life to God, why didn't he do it nobly?

Pietro sat on Francesco's bed. His bed with fine sheets, plump and soft, where, as a child, he would cry out with night terrors. His bed, empty that endless year after the war. This bed, where Pica wouldn't let him die.

Up to now, I have called Pietro di Bernardone my father . . .

So, Francesco no longer wanted to be part of his family? It was as if he had died. What do you do with the clothes of a dead son?

Up to now, I have called Pietro di Bernardone my father . . .

He had said God would be his Father. God didn't shower down clothes, bread, or coins on His children. What would Francesco wear tonight? What would he eat? Where would he sleep? Was Bishop Guido going to care for him? Why would the bishop want to care for such an ungrateful son? But then Pietro had never understood religion. The scandal of the cross mystified him. Why would God come to earth, poor and helpless, to die a shameful and torturous death? It made no sense. God as Father? Not a good father like Pietro. Not a good father like Pietro's father and grandfather. God was a capricious Father,

Who would let Pietro's son escape an honorable death to die a living, shameful death in front of all his neighbors. What kind of God was this?

Pietro could not answer his questions. He buried his head in his hands and tried to squeeze out the refrain that kept up its relentless beat.

Up to now, I have called Pietro di Bernardone my father . . .

He heard the door open downstairs. Pica and Angelo must be home. No one was speaking. What would they say?

What do you do with the clothes of a dead son? Who would want to wear them? Only beggars, and that is what his son had become. Pietro clenched his teeth. He would rather burn the clothes than have beggars wear them.

NOTES

1C (first book, chapter VI) records the scene at the bishop's palace. Pietro's response is conjecture.

35

Unocchio

Wooded Valley of the Tescio River, Assisi (Late January 1206)

The snow had turned to rain. In a makeshift shelter of logs and branches, a band of six thieves were dozing around a campfire in the thick woods near the Tescio River when Unocchio heard a French troubadour singing on the road. Only Unocchio jumped to his feet. Perhaps his hearing had grown keener to compensate for the loss of his left eye in last spring's scuffle.

The singing was approaching. Unocchio shook his partners awake. A troubadour meant a caravan. A caravan meant money. Quietly the thieves took their knives, swords, and clubs, and stealthily moved toward the sound.

Through the trees, they could see the road and the . . . penitent? The fool—or was he a heretic? —was dressed in a soaking wet, black tunic, belted at the waist, and brandishing a walking stick like a baton while dancing and singing lustily. But a caravan? None in sight.

Springing out of the forest, the robbers surrounded the figure.

"Who are you?" the bandit leader demanded.

"I am the herald of the great King! What does it matter to you?"

What mattered was money. In a quick, well-practiced routine, the bandits jumped the man while Unocchio pulled off his tunic, leaving him clad in a hair shirt and breeches. After roughing him up a bit just for show, one bandit shoved the penitent into a trough of snow. “Lie there, you stupid herald of God!” he sneered. Then the bandits tore at the tunic. Not one coin could they find. Tossing the tunic onto the snow, they disappeared into the woods as quickly as they had come.

The fool called after them, “Many thanks! Pace e bene!”

Crazy.

Back at the campfire, Unocchio heard the penitent French troubadour singing again. He listened disinterestedly until the singing faded.

NOTES

1C (first book, chapter VII) records this incident of unnamed robbers attacking Francesco. According to Pazzelli (p. 39), Francesco’s garb of black tunic, belt, and walking stick was that of a lay penitent. Unocchio translates as One Eye.

36

Frater Indosarre

Abbey of San Verecondo, Gubbio (Late January 1206)

Having prayed Vespers with his fellow monks, Frater Indosarre had retired to his cozy mattress in a corner of the porter's room at the Abbey of San Verecondo. To ease himself to sleep, he spun mental tales of Saint Verecondo, a French knight. Eight hundred years ago in this area, pagans had murdered Verecondo on his journey from Rome back to France.

By day, Indosarre was a meek, stubby porter whose gentle, penetrating gaze encouraged visitors to confide their needs to him for prayer. By night, however, he became Verecondo's gallant squire, accompanying his master on countless heroic exploits. Tonight, he and Verecondo were chained to the deck of a pirate ship in the Mediterranean, having been abducted three days ago from Brindisi. A storm was lashing the ship, lurching in the turbulent waves. Something crashed. A mast? Another thud. A second mast? Were they chained in the hold instead, where kegs were bashing the hull? Thud! Thud!

Indosarre was awake. The ship had disappeared but not the storm. A screeching wind was lashing a torrential rain against the monastery.

Thud! Thud! Knocking? At this time of night? In this storm? Bandits! Indosarre's bravado vanished. Timidly he approached the door.

"Who's there?" he called in the deepest voice he could muster.

"A penitent."

Indosarre was skeptical. "From where?"

"Assisi."

"Why are you here?"

"I'm going to Gubbio. May I stay the night?"

Indosarre imagined Verecondo and himself in a furious storm like this one. He must show pity to the penitent just as Verecondo would have done.

Indosarre unbolted the door. A drenched, dripping penitent in a tattered tunic stepped into the room.

"Grazie. May I sit by the fire?"

Indosarre led him to the hearth. The monk stirred the dim embers into flame and added more wood until the fire flared. The penitent was shivering. Chivalrously, Indosarre took the blanket from his bed and draped it over the man's bony shoulders. Huddled in it, the man moved as close to the fire as he safely could and sat down.

"May I work here for food? I haven't eaten in three days."

Sharing his blanket was one thing. Working here for food was something else. "I'll ask the prior in the morning."

"Grazie." The penitent drew the blanket tighter about himself and bowed his head. Within moments, he was snoring.

Sighing, Indosarre returned to his cozy mattress. He grabbed his mantle from the peg by the door and, pulling his legs up under his tunic, tossed the mantle over himself. It was shorter than a blanket, and he had to keep his legs tucked up or his toes would stick out. Lashed by wind-driven rain, he and Verecondo fell asleep on the pitching deck of a pirate ship caught in a Mediterranean storm.

When the Office of Lauds ended the monastery's night silence, Indosarre approached the prior. "A penitent arrived last night from Assisi and asked if he might work here for food."

"Probably wants to become a monk," the prior muttered. "You know how we test vocations. Treat him harshly. Give him broth. Have him clean the kitchen. Take out the dung. Split wood. Wash dishes. If he still wants to stay after a few days, have him come and see me."

"His clothing is in tatters. Shall I give him a new tunic?"

"No. He's a penitent. Let him dress like one. And find out his name, if he has one."

Two days later, the storm ended. Two more days and the roads were passable. Indosarre found the prior after Lauds. "The penitent has left. He said his name was Francesco."

NOTES

1C (first book, chapter VII) records the incident of Francesco asking for shelter and work at an unnamed monastery on his way to Gubbio. Most historians now concur that the Benedictine Abbey of San Verecondo, now called Vallingegno, was the monastery. The *Rule of Saint Benedict*, chapter 58, details how the monks ought to test vocations by treating newcomers harshly, the treatment Francesco received. The histories do not record the monks' names. Indossare translates as "to wear" or "to put on."

37

Count Federico Spadalunga

Great Hall of the Spadalunga House, Gubbio (Early February 1206)

Clad in lightweight armor, Count Federico Spadalunga was sparring with his brothers, Antonio and Giacomello, in the great hall of his family's fortress-like home near the mercato in Gubbio. Since Terce, the counts had been practicing thrust-and-parry moves, drilling two against one, and this time Federico was the one.

In their prime of life, the three men were in splendid physical condition. Daily practice kept their muscles strong and their moves swift. Periodically, some other noble challenged their family for lands and houses. The brothers had determined that no hired knights would surpass themselves in bravery and fitness.

The doors to the great hall swung open.

"Lord Counts, a guest has arrived."

Federico bashed aside the two dulled swords that had swung against him. The three turned to the servant. "Who?" Federico asked.

"Messer Francesco di Bernardone from Assisi."

"Francesco! Show him in!"

Francesco! He must have come to solicit the family's fabric order for the Bar-sur-Aube fair in mid-Lent. Four years ago, Francesco had come soliciting, but that fall both he and Federico had been taken prisoner after the battle of

Colle della Strada. Federico had been in prison only a few days when a shoulder wound festered and threatened his life, forcing the Perugini to offer to his family the price of his ransom. He had left a battle-stunned Francesco in prison and had heard no more of him until a year and a half later. Then, Pietro di Bernardone toted his wares to the Spadalunga house and told the counts that Francesco was ransomed but very ill. Now the young merchant-knight was well enough to solicit business again! *Grazie, my Lord*!

Why was this unkempt penitent striding into his great room?

"Lord Counts!" the penitent hailed.

"What dog dragged you in?" Antonio demanded.

"I thought we were seeing the merchant," Giacomello addressed the servant. "Who's this?"

"Francesco?" Federico was jolted by the recognition of his friend. "What happened?"

"I was beaten by robbers."

Antonio scoffed.

Giacomello stared dumbly.

"Bring him some clothing," Federico ordered the servant.

"An undyed black tunic," Francesco requested.

"Nonsense!" Federico protested. Black wool was the lowest grade, a pauper's garb. "A coif. Surcote. Leggings. Mantle."

"Count, I am a penitent. An undyed black tunic, please."

Federico's dark eyes widened.

"I know it's difficult to believe."

"What's happened, Francesco?"

"Perhaps we can talk over a meal?"

Federico bellowed with laughter. "So, the penitent is hungry. Bring a black tunic and some bread, cheese, and wine," he spoke to his servant. "Set a table and we'll talk."

Antonio punched his dumbstruck brother's shoulder. "Let them share their war stories. We can duel in my room." Bowing to Federico, they took their swords and left.

The servant obediently set in place two trestles and lay a small board on them. Then he carried near it two chairs that had been pushed against a side wall. The count and penitent sat to talk while awaiting their meal. They were washing down their last morsels with wine when Francesco finished speaking.

"Since you're not soliciting my business, why did you come to Gubbio? Just to see me?" Federico laughed.

Francesco's eyes twinkled as he smiled. "Perhaps. When I left Assisi, I asked my Lord to direct my steps. Then I twirled around and, when I stopped, I was facing in the direction of Gubbio."

Federico slapped his big hands on the table. "So, the Lord sent you to me! Does He want you to tell me something?"

"I think He wants you to tell me something."

"What could He possibly want me to tell you?"

"That I'm not insane."

"Are you?"

"I don't think so. Count, you and your family are wise and wealthy, strong and respected. All my life, I aspired to these things. Now I aspire to nothing. I've given everything to my Lord Who's given me everything. I've sinned much, but He's forgiven me. I want to sin no more. So, I must avoid the causes of these sins. No more rich food or fine clothes. No comfortable bed. Turn the other cheek rather than fight back. Be a fool, *un idiota*, rather than admired and praised. I'm to live no better than my Savior. This is my penance. For all of my life."

Federico leaned back in his chair, his small, dark eyes scanning the vaulted ceiling with its tightly mortised joists. This great house, built like a fortress by his father Spadalunga, was massive and secure, housing his family as well as servants and knights. With his mother's sumptuous furnishings, the house's beauty rivaled that of a palace. His family wore the best clothing and armor and ate like kings. Was anything wrong with that?

To the anomaly of the man before him, Federico offered an invitation. "Stay with us."

"Grazie, but no. I'll stay with the lepers."

Lepers? Federico had forgotten that lepers existed. Francesco must be insane to wish to stay in that stinking hovel of moral degradation. Nevertheless, a thought intruded. WHAT YOU DO FOR THE LEAST OF MY BRETHREN, YOU DO FOR ME.

"My insane friend," Federico smiled. "There's another way to do penance. Alms. I'll have a servant accompany you to the leper hospital and bring with him a cart of clothing, bedding, medicine, and food. Will you wait until it's readied?"

NOTES

1C (first book, chapter VII) records that Francesco went to Gubbio to seek out a friend who could help clothe him. Johannes Jörgensen (*Saint Francis of Assisi*) mentions in a footnote (p. 297) that Giuseppe Mazzatinti (in the journal *Miscellanea Francescana*, vol. V, pp. 76–78) named the friend as Federico Spadalunga, the oldest of three brothers, the other two being Antonio and Giacomello. The father's name Spadalunga means "Long Sword," a possible indication that this was a warrior family.

38

Fazio

Leper Hospital, Gubbio (Early February 1206)

With a load of damp wood on his shoulder, teenaged Fazio slogged through the mud at the leper hospital outside of Gubbio. Being tall and strong, his disease still only a rash of facial bumps, Fazio was doing the task he'd done for his lord until being brought here two years ago.

The rumbling stopped him as he was about to enter the front hall. An oxcart, pulled by two massive, straining beasts, sloshed toward the hospital. Fazio hurried indoors and piled the wood by the hearth to dry.

"Provisions," he smiled to Orfelina, who was sitting near the fire, her thick auburn hair shimmering in the firelight. Fazio sat next to her, basking in her innocence. Once the donor piled the provisions near the door and left, she and Fazio would bring the supplies indoors. Then they could resume sitting by the fire and chatting.

A knock sounded at the door. "Provisions. May I bring them in?"

At this odd request, Fazio and Orfelina looked questioningly at each other.

"Leave them by the door," Fazio called out. "We'll bring them in."

Outside, Fazio heard scratching and thudding, then another knock.

"We're unloaded."

"Grazie!" Fazio called out. He heard the cart creak and rumble. Then the sound faded. The donor had left. With Orfelina, he opened the door to bring in the provisions. Sitting on a keg, a scruffy man in an undyed black tunic startled him.

"I'm a penitent," the man explained. "May I stay with you?"

Fazio and Orfelina exchanged glances. Two penitents were already staying at the hospital to care for the lepers. They were a tremendous help and comfort.

"If he wants to," Orfelina offered.

"How are you called?" Fazio asked.

"Francesco."

Francesco stayed. He slept in an empty cell, ate the lepers' meager fare, repaired their hospital's walls, and tended their sores, draining pus from them and cleansing them. Francesco spoke little about himself but much about our Lord Jesus Christ, even singing to Him while prancing about like a troubadour. He brought joy to the lepers. They wanted him to stay with them forever.

However, one warm day in spring, when the leaves had begun to stretch out of their buds, Francesco embraced each leper and said, "I have a church to rebuild in Assisi, and now the weather is good enough to begin. I must leave to do my work. Grazie for all you have given me, my brothers and sisters. I promise I'll see you again."

NOTES

1C (first book, chapter VII) records that Francesco "moved to the lepers and stayed with them." The author of this work postulates that these unnamed lepers were in Gubbio and that Francesco stayed with them until spring, when he returned to Assisi.

Part Six

"And the Lord Gave Me Such Faith in Churches"

39

Alonza

Mercato, Assisi (May 1206)

On this brilliant spring afternoon, Alonza felt deliciously comfortable in her undyed, thin gown and sleeveless brown tunic, tight over her ample chest, just the way she wanted it. Such days made her realize her good fortune in being the Bernardone's servant. With their ample funds, she could purchase the best for dinner.

Like a beetle, Alonza scurried from one merchant to another as she selected today's foodstuffs and flirted with the younger vendors. Dried beans. Cabbage. Fresh bread. Pork. A fine dinner! If Angelo and his new bride visited, there would be food for all!

"Pace e bene!" Her heart leaped at the deep singing voice that rang out above the banter and gossip of the mercato. The voice sounded so like . . .

Francesco! She paled, catching sight of him across the piazza. Above the jeering and mockery, she heard his joyful song. "Pace e bene! Praise Him, all His angels; praise Him, all His heavenly hosts. Praise Him, O sun and moon; praise Him, all you shining stars. Praise Him, O highest heavens, and you waters above the skies!" The tune could have been that of a troubadour's love song but with holy words. Where had she heard those words? At Mass? Were they from the Bible?

"Come, praise the Lord, good people. Let your praise extend to God's house! Who will give stones to build the house of God? God will reward you! One stone for one reward! Two stones for two rewards! Three stones for three rewards! Messer, can you give a stone or two?"

Francesco! Dancing about in a penitent's tunic. Praising the Lord! Pleading for stones!

Despite herself, Alonza smiled. He seemed to take ridicule as approval of his antics! When he had been a cloth merchant, he had loved to perform for her, and she had laughed at his foolishness! They had been close, she and he. Maybe too close. Alonza blushed.

Now here he was. Practically a religious! Was he sane? Was he safe? Who would give him anything? Months ago, following that disgraceful display in the Vescovado, he had disappeared. Why had he returned? What church was he talking about? Around here, a lot of churches needed repair. So what?

What if he recognized her? She'd die of embarrassment. Alonza scurried around a cheese vendor and pressed herself against the back of the vendor's booth where, hopefully, she'd be out of view. *My Lord*, she prayed, *please don't let him see me*!

NOTES

The opening quotation for Part Six is from Saint Francis' *Testament*, 4.

We know neither the names of the Bernardone servants nor when Angelo married.

Francesco returned to Assisi where he praised God and begged for stones to rebuild San Damiano (1C, first book, chapter VIII), reminding his listeners of heavenly rewards for their donations (L3C, chapter VII). Although Francesco had memorized the Psalter, we don't know what praises he sang when begging. The praises in this chapter are from Psalm 148. L3C (chapter VII) records the people's response to him and his response to them.

40

Dom Pietro

Church of San Damiano, Assisi (June 1206)

Dom Pietro stood at the hearth and stirred the pot cooking over the low flame. The delectable scent of kale and bean stew, seasoned with garlic, red pepper, and olive oil, tickled his nose. He and Francesco would eat well tonight.

He worried about that young man. Lugging up stones from the crypt under the church to rebuild the upper walls. Haranguing Assisi citizens for stones and then carting them down to San Damiano. The hill to the city was so steep that Francesco could barely hold the cart back as he descended to the church. Pietro chuckled at a vision of Francesco jumping into the cart and letting it rush down the hill of its own accord. If there were some way to steer the cart, that would be an easy way to transport the stones.

Francesco was sincere, but he was delicate. How was he tolerating his rough tunic? The painful blisters that had erupted on his hands when he first began the rebuilding had turned to callouses. Were his muscles stiff from sleeping on the church floor? No matter how much Pietro objected, his young oblate wouldn't moderate his penances: "I'm to follow my Lord Jesus Christ. My life shouldn't be easier than His."

Thankfully, Pietro could care for Francesco's weak digestion. The priest had been asking his benefactors for appealing, wholesome foods that he would cook in tantalizing ways. Eating well would keep Francesco healthy. However, recently Francesco had been taking smaller portions. Was he fasting? Ill? Pietro would ask him when he arrived for dinner.

The priest was dozing in a chair next to the hearth when he heard the door to the house creak.

"Dom!" Francesco embraced the priest. "Look what I've collected!" He handed the priest a wooden beggar's bowl piled with table scraps and fragments of bread trenchers. Disgusting.

Francesco beamed. "Aren't you proud of me?"

Pietro was puzzled. "Where is the dog you're feeding? Or is it a wolf?"

Francesco's wolf howl ended in laughter. "It's for me! Dinner!"

Pietro stared. "I've cooked dinner for us." He stood, placed Francesco's bowl of leftovers on his chair, and removed the lid from the simmering pot. A delectable aroma filled the room.

"Magnificent!" Francesco laughed. "You'll enjoy it."

"We'll enjoy it."

"I'll taste it, but, after this, no. I've been thinking. Where else will I find a priest who will show me such human kindness as you? This isn't the life of the poor that I've chosen. Like a beggar, I should go from door to door with a bowl in my hand and eat the scraps I collect."

"Francesco, this is unnecessary."

"Not for me. I must do this willingly out of love for Him Who was born poor, Who lived poorly in this world, Who remained naked and poor on the cross, and Who was buried in another's tomb." Francesco pointed to the bowl. "Would you like to share my dinner?"

"Are you really going to eat that mess?"

"I've been eating such messes for days. At first, my stomach turned sour to even consider it, but then I prayed and asked my Lord to help me conquer myself. That mess will taste delicious."

NOTES

L3C (chapter VII) tells how Francesco tried begging and, overcoming his revulsion, asked Dom Pietro to cease cooking delicacies for him.

41

Alberto

Porta Moiano, Assisi (June 1206)

Sitting to beg always made Alberto restless, but lately his sapling-thin, old body grew stiff as a dry board if he didn't keep walking. He was approaching the Porta Moiano, a few coins in his dusty purse, when he spied that crazy penitent Francesco. He was walking up the hill from the direction of that derelict chapel he was rebuilding. No point in begging from him. He had no coins to give.

Instead of prancing past, Francesco bowed to Alberto as if he were a baron. "Alberto, would you like to eat every day without begging?"

Alberto's flat stomach suddenly felt ravenous. "Sì!"

"Come with me, and I'll beg for both of us. Only you must be papà to me and bless me when Pietro di Bernardone curses me."

Pietro di Bernardone. Alberto recalled one scene a few weeks ago. Francesco begging stones right here near the Porta Moiano. Children pelting him with pebbles. Him laughing and calling out, "Bigger ones, please! The church is for people, not for mice!" The children giggling and scampering off as Pietro di Bernardone strode up to his son and raised his fist to strike him, then dropped it, for striking a man dedicated to God was a sin.

"Why did you return? May you rot in hell!" Pietro cursed his son.

Saying nothing, Francesco resumed begging for stones.

To accompany Francesco seemed simple enough. Alberto agreed.

NOTES

1C (first book, chapter X) mentions "a man from Assisi with a holy and simple character, who was the first to follow devoutly the man of God," but gives no name. L3C (chapter VII) records this scene while AP (chapter I) states that the old beggar was named Alberto. Alberto is mentioned only at the very beginning of Francesco's spiritual life. He either left Francesco early on or died.

42

Ghita

Tavern, Assisi (June 1206)

Ghita was a little frustrated. She had not yet completely cleared the table of trenchers from their meal when Assisi's hooligans began rolling dice and calling out bets. With tipsy men hunched over the gaming table, collecting trenchers required dexterity. As she reached for Messer Rufino's trencher, she heard a familiar voice. *"De l'huile, s'il vous plaît."* Was that French?

Before she could put a name to that voice or her mind recognize the dingy penitent, Morico leaped to his feet.

"Francesco!"

Ghita's heart skipped a beat. Francesco? She thought she had stopped loving him months ago.

The scene seemed frozen—Francesco and the men with whom he used to party, staring at each other.

"Morico. Sabbatino. Rufino." Francesco greeted each by name. "Ghita."

She smiled weakly at him.

He presented a small flask. "Would anyone give me oil for the lamp in the Church of San Damiano?"

Rufino stood hesitantly. "Ghita, get him some oil. I'll pay for it."

Ghita nodded dumbly. Just before the dinner hour, she had filled an oil lamp on an adjacent table. She took the flask from Francesco, barely touching his fingers. He smiled at her. Then he turned to his friends. "And something to eat, perhaps."

Sabbatino pushed aside his trencher and called to Ghita, "Bring something for him!"

"No," Francesco said. He held a beggar's bowl toward Sabbatino. "Your trencher is fine, unless you're going to eat it yourself!" Francesco was grinning at the preposterous idea.

Ghita almost spilled the oil as she poured it from lamp into flask.

Sabbatino picked up the soppy bread trencher and plopped it into Francesco's bowl. "You'll like it, you *idiota*," Sabbatino said with good humor. "Fowl with zucchini and peas."

"You can imagine the meal," Morico said. "The trencher will be tasty. Take mine, too."

"Sabbatino's is enough. Give yours to another beggar." Francesco looked at his friends. "You all look well," he smiled.

"Are you well?" Rufino asked.

"You have all made me feel very well!" Francesco grinned. "Do you know how long I stood at that door, getting up courage to come in and beg from you?" Francesco performed a short, dancing mime of an indecisive man vacillating between decisions. Ghita laughed. His friends clapped. "I see you're still my friends."

"And you're still Francesco!" Sabbatino bellowed.

Francesco looked at Ghita, who was standing awkwardly nearby. She handed him the flask.

"Grazie," he said, taking it from her and kissing her hand. Then, bowing to all of them, he left as quietly as he had come.

NOTES

L3C (chapter VII) records this incident without naming the men who were gaming or the tavern worker. It does mention Francesco's embarrassment and that he overcame it by begging in French, a tactic he used to combat discomfort.

43

Messer Pietro di Bernardone

Piazza del San Rufino, Assisi (July 1206)

Pietro di Bernardone was huffing as he entered the Piazza di San Rufino, carrying with him a roll of saffron silk for Madonna Ortulana, wife of Messer Favarone di Offreduccio. Unlike the previous sweltering days, today was so deliciously cool that he had decided to carry the parcel himself rather than send a servant with it. However, he had not considered the high sun's warmth. Now he was sweating.

Pietro spotted two girls cavorting and laughing in front of Favarone's massive house. Madonna Chiara and her sister Madonna Catarina. Chiara was almost a woman. Soon her freedom to play would end and she would remain indoors under watchful eyes, awaiting suitors.

Pietro brushed the back of his right hand over his sweaty brow and bowed to the girls. "Would you carry this cloth to your mother?"

Each holding one end of the parcel and laughing at their clumsiness, the girls lugged it toward their home.

"One stone for one reward! Two stones for two rewards!" To Pietro's right, the disgustingly familiar call rang across the piazza. Pietro moaned. Francesco. Again. Would he never be free of that son?

Pietro turned toward the voice. "You! Do you dog me, you, worse than a dog? May your stones drag you to hell!"

Francesco looked at Pietro and then knelt before an old, thin beggar at his side. "Bless me, papà," he calmly addressed the man.

The beggar raised his hand and traced the sign of the cross over Francesco. "May God bless you, my son," he intoned.

Pietro was speechless. Francesco was looking at him. His quivering voice came gently, "Don't you believe that God can give me a papà to bless me against your curses?" Then he turned away, approaching the girls who had stopped in their tracks to gawk at the confrontation.

Francesco bowed to them. "May I carry that?"

The girls nodded dumbly. Deftly Francesco heaved the parcel to his shoulder and carried it toward the Offreduccio house. The girls ran ahead of him and entered the doorway. When Francesco reached the threshold, a servant appeared and took the parcel from him. Francesco bowed, turned away, and began to sing a blithe melody. "Great is the Lord and greatly to be praised in the city of our God, His holy mountain!"

His cheeks stinging with embarrassment, his blood hotter than the sun could make it, Pietro hurried down the streets to his cloth shop.

God, he still loved Francesco! Why had he disgraced himself? Every jeer stabbed Pietro's heart. Francesco was gaunt, that belt cinched tightly around his narrow waist. Starvation, penance, and hard labor were killing him. Pietro would have given anything to save him. But he had rejected it all, rejected even Pietro. *From now on, I shall say, "Our Father, Who art in heaven," and not my father Pietro di Bernardone. Do you not believe that God can give me a papà to bless me against your curses?*

Pain broke Pietro's heart. Why had Francesco returned? Why was he staying here? Why didn't he leave Pietro in peace?

No matter what anyone said or did to him, Francesco seemed always at peace. Why? Could a lunatic be at peace? The question nipped at Pietro like the dog he had called Francesco.

Pietro was extinguishing the lamp to climb into bed when he finally understood. This penance thing was just Francesco's latest whim. Soon he would abandon it and go on to something else. Would Pietro then be at peace?

The question followed him under the sheets. His dishonored son, who had given up everything for nothing, seemed to dwell in perpetual peace. Pietro, who had gone from having nothing to having everything, was agitated and tense. Francesco was free of all goods. Pietro was chained to them. Who was the crazy one?

NOTES

In medieval Italy, according to Fr. Joseph Tuscan, OFM Cap., sons who met their fathers in the street customarily knelt before them to request a blessing. Pietro not only refused to bless Francesco but instead cursed him. L3C (chapter VII) records Pietro's concern and love for his son, this incident, and Francesco's words to his father. While the Offreduccio girls are not mentioned, the details concerning their ages, parentage, and home are accurate (see Nugent, *Chiara: A Story of Saint Clare of Assisi*). The praises Francesco sings here are the first verse of Psalm 48.

44

Messer Angelo di Pica

San Damiano, Assisi (February 1207)

Pulling his mantle tightly against himself to keep out the penetrating cold, Messer Angelo di Pica strutted as he led Messer Patrizio toward the potter's shop. Since their school days at San Giorgio, the exquisitely cultured Patrizio and he had been friends, and now Patrizio had finally succumbed to Madonna Milana's charm. Although she was selecting most of the household items, Patrizio wanted to choose a few to satisfy his own taste and to surprise his bride. After meticulously comparing Angelo's finest fabrics and seeking Angelo's advice, Patrizio had selected the best. Now he wanted Angelo to advise him on purchasing pottery. Then furniture. And bedding. Since Pica was minding the cloth shop today, Angelo was free to accompany his friend.

The bells had just rung for the hour of Sext when they arrived at the potter. Near a weathered cart holding two large stones stood a penitent, his head bowed, his hands clasped in prayer.

Angelo groaned and turned to Patrizio, "My crazy brother."

Despite his infatuation with penance, Francesco was still a merchant underneath. Angelo liked to goad him with that reality. He nudged Patrizio and said, loud enough for Francesco to hear, "You might tell Francesco to sell you a penny's worth of his sweat."

Francesco looked up, his eyes twinkling. *"Je vendrai cette sueur à mon Seigneur à un prix élevé."*

"Is your brother French?" Patrizio asked.

"No. He talks like that to pretend that he's some chivalrous knight." As if to prove the truth of that, Francesco made a flourishing grand bow to the two men.

Angelo scoffed. "Our mother is French. She spoke French to us and used to sing us French lullabies." Francesco bowed again, then again clasped his hands and lowered his head.

Ignoring him, the two buyers entered the potter's shop. "So, what did he say?" Patrizio questioned.

Angelo translated Francesco's retort into Umbrian. "I will sell that sweat to my Lord at a high price."

NOTES

L3C (chapter VII) records this winter incident without giving details of who was accompanying Angelo, where the encounter took place, or how Francesco was praying.

Part Seven

"The Lord Gave Me Some Brothers"

45

Dom Bonifacio

Porziuncula, Assisi (October 18, 1207)

Had Dom Bonifacio just seen that? Of course, he had. Here in his hands were Francesco's shoes, walking stick, leather belt, money pouch, and provisions sack. Just now, barefoot Francesco, clad only in tunic and undergarment, had danced out the doorway of this tiny sacristy, singing.

What had just happened?

Bonifacio placed Francesco's possessions on the floor where, moments ago, he'd been sitting while Bonifacio explained to him, as he did daily, the Mass Gospel reading. As usual, the young man had fixed his large brown eyes on Bonifacio's beady black ones and listened.

Bonifacio screwed up his tiny mouth and rubbed his plump, clean-shaven cheeks. He stared at Francesco's possessions.

Today's Mass had been for the feast of Saint Mark the Evangelist. Francesco had attended, as well as two other penitents and two swineherds who used to house their pigs here at the Porziuncula, "the little portion." Francesco had reclaimed the pig sty as a church and rebuilt it as he had San Damiano and San Pietro della Spina. The monks at the Benedictine Abbey of San Benedetto, perched below the pastureland on the top of Monte Subasio, owned this small country chapel. They were delighted at its transformation. With the hogs gone, the church's name again seemed appropriate—Santa Maria degli Angeli, "Our Lady of the Angels." Country folk swore they heard angelic music here. Bonifacio had heard it—breezes singing through the pines in angelic harmony.

In the wake of what had just happened, Bonifacio could almost hear angels singing now. Today's Gospel reading had been from Saint Luke. The Scripture was still resting in his lap, from when he had reread it to Francesco, translating the Latin into Umbrian. Bonifacio cross-referenced the reading with similar passages in the Gospels of Matthew and Mark. He reread Luke's words slowly, marveling that they could have caused Francesco's immediate response.

> After this the Lord appointed seventy others, and sent them on ahead of him, two by two, into every town and place where he himself was about to come. And he said to them, "The harvest is plentiful, but the laborers are few; pray therefore the Lord of the harvest to send out laborers into his harvest. Go your way; behold, I send you out as lambs in the midst of wolves. Carry no purse, no bag, no sandals; and salute no one on the road. Whatever house you enter, first say, 'Peace be to this house!' And if a son of peace is there, your peace shall rest upon him; but if not, it shall return to you. And remain in the same house, eating and drinking what they provide, for the laborer deserves his wages; do not go from house to house. Whenever you enter a town and they receive you, eat what is set before you; heal the sick in it and say to them, 'The kingdom of God has come near to you.' But whenever you enter a town and they do not receive you, go into its streets and say, 'Even the dust of your town that clings to our feet, we wipe off against you; nevertheless know this, that the kingdom of God has come near.' I tell you, it shall be more tolerable on that day for Sodom than for that town.

Francesco's possessions were on the floor. What had he exulted as he danced out? "*This* is what I want! *This* is what I seek! *This* is what I desire with all my heart!" Was he going to try to do what Bonifacio had just read?

NOTES

The opening quotation for Part Seven is from Saint Francis' *Testament*, 14.

1C (first book, chapters VIII and IX) describes how Francesco repaired the three churches mentioned in this chapter. Historians believe that the second church, unnamed in the early sources, was the Church of San Pietro della Spina (*Early Documents*, p. 201, footnote).

Henri d'Avranches, in *The Versified Life of Saint Francis* (fourth book, section 200, written between 1230 and 1235) states that the Porziuncula, owned by Saint Benedict's Abbey, had been used as a pig sty before Francesco's renovations.

Deducing from what Fortini records about the Porziuncula, Franciscan scholar Bret Thoman believes that this church, as well as several others under the dependency of the abbey, "were not monastic churches but were secular churches and, as such, would have had a secular priest in residency nearby" (email to the author, September 28, 2019).

1C (first book, chapter IX) states that, at Mass one day at the Porziuncula, Francesco heard the Gospel "about how the Lord sent out his disciples to preach" and asked the priest "to explain the Gospel to him." Francesco included Christ's directives in the *Earlier Rule*, chapter XIV. These directives are found in Luke 10:1–12, the passage proposed for the feasts of Saint Mark (April 25) and Saint Luke (October 18). Directives to the apostles in Luke 9, Mark 6, and Matthew 10, are similar. Knowing the Scriptures, the unnamed priest could likely intertwine the Gospels in his explanation.

After hearing the priest's explanation (the histories provide no details), Francesco exclaimed, "This is what I want, this is what I seek, this is what I desire with all my heart," and then "Immediately, he took off the shoes from his feet, put down the staff from his hands, and, satisfied with one tunic, exchanged his leather belt for a cord" (1C, first book, chapter IX). A tradition that Francesco heard this Gospel on the feast of Saint Mathias, celebrated on February 24, is unlikely. In 1208, the Gospel text for the feast of Saint Matthias was Matthew 11:25–30, which mentions nothing about the garb of the disciples (*Pro Monialibus* [internal newsletter of the Poor Clares], 1979 [71]).

46

Bishop Guido

Bishop's Palace, Assisi (Late October 1207)

Although a secretary organized the bishop's schedule, Guido preferred to know his responsibilities in advance. As he stood beside his large table, his big hands spread wide a parchment that listed November obligations. Blessing the harvest. Leading processions. Dispensing sacraments. Visiting pastors. His secretary had begun by writing each activity neatly on a line, then skipping two lines so that other obligations could be written in. But most of the blank spaces were already filled, and the secretary was inking in the margins.

The door to the study opened and his secretary entered. "Messer Bishop, Francesco is here to see you."

Gladly putting aside the parchment, Guido pulled over a chair and sat down. He beckoned Francesco to enter. If only Guido could be as spontaneous and free as that young man!

"Francesco, where did you get that outfit?" Guido asked. The former black-robed penitent in the belted tunic was now garbed in a dingy, gray wool tunic tied at the waist with a length of rope.

Instead of answering, Francesco opened his arms wide. The sleeves of the tunic were the same width at the cuff as at the shoulder. Standing like that, Francesco formed a cross.

"I made it, Messer Bishop."

His own pattern, Guido surmised. "Where are your pouch and shoes?"

"When Jesus sent his disciples to preach, he told them to take no purse or bag, no money or walking stick, no bread or sandals. I'm the least of his disciples."

Taking the Gospel literally. Again.

"You're not preaching, Francesco."

"I came to ask if I may." Before Guido could object, Francesco moved on. "I've been telling people about our Lord, and we talk. I've asked Dom Pietro about preaching. He said to ask you."

"You have no training to be a preacher, Francesco."

"The disciples weren't trained. They were fishermen."

"They had Jesus with them, teaching them."

"Isn't He with us through the Scriptures? In the Gospels didn't He tell us what to speak?"

"What do you think the people need to hear? What would you tell them?"

"What Jesus told the disciples to tell them. 'Where two or three are gathered in His Name, the kingdom of God is near.' I'll remind them."

They do need reminding, Guido thought. "That's not preaching. Preaching involves theology. Learning. Doctrine. Reading Scripture commentary. You have none of this training."

"Does it require training to tell people about Jesus, Messer Bishop?"

"Not if you tell them to listen to the Scriptures and follow what their priests tell them."

"That's what I'll do."

"You want to tell more people this message, more than you are reaching by talking to people here and there?"

"Sì."

"Then you may spread this message in Assisi and all my territory to as many people as you like. However, only that message. Don't try to argue about what the Church teaches. You're not trained."

"Only that message, Messer Bishop. Jesus Christ is near. Listen to Him. Come to Him."

"If I hear any complaints, I'll reconsider this permission."

"May I spread this message in churches? Dom Pietro said to ask you."

In churches? That would confuse people. "You don't have my permission to gather people in a church to speak to them as do priests and clerics. You're a layman. Outside the church you may gather the people, but only if the priest permits it. However, if I receive complaints or questions about heresy or hear that you're trying to teach doctrines that only priests fully understand, you'll be hearing from me."

NOTES

While the histories do not mention Francesco obtaining the bishop's permission to exhort the people, protocol would suggest it. Guido's reticence reflects the attitude of the hierarchy to lay preaching.

47

Messer Bernardo di Quintavalle di Berardello

Bernardo's House, Assisi (Early April 1208)

Messer Bernardo di Quintavalle di Berardello had heard the church bells ringing for Prime, but he had stayed in bed, trying to calm his heart. By now, in the Church of San Gregorio across the street, the Office of Prime must have ended, and the church would be deserted. If only he could disappear from his room and reappear inside the church to pray alone! But the bustle in the Piazza del San Gregorio had intensified, as had the early morning light pushing through cracks in his shuttered third floor window. If he left his house, even to walk across the street, he could meet someone. He didn't want to talk to anyone.

Why was he so agitated? He rubbed his hands across his usually clean-shaven cheeks, prickly under a day's growth of stubble. He needed to shave, to comb his unruly black hair, to wash his face. Why? Why did all these comfortable conventions trouble him? For thirty years, he'd been meticulous, having learned cleanliness and order in his substantial and respected family home. Now all those niceties seemed pointless.

He needed to get up. It was too late to be in bed. He needed to get up and go to San Giorgio, where Francesco had promised to speak again today after Terce.

He pushed out of bed and shaved, combed his hair, washed his face. Carefully he drew on his clothing, stretching the wrinkles out of his hose, smoothing his orange-colored tunic, and fastening it at the waist with a fashionable leather belt. He slipped on his red pointed shoes and decided to leave his lavender mantle behind. The day was warming nicely.

When he emerged from his house, he genially offered a "Good morning" to his fellow Assisiani. They returned the greeting with the respect they felt for this intelligent and wealthy man, who had earned degrees in both civil and canon law from the prestigious University of Bologna. Near the Piazza Santa Maria Maggiore, Madonna Camelia asked him how best to approach the consuls about repairing the street in front of her palazzo. At the Porta San Giorgio, Dom Faustino and Dom Mateo sought his opinion about the spiritual status of a hypothetical baptized orphan raised by infidels. "Since the child doesn't know he's Christian, he can't be held guilty for not following the faith," Bernardo reasoned.

Upon reaching San Giorgio, he was more agitated than when he had left home. As he stood among the small crowd in front of the church, he wanted to bolt, yet he felt rooted to the spot.

Francesco, why are you doing this to me? I don't even know you!

Francesco was a few years younger than Bernardo. They'd been acquaintances, opposite in temperament. Francesco was gregarious; Bernardo preferred solitude. Francesco was a wildly joyful, impulsive attention seeker; Bernardo was a thoughtful hermit of sorts who carefully thought through every decision. Francesco's schooling was passable; Bernardo's was brilliant. Francesco concocted pranks Bernardo never would have dreamed of. Now here in San Giorgio stood Bernardo, fascinated by the change in Francesco. Having never paid him much attention before, Bernardo had been paying the closest attention to him for the past two years. Without exchanging a single word, Francesco was challenging him.

How Francesco could speak! Not the words so much, but his conviction, his animated gestures and the exuberance that transformed his thin body and voice into a lute, throbbing and dancing with melody. When Francesco finished his brief exhortation, thoughts of penance, peace, and love of God hung in the air like invisible vapors. In silence, the thoughtful small crowd began to disperse.

For Bernardo, one phrase burned, word for word, in his soul. "Where there is rest and meditation, there is neither anxiety nor restlessness." If only he could rest and meditate! One way or the other, this anxiety must end. He needed information. Resolution. Peace.

A few people waited to speak to Francesco, who gave his full attention to each in turn. Bernardo could hardly keep still as he waited near the door. His heart pounded more rapidly with the departure of each satisfied questioner. He wanted to speak to Francesco. Alone.

What was the point of imagining Francesco's sins and his reasons for becoming a penitent? Bernardo needed to examine his own life. Niggling habits and attitudes that proved that Bernardo's real god was Bernardo. He liked his life's order and neatness. He took for granted the respect shown him. He knew that he was better educated than almost everyone else. He was foolishly proud of his degrees, which were impossible for poorer people to afford. He gave alms because he had spare money. He never lusted after women because, keeping so much to himself, he had never been tempted. How could he be proud of a never-challenged holiness? Holiness was not so much in what you did but in who you realized you were. Francesco knew that he was nothing. Bernardo needed to know that about Bernardo.

Finally, only Bernardo was left to consult Francesco.

"Messer Bernardo," Francesco said, bowing to him.

Bernardo blushed. "Frater Francesco, there is no need to bow. I am but a man like you. But I'm not like you. I'd like to learn more about you and how you live. Would you be so gracious as to come to my home for dinner tonight, so we can talk?" He would send his elderly servant Pietro to the mercato to purchase some simple foods.

Francesco broke into a grin. "Grazie. I'll come."

Having served Bernardo for over a decade, Pietro always seemed to understand exactly what Bernardo wanted. Bernardo had requested a simple but substantial meal, and that is precisely what Pietro prepared. Sweet peppered sausage *corallina*; hard-boiled eggs; savory, cheesy *torte al formaggio*; and red wine.

Francesco and Bernardo spoke late into the night. As Francesco shared his experiences, Bernardo became increasingly convinced of what he had begun to suspect over a year ago, namely that Francesco was possibly the sanest person in Assisi. The candles had burned to stubs when Bernardo finally said, "Francesco, grazie for staying this late. By now, it must be nearly midnight. Why not sleep here tonight on the extra bed in my room?"

Francesco agreed and soon both men were in bed. *Will he really sleep?* Bernardo wondered. Facing Francesco's bed, Bernardo snuggled under his blankets and closed his eyes. He waited a few moments and then began to snore. He heard Francesco snoring across the room. But not for long. After a few moments of Bernardo's snoring, Francesco quietly pushed back his blankets and gently eased himself to the floor where he knelt by the bed, his hands clasped in prayer. In the night stillness, Bernardo could hear him occasionally sighing, and sometimes whispering, "My God and my All . . ." or "O, sweet Virgin Mother . . ." or "My precious Jesus . . . ." Bernardo lay very still. Occasionally he may have dozed. But each time he opened his eyes, Francesco was kneeling, his head resting on the bed. As morning sun began to lighten the room, Bernardo saw Francesco quietly crawl into bed, his face to the wall. Later, when Bernardo shook him, he yawned as if awakening from a sound night's sleep. "Grazie, Messer Bernardo. Your bed is comfortable."

Too much so, Bernardo thought. He had heard where Francesco slept. In caves. Abandoned churches. Wooded hollows.

Bernardo's pressure to decide intensified. He had to think. He thanked Francesco, gave him a roll and cheese for his meal, and invited him back to speak with him the following week.

That week was torturous. Increasingly he felt God pressuring him into an unimaginable decision. Inside his spirit raged a battle far worse than that of

Colle della Strada. He was eternally grateful for surviving that confrontation. But this inner struggle? Maybe he'd tell Francesco not to come. Maybe he'd return to Bologna for more studies. Tantalizing but foolish tactics! He could escape Francesco but not the Holy Spirit, Who was dueling Bernardo into a corner.

Bernardo hadn't planned on asking Francesco so bluntly, but the words spilled out while they were enjoying their dinner of *salame* and *asparagi selvatici*. "Frater Francesco, if, for many years, someone holds on to the possessions, many or few, he has acquired from his lord, and no longer wishes to keep them, what is the better thing for him to do with them?"

"He must give them back to the lord from whom he has received them."

"As you did."

Francesco's dark face blushed. "With more charity than I showed."

Bernardo understood. He had witnessed Francesco's relinquishment in the Vescovado. "Then, Brother, I want to give away all my worldly goods for the love of God, who gave them to me, as it seems best to you." There. He had said it. His soul had not burst. Instead, it swelled with an inexplicable peace as if he, having survived a bloody battle, now saw unfurled the flag of victory.

Francesco's eyes widened, and his face seemed to radiate joy. "Then we will go to the church early in the morning and, through the book of the Gospels, we will learn how our Lord instructed his disciples."

NOTES

This incident, first mentioned in 1C (first book, chapter X), is in all the Franciscan histories. L3C (chapter VIII) records Francesco and Bernardo's conversation regarding relinquishment of a lord's goods. The phrase "Where there is rest and meditation, there is neither anxiety nor restlessness," is in Francesco's *Admonitions* (XXVII).

48

Pietro

Home of Bernardo di Quintavalle, Assisi (Early April 1208)

As he served and cleaned up the meal, Pietro couldn't help overhearing the conversation between Francesco and Bernardo. Was his master poised to join the merchant? When Francesco first began his odd adventure, people deemed him insane. Many still thought that way, but could they be wrong?

Pietro remembered an inexplicable parable. If a merchant found a pearl of great price in a field, what sense would it make to sell all that he had to buy that field? If he wanted to recoup his material wealth, he would have to sell the pearl because all his funds would be invested in it. What was the point? Either the merchant has money and lands with which to live a good life, or else he has a pearl that can neither feed nor support him.

As he lay in bed that night, Pietro wondered if Francesco might be smarter than everyone else. He had relinquished everything to obtain the pearl of great price. Now that he had only God and nothing else, he wasn't starving. Humbly, jubilantly, he was working and begging to support himself. Had Francesco found the path on which no one else was courageous enough to walk?

Pietro's old bones were poking his body, and his old mind was poking his memory. As he tried to find a comfortable sleeping position where hips and neck didn't hurt simultaneously, his memory was evaluating his long life.

Ever since his boyhood, he had served the Quintavalle family, starting with Bernardo's grandfather, Messer Berardello, who always found fault with Pietro's work. He could still hear the old man's drone: "Train the servants well when they're young, and they'll serve well when they're old."

Berardello had certainly made Pietro perform his duties perfectly, so that, when Berardello died and Pietro became his son Quintavalle's servant, Messer Quintavalle hardly spoke a word of correction. Under Quintavalle's service, Pietro had given alms to the poor and even brought some destitute and ill paupers to the Hospital of San Giorgio.

When Quintavalle's son Bernardo was old enough for a servant, Quintavalle had assigned Pietro, who accompanied his young master to Bologna for his schooling. Exceeding Quintavalle in generosity and compassion, Bernardo would give Pietro many alms. Pietro joyfully distributed them to the poor, with whom both men conversed as equals. "All people have dignity," Messer Bernardo asserted. "Dignity comes from God, Who made us in His image." What an honor to serve such a master! He wanted to serve Bernardo for the rest of his life and die near him. There was only one way to do that.

In the morning, the three men left to consult the Gospels. Francesco led the way to the quiet Church of San Nicolo, deserted at this time of day. In the dark crypt lit by numerous candles, the men knelt in a tight cluster before the altar and prayed.

After a few moments, Francesco whispered, "My Lord, how are we to renounce everything? Please show us Your Will." Then he took the closed book of the Gospels from the altar and, kneeling again with eyes closed, opened it at random and pointed to a verse. His eyes widened. "Messer Bernardo, your Latin is better than mine. Will you read this?"

In the flickering light, Bernardo read the Latin, then translated it. "If you wish to be perfect, go, sell everything you possess and give to the poor, and you will have treasure in heaven."

In joyful astonishment, the men looked from one to the other. Pietro felt prickly with wonder. In his long life, he had never felt the Presence of God as intensely as now.

"The Trinity is three," Francesco said. "Let's consult the Gospel two more times." Closing his eyes and the Gospel, Francesco opened the book again at random and pointed to a verse. He handed the book to Bernardo, who read and translated, "Take nothing for your journey, no staff, nor bag, nor bread, nor money; and do not have two tunics."

"That's the verse," Bernardo said in a hushed voice, "that you shared with me. The verse that God gave you on the feast of Saint Mark."

"Sì." Francesco bowed and slowly, with exquisite tenderness, kissed the pavement before the altar. "Grazie, my Lord. You have confirmed what You have already shown me." After a few moments of silence, Francesco raised his head. "Please show us one more time how we are to live."

For the third time, he closed his eyes and opened the Gospels. This time Bernardo read and translated where his finger pointed. "If anyone wishes to come after Me, he must deny himself, and take up his cross, and follow Me."

The men's eyes were fixed on the Gospel in Bernardo's hands. Then they looked at each other. Pietro saw astonishment and wonder on each face. Peace engulfed him. *They feel it, too*, he realized. *God's peace.*

Francesco hardly had to say, because the three of them knew, "Brothers, this is our life and rule and that of all who will want to join our company. Go, therefore, and fulfill what you have heard."

NOTES

1C (first book, chapter X), notes that "Immediately [after Bernardo] another man from the city followed him. This man was highly respected in his way of life, and what he began in a holy fashion he completed within a short time in an even holier way." AP (chapter II) and L3C (chapter VIII) record the man's name as Pietro and state that he followed Francesco at the same time as Bernardo. AP (chapter II) also states that, at this time, neither Bernardo, Pietro, nor Francesco "knew how to read very well" (which might mean "interpret the Scriptures"), so they consulted a priest to help them.

The Life of Brother Giles (24Gen, section 75), believed to have been written by Brother Leo (Leo joined Francesco in 1210 and died in 1271) after Egidio's (Giles') death in 1262, is the first history to identify this early follower as Pietro di Catanio.

However, Giordano (Jordan) of Giano, in section 11 of his *Chronicle* (13CC), calls Pietro (Peter) di Catanio "a doctor of laws" and in section 12 states that he "was educated and of noble birth." *The Mirror of Perfection* (IMP, section 61), believed to have been written in 1318 from scrolls (*rotuli*) preserved by Brother Leo, states that Pietro (Peter) di Catanio had been a canon of San Rufino. AP (chapter II) states that "Brother Peter . . . was poor in worldly goods." A canon would have been poor in worldly goods but literate and trained in Scripture scholarship.

Many modern historians postulate that Leo erred in identifying the first Pietro as Pietro di Catanio because the early histories do not mention his full name until 1219 or 1220. This book postulates that the first Pietro was not Pietro di Catanio, but another Pietro who joined Francesco at the same time as Bernardo. Bernardo's servant—simple, uneducated, and not wealthy—would be a plausible possibility as the first Pietro.

49

Dom Silvestro

Hospital of San Rufino, Assisi (Late April 1208)

Dom Silvestro was carrying a tray of four bowls of soup to the bedside of Enrico, a middle-aged beggar from the piazza, whose wife and two small sons were seated around him. Five days ago, Enrico had been trampled by the galloping steed of a knight who was in hot pursuit of a rival. Since Enrico had not been killed, the comune was ignoring the incident.

In his forty-some years, Silvestro had witnessed a great deal of suffering. Each gray hair in his black beard could attest to a tragedy of someone whom he had helped. Senseless incidents like this one angered him. Enrico was no dog. Poverty didn't erase his human dignity.

Silvestro handed the two bowls of soup to the boys, who took them politely and thanked him. The children looked longingly at their meal but didn't taste it. They were waiting, Silvestro knew, for their parents to receive their portions. *Manners*, Silvestro thought, *have to do with good teaching, not good breeding*. He handed Enrico and his wife their portions.

"Grazie, Dom. Will you please lead us in prayer?" Enrico asked, his swollen, battered lips mumbling the words.

The priest bowed his head and led the family in praying an Our Father.

Silvestro was returning to the kitchen to get more soup for other patients when three gray-clad penitents walked into the hospital. *Probably come to help*, he thought. They could feed the most infirm. As he approached them, his old eyes began to focus, and he could now see what could not be. Francesco, sì. He was a common sight in Assisi hospitals. However, that taller penitent had to be Messer Bernardo di Quintavalle and that shorter one his old servant, Pietro.

Were they joining Francesco? A few months ago, that old beggar Alberto, who had traipsed around with Francesco, had died. Not three weeks ago, that gullible priest at San Damiano, who had been enamored of Francesco's charms, had been found dead in his home. Francesco's only additional support, other than beggars and lepers, was the bishop, but who would have much time with that busy prelate? Gregarious Francesco must be recruiting. How did he persuade a dignified jurist and his well-respected servant to join him?

Before Silvestro could ask questions, Bernardo opened his bundled mantle and began to hand out coins to the patients. Pietro opened his mantle and began to do the same. Pietro quickly distributed his small alms and then dipped into Bernardo's very ample coffer and began to distribute the nobleman's wealth. Silvestro, who owned houses and properties, seized the opportunity. "Francesco, you didn't pay me well for the stones you bought from me."

With a swift hardness in his face that quickly faded into a genteel nod of the head, Francesco dipped into Bernardo's mantle and extracted a fistful of coins, which he handed to Silvestro.

"Do you now have full payment?"

Startled by the extravagance, Silvestro replied firmly, "I have it fully." Then, thinking he had better hide the money, Silvestro quickly returned to his room and stashed the coins in a corner behind a knapsack. When he returned to the hospital, the patients were ecstatic at their new riches and the penitents were gone.

NOTES

AP (chapter II) describes how Silvestro asked for some of Bernardo's coins in payment for stones that Francesco had begged.

50

Egidio

Assisi (April 23, 1208)

Wrapped in his woolen mantle against the morning chill, Egidio left his master's flock grazing under the vigilant eye of old Leopoldo. Insisting that watching jousts exhausted him, Leopoldo promised to tend the sheep alone while Egidio headed to the Semetone fields. Having seen fourteen summers, Egidio was not yet a man, but the soft stubble on his cheeks indicated that he was beginning to leave behind his boyhood. The boy in him, however, was almost running to get to a man's event, although the crowd impeded his progress. Wending his way through nobles on horseback and numerous families herding youngsters, Egidio made slow headway.

Today, to celebrate the feast of Saint George, Assisi knights were jousting in the Semetone fields. Egidio wanted to arrive before the games began so that he could walk among the knights, admire their armor, and imagine himself one of them. His master's son, Messer Reynaldo, a little older than he, often rode out to the meadows to escape boredom. Then he would regale Egidio with tales of Roland, Charlemagne, and King Arthur. Messer Reynaldo was squire to one of the tournament's knights. When he came of age after being trained in valor and humility, Reynaldo, in a religious ceremony both regal and sublime, would prostrate himself before his lord and extend his arms in the form of a cross. His petition? To be knighted. If the lord deemed him prepared and worthy, he would have him rise and grant his request. "I'll invite you," Reynaldo promised.

"Egidio!"

He heard the voice at his ear as he felt a hand on his shoulder.

"Lucio!" Egidio's eyes widened at his cousin's garb. Instead of wearing his usual short, plain tunic and baggy leggings, Lucio was outfitted in a crisp, new, bright blue tunic, ochre mantle, blue pointed shoes, and a jaunty blue cap, all fit for a noble.

"What do you think?" Lucio strutted even as they walked.

"I think you must have stolen those."

"Papà bought them," Lucio said with mock indignation.

Egidio gawked. His uncle had no more money than Egidio's papà.

"Some rich man was giving away all his money, and he gave a big handful to papà. Papà bought us all new clothes."

"That makes no sense. Why would a rich man give away all his money?"

Lucio shrugged. "He became a penitent."

Egidio pushed past an oxcart of children. "Why? Did he murder someone?"

"No! He's a rich notary," Lucio said, following Egidio. "He did it because he wanted to."

"He wanted to?"

"Something to do with Francesco." Lucio laughed. "You know. Saying you are a sinner. Worrying about your salvation." Lucio waved his hands as if to brush off the idea. "Papà says they acted like knights. Told him 'God be with you!' Even bowed to him."

"They?"

"Francesco. The rich man. And some old servant."

Lucio suddenly broke into a huge grin. "Tito!" he shouted over the crowd. "Excuse me," he said to Egidio. "See you at the tournament!"

Egidio watched him run off to join Tito, another cousin.

The crowd was pushing past Egidio, who wondered why he had stopped moving. He had an odd sensation of being outside of himself, way up in the sky.

In one direction were knights who served earthly masters and who would joust, shout, and compete for honors that lasted until the next tournament.

In the other direction were three penitent men from Assisi who acted like knights but who served a heavenly King Who would grant them eternal salvation.

Am I going in the wrong direction?

Confused by this sudden revelation, Egidio felt an overwhelming compulsion to stop and think. With longing, he looked in the direction of the joust and became aware of a joust already in progress, within himself.

The jousting at the Semetone fields was today only. If he attended, he could deal tomorrow with this uncomfortable inner turmoil. He took a few steps in the direction of the determined crowd. No. This didn't feel right.

Egidio, you're dim-witted, he thought. Saint George became a saint, not because he was a knight who had served a human lord, but because he had relinquished that to serve the Lord of All. To honor Saint George on his feast, Egidio shouldn't be attending a raucous joust. He should pray in the saint's church and ask his intercession.

Long ago, Egidio had learned to ask the Lord what to do when he couldn't decide. The answer always came swiftly to mind. Obeying the first thought that came, he'd never been led astray.

Lord, what should I do?

RETURN TO ASSISI.

Assisi. A bit disappointed, Egidio worked his way back through the crowd to Assisi where he entered the deserted Church of San Giorgio and knelt before the altar.

Saint George, pray for me.

Egidio was still, his eyes closed. Saint George, he felt, had heard his prayer. However, his spirit was still in turmoil. He wanted to be at that joust.

My Lord, what should I do?

GO TO FRANCESCO.

What? Egidio had expected the answer to be either go to the joust or stay here and pray.

What, Lord?

GO TO FRANCESCO.

Where, Lord?

No answer came, but a cleric walked into the church, so Egidio asked him. "Where is the penitent Francesco staying?"

"San Lazzaro d'Arce," the cleric whispered.

Egidio had heard that Francesco stayed with lepers. That scared him. But the Lord wanted him to find Francesco. So, he had to go.

Through the deserted city, he made his way to the Moiano gate, which opened to the Strada di Collemaggio. The road led into the forest. What should he do when he met Francesco? The Lord would have to tell him. He walked on.

Unexpectedly, the road forked into three.

My Lord, which way?

The answer came. TO THE LEFT.

Grazie, my Lord.

What a day! In the brilliant sunlight, the roadside was brimming with greenery laced with blossoms of violet, lemon, rose, and ivory. Warmed by the sun and his walking, Egidio removed his mantle and slung it over his shoulder.

A rustling startled him. A wolf? Deer? A gray form pushed aside a branch and stepped into the road.

Francesco.

Without any conscious thought, Egidio fell to his knees, then to his face, lying flat on the forest floor, his arms stretched out on either side in the form of a cross. He knew no position more humble than this of a squire requesting knighthood.

Egidio felt a firm grip on his shoulder.

"Kneel, my brother."

Egidio knelt before Francesco, his head bowed.

"Accept me into your company."

With his gaze lowered, he waited.

"What is your name?"

"Egidio."

He felt something hard touch his right shoulder. He looked up. Francesco was brandishing a thick stick, with which he graciously touched Egidio's left shoulder. A knighting ceremony with stick, not sword.

"Fra Egidio, what a grace the Lord is giving you. If, at this moment, the emperor himself came to Assisi and wanted to assume some person from the town as his knight, servant, or friend, wouldn't that man be overjoyed? How much more should you feel overjoyed since the Lord has chosen you as his knight and most beloved servant!"

Egidio was breathless. The Lord had chosen him? Chosen Egidio? As His knight and servant? Could it be true?

"Welcome to our company, Egidio, noble knight of Christ. Remain faithfully in this vocation to which the Lord has called you. In that way, you will someday go to live forever in His presence. Now rise, and we shall begin."

Dazed, amazed, overjoyed, Egidio rose. When their excited, spontaneous embrace ended, Francesco led the way through the woods to three small, makeshift huts of branches and leaves. Nearby, a middle-aged man was sitting by an open fire, stirring a pot from which wafted a delicious aroma. An old man was sitting on a log, mending his tunic's hem.

"You've returned early from prayer," the old man said.

"Perhaps he smelled the soup!" the other man teased.

Francesco laughed. "My brothers, soup didn't bring me back. Our Lord has sent us a good brother! Egidio!"

Exclamations of joy. Embraces. Introductions. A prayer of praise for Egidio. A prayer of thanksgiving for the savory soup of wild herbs and greens and for the soggy bread trenchers, which the younger Bernardo and older Pietro had begged that day. Then their meal, eaten while sitting on the ground.

As they tore the trenchers into bite-sized pieces and dipped them into the soup, the men shared about their trades and occupations and how they continued in them now while serving the poor. Francesco explained, "The Apostle says: 'Whoever does not wish to work shall not eat' and 'Let everyone remain in that trade and office in which he has been called.' So, you will work, Fra Egidio, and, for it, you may receive whatever is necessary. Except money. Money is nothing but dung."

"We aren't to be in charge," Bernardo added. "We must be the lesser ones, subject to all in the house."

"That's difficult for you, Messer!" Pietro laughed. "Everyone wants you to be in charge of their affairs."

Bernardo smiled. "No 'Messer' here. Here, only 'Fra.'"

Pietro looked flustered. "I'm sorry. I forgot."

"It's fine. Just so I don't forget," Bernardo said with a gentle smile. "It's difficult when people ask for advice. I advise them, but I now tell them that they must care for their own affairs." He paused. "Enough about me. Now, about Fra Francesco. He has sewn our tunics."

"If no one gives him thread, he uses vines." Pietro pointed to the seams that fastened the sleeves to his tunic.

"Maybe we'll sprout leaves!" Bernardo teased.

The men burst into laughter.

"Fra Pietro—he cooks for us. He tends the lepers and the poor," Francesco explained, "as we all do. As we work, we ask people to serve the Lord."

"So, Fra Egidio, what's your trade?" Pietro asked.

Egidio thought. "My family are poor farmers. I have no trade. What I don't know how to do, I learn." He focused his gaze on his sturdy hands and began to think of all he had done with them. He had been working ever since he could remember. "I've gathered nuts. Olives. Wheat. Grapes. Berries. Made fences. Minded children. Hauled water. Herded sheep. Pulled weeds. Made brooms. Cut trees. Chopped wood. Built houses." There was more, he knew. If he thought, he'd remember.

Francesco's words interrupted his remembering. "The Lord has *truly* sent you to us." His emphasis on the word *truly* betrayed his awe. "These skills will greatly help."

The men continued to share until the soup pot was empty and the trenchers eaten. Then together they prayed an Our Father in thanksgiving.

Francesco laid his hand on Egidio's arm. "Fra Egidio, we must beg cloth for a tunic for you." Egidio understood. His short tunic and loose leggings were the garb of laborers, not of penitents. "Once you're clothed, we'll tell your family and your master that you're in our company. Keep your tools to serve the Lord but give whatever else is yours to the poor."

NOTES

Egidio (Giles) was the third companion. In *The Life of Brother Giles* (24Gen), written by Brother Leo, Egidio called himself "a sinner, a rustic man, a simple and unlettered person" (section 97). An Assisi laborer, Egidio, who died in 1262, must have been quite young when he joined Francesco. While we know nothing about Egidio's family, we do know that he heard a relative talking about Bernardo and Pietro and felt the need to get his own salvation in order. The details of Egidio's decision follow closely the account in *The Life of Brother Giles* (24Gen, sections 74–76).

The meal is an imaginative account of how the early brothers must have eaten. The words about work are taken from chapter VII of the *Earlier Rule*. Fathers Blasic, Hammond, and Hellmann (*The Writings of Francis of Assisi*, pp. 62–72) believe that the places the brothers worked were charitable institutions and homes of the poor.

In this chapter, Francesco quotes the apostle Paul, from 2 Thessalonians 3:10 and 1 Corinthians 7:20.

L3C (chapter XI) states that Francesco considered money "as equal in worth and weight to the dung of an ass."

Historians disagree on when Francesco moved to Rivo Torto. Was it at the beginning, when the first brothers joined, or was it later? Since Francesco seems to have been staying at the Porziuncula when Bernardo and Pietro joined him, the author of this work believes it more plausible that the men simply built two more huts and joined Francesco as squatters at the Porziuncula. As other brothers joined, the huts the brothers made from woodland vegetation would serve them well until the weather grew too cold. The author of this book proposes that, at the beginning of winter in 1208, Francesco would have sought warmer accommodations, moving the brothers to Rivo Torto at that time. The decision must have been difficult, since at the Porziuncula the brothers could pray in the church and be in the Lord's presence, while Rivo Torto had no church. Francesco partially solved this dilemma by making a prayer chapel out of the middle space between the two Rivo Torto stone huts.

51

Prepotente

Road to Assisi (April 23, 1208)

Grumbling, Prepotente tried to hurry toward Assisi to beg, but the going was slow. Her two small sons, Demarco and Elmo, were dawdling, and she was big with child. If only six-year-old Bonfilia were here! She could mind those boys! But Bonfilia had just been hired out as a milkmaid.

Boys were certainly different than girls! Every shiny stone and every out-of-place twig caught their attention. Prepotente wanted to get what the family needed and return home to weed the garden. With her husband continuously busy working his master's fields, she did all the work at home. If Prepotente didn't weed the garden soon, weeds would overtake the vegetables while she was abed after childbirth.

If only her husband made enough money to support them! But money's value changed. No one knew from day to day what a day's work was worth.

Prepotente spied two approaching figures. The penitent Francesco and a laborer. Francesco would give something if he could. Others might not beg from him, but she did. So what if her bossiness had spawned her name? She usually received what she sought.

"Put those stones down," she commanded the two boys, who began to whine. "Be quiet. We're going to ask for alms."

She turned toward the travelers. “Have you any alms for a poor mother?” she called.

Francesco stopped. He tousled the heads of the two boys and bent down to speak to them. Prepotente tried to be patient. “Stones?” he said when they opened their fists. “That’s a pretty one.” He pointed to one in Demarco’s grimy hand. “Do you know our Lord Jesus Christ walked over stones just like these? Do you know that He made them? They’re beautiful as He’s beautiful. He made you. And you, too, are beautiful.” The boys giggled.

“Alms?” Prepotente reminded him.

Francesco stood. “Dear brother, let us give your mantle to this woman.”

Francesco was like an angel, Prepotente thought. She could sell that warm wool mantle and have alms for many days.

Without hesitation, the laborer bowed to Prepotente, took off his mantle and handed it to her. Demarco and Elmo jumped up and down and clapped.

NOTES

The Life of Brother Giles (24Gen, section 76) states that, on their way into Assisi to obtain cloth for a tunic, Francesco had Egidio give his cloak to an unnamed poor woman (no other details are given) who requested alms. “Prepotente” translates to “arrogant, bossy, or overbearing” and “Bonfilia” to “good daughter.”

Michael F. Cusato (*The Early Franciscan Movement,* p. 34) explains how, at this time, the poor were paid in Luccan coin, *piccolo,* the value of which the wealthy changed at whim. For their own transactions, the wealthy and powerful used the more stable Pavian coinage, *grossa.* Francesco didn’t want his brothers to handle money partly because it exploited the poor.

Part Eight

"Let Everyone Remain in That Trade and Office in Which He Has Been Called"

52

Fra Egidio

Porziuncula, Assisi (Late April 1208)

Near the Porziuncula, Egidio and the three other penitents stood in a swath of early morning sunlight dappled with shadows cast by overhead leaves. They had finished praying Lauds, and now their little band was about to split.

For the past days, the men had been discussing the slovenly condition of many churches. The golden vessels were rightly fit for the King of all Creation, but why were they so often unpolished and dirty? Would an earthly emperor be served dirty tableware? Why did people allow the house of God to look like a stable? Sì, Jesus came and lived in poverty, so He wouldn't expect a lavish house, but shouldn't it be clean?

Maybe the condition of churches reflected the condition of souls. When people don't care if their souls, where the Lord dwells, are smudged, why would they care about the cleanliness of their churches, where the Lord resides in the tabernacle? If someone cared more for the churches, would people care more for their souls?

One broom had served Francesco. He had replaced the worn straw many times. Now Egidio, crafting a handle from a tree limb, had made a second broom. With begged straw, he had made the bristles and tied them to the handle with cords.

They had their mission. To sweep churches and to tell others of God's love. Today they'd begin. Francesco grabbed the older broom from where it leaned against the church wall. He thrust its handle toward the sky as a knight might thrust a sword. "We'll return when the Lord brings us back!" he proclaimed.

Bernardo seized the new broom and thrust its handle skyward. "Pietro and I will await you!"

Bernardo and Francesco touched the tips of their broom handles together as knights touch the tips of their swords. Then all four men blessed themselves.

Egidio was curious. "Francesco, where are we going?"

Francesco's eyes were sparkling. "You'll tell us. Twirl around like a top until you can no longer stand." Then Francesco knelt, closed his eyes, and clasped his hands together in prayer. "My Lord, show us where to go."

Having vowed to obey Francesco as his liege lord, Egidio twirled and twirled until his stomach began to heave, his legs gave way, and he toppled with a splat to the ground.

The three men hurrahed. Egidio joined in the jest against himself.

"My brother, when you're no longer dizzy," he heard Francesco say, "then stand up and we'll go in the direction in which your head is pointing. When we return," he chuckled, "we'll find every church in Assisi clean."

"That you will," Bernardo assured.

"Agreed," Pietro assented.

NOTES

The opening quotation for Part Eight is from Francis' *Earlier Rule*, chapter VII, verse 5.

According to AP (chapter III), shortly after Egidio joined Francesco, the two men went on a mission in the direction of Ancona, leaving Bernardo and Pietro in the vicinity of Assisi.

Why Ancona? Why other locations? Francesco generally left those decisions up to God. His idea of twirling until collapsing and then walking in the direction in which one's head lay is told in *The Life of Brother Masseo* (24Gen, section 116). Unless he were going to a certain location, Francesco likely used this twirling technique to decide the directions of the missions.

AC (section 60) describes how Francesco used to carry a broom to sweep out churches, and how he instructed his friars to keep churches clean.

53

Dom Amedeo Magnani

Ottiano, Outside of Assisi (Early May 1208)

Dom Amedeo Magnani strolled majestically down the main road that ran through Ottiano, his red cape blowing in the warm breeze and his black curls dancing around his tonsure. He was too young and hearty to stay indoors, but the preceding rainy days had forced him into boring confinement. At last he could walk outdoors without mud soiling his soft shoes. Today was dry and sunny, a perfect day for letting his parish see that he cared for them. He could hail the farmers, talk to some at the edge of their fields, and visit families in their homes. Somebody would ask him to dinner, and he would, of course, accept. Even if they had to deprive their family, these poor farmers would feed Amedeo well. That was how one treated a rotund, respected priest.

As he walked by a newly planted vineyard, he spied an unfamiliar figure among the others hoeing the vines. A barefoot, sturdy, young man in a dark gray tunic. A penitent. Or a heretic.

"Good morning!" he called loudly. The men turned toward his voice, paused in their work, and returned his greeting.

"Good morning, Dom!"

Enough with the greetings. He had that new man's eye. Amedeo beckoned him to come.

The penitent, or heretic, laid down his hoe, approached the priest, and knelt before him. Goodness, this was more boy than man. Amedeo offered his hand, and the boy-man kissed it. A heretic wouldn't do that.

"You may rise," Amedeo said.

The young man did so.

"Who are you?"

"A penitent from Assisi, Dom."

Amedeo nodded. "Fine. You may go now."

The penitent bowed and scampered back to work.

A penitent from Assisi? Why come to Ottiano?

A short while later he came to his small, stone church, the Church of San Michele Arcangelo. From inside came a rhythmic *swish, swish, swish*. What? He peered in the open doorway. Another penitent? Older than the boy. Homely, with big ears. Sweeping the church.

Amedeo hopped up the stone step and into the nave. The man looked up. Seeing the priest, he lay down his broom, knelt, and waited. Amedeo offered his hand, and this penitent kissed it. Amedeo was sure now. Another penitent.

"Rise."

The penitent did so.

"What are you doing?"

"Dom, the church was dusty."

Amedeo felt insulted. "Do you think I can't keep my church clean?"

"I think you're busier tending your people."

The gentle words stung Amedeo's conscience. He was meticulous about his own appearance. Only that.

"May I speak with you?" the penitent asked.

"Speak."

"I'm sure that you wish the church to be clean. The altar vessels. The linens. The sacred words of Scripture. You're busy, so perhaps some good women can help?"

Amedeo had never thought of asking. He never thought much about the church. Dirty farmers came in. Occasionally a noble rode his horse in. The church had been a place to offer Mass out of the rain, a sort of covered outdoors. Who sweeps outdoors?

"Our Lord dwells here," the penitent said.

The words stung. His own house he kept fit for a king. But the King's house? Maybe he should think about asking some women to help.

NOTES

Ottiano is a small village of Assisi through which Francesco and Egidio could easily have passed on their first mission. Francesco admonished priests to keep clean the churches, sacred vessels, altar linens, and "holy words" [Scriptures] (see AC, section 60). The description of Ottiano's Church of San Michele Arcangelo (still standing) is accurate. However, we don't know the priest's name or anything about him. Francesco periodically visited Ottiano, the people "enjoyed seeing and hearing him," (AC, section 61) and he swept the church. He taught his brothers to reverence priests (AP, chapter VIII) as he reverenced Dom Amedeo, because Jesus comes to the faithful through the hands of a priest.

54

Elisa

Mercato, Fabriano (June 1208)

Thirteen-year-old Elisa was sitting on a stool in her mother's booth in the mercato of Fabriano. Trained for over half her life, Elisa made and sold laces with her mother and sister. She was deft with the two-pronged lucet, with which she could quickly braid laces—strong cords of leather or thinner ones of woolen or linen thread to lace up a bodice, sleeve, or waist. Her mother had various colors and thicknesses of threads, enough to keep Elisa and her ten-year-old sister Jacobella busy while mamma spoke to the customers and noted their orders. Elisa was working on a fine, white lace of twenty hands long for Madonna Marsala. Jacobella was crafting five leather laces of five hands' length each for Messer Dario. Both customers would fetch them after siesta.

Thinking about siesta made Elisa groggy. That was bad because she could miss a turn of the lucet or a slip of the thread and ruin the lace. She widened her big, brown eyes and wrinkled her nose. That might make her sneeze. A sneeze would wake her.

"Pace e bene." What a strange greeting in a deep voice! Elisa looked up and saw the most gorgeous young man in a gray tunic holding a broom and towering above a rather homely-looking man with big ears. The homely one bowed to her mother and the gorgeous one did the same. Then the homely one said graciously, "My good women, permit Fra Egidio to sweep out your stall."

He nodded to the gorgeous one who immediately began sweeping. Elisa and Jacobella lifted their bare feet so he could sweep beneath them. Goodness, the gorgeous one seemed so muscular and strong. He swept quickly and soon the little booth was clean.

The homely one cocked his head toward them. He called them closer with a beckoning of his finger and what Elisa thought was a prankish grin. When the three women had come a bit closer, he lowered his voice. "My good women, now that your booth is clean, may I share a secret to cleanse your souls?" Something about his manner was captivating. The women nodded.

"The secret is this," the homely one whispered. "Always remember that God is near. Therefore, let us refer all good to the Lord, God Almighty and Most High."

He paused.

"Acknowledge that every good is His."

He paused again.

"And thank Him, from Whom all good comes, for everything."

The smile on the man's face spread into his eyes until they twinkled.

"Now you know the secret. Will you remember always that the Lord is near? Will you see Him and thank Him in every good?"

Like puppets, the women nodded.

The penitent grinned. "Wonderful! May the Lord bless you this day and every day."

"Listen to him," the gorgeous one said in his deep, warm voice. "What he says is very good."

The gray-clad men bowed again and, taking the broom, walked to the next booth.

"Mamma, are they heretics?" Jacobella asked.

Mamma was staring after them as they stood at the tassel-maker's booth next to hers. From what Elisa could overhear, the men were delivering the same message.

"They look like heretics," mamma said, "but I don't know if they are."

"They're scary," Jacobella said.

Maybe one of them, Elisa thought. *But not the other*.

Two days later, the other returned. "My good women," he said, "may I beg a lace of you? All that's good on my poor broom is the handle."

Elisa's mother dismissed the straggly instrument with a flourish of her hand. "Looks like you've done much sweeping," she smiled.

The gorgeous penitent bowed. "So much that not only are the straws worn down, but the lace . . ." He shrugged and pulled at the lace wrapped around the battered straw. He held up the jumble of knots that had broken off. "I've knotted this so many times that it's now too short to use."

Elisa blurted out. "Mamma, may I make him a lace?"

"Certainly," mamma nodded.

"Grazie."

The young penitent sat at the foot of mamma's stool while Elisa lightly cinched the unfinished lace that she was making for Messer Bernardo. Setting that lace aside, she took another lucet and, with gray thread that matched the penitent's tunic, began a new lace.

"Let's offer a prayer for this lace and this lace-maker," the penitent said.

For me? No one ever prayed for Elisa except mamma.

"My Lord, in Your kindness, bless these good women for their kindness." The penitent then directed a question to the women. "Do you pray?"

Elisa and Jacobella shook their heads.

"Sometimes," mamma said.

"Shouldn't we always pray to our good God?" the penitent asked.

"I don't know how to pray," Jacobella blurted out.

"And you?" the penitent asked Elisa. "Do you know?"

Elisa felt the blood rushing to her face. She knew how to pray, but did she pray? She worked furiously at the lucet. "You pray for me," she said.

"Why not pray for yourself?"

Elisa could hardly speak. The gorgeous penitent probably prayed all the time. If she said she didn't think of praying, or was too lazy or thought it unimportant, she'd scandalize him. What holy excuse could she give? Well, she sometimes disrespected mamma. She argued with Jacobella. She nursed bad thoughts toward others. "You pray for me because I'm a sinner," she said softly, "and you're a holy man."

"I'm a sinner, too," the penitent said. "We're all sinners." Elisa blushed at this dismissal of her excuse. "Let's suppose that, tomorrow, the emperor comes to Fabriano and fills the piazza with gold and silver. The announcement goes through the city that everyone can come and take what they like. Would you send someone else to get you some treasure? Would you send me?"

"I'd go and get it myself," Elisa said. "Then I can take what I want."

"Naturally," the penitent said. "It's the same with God. He fills the whole world, and everybody can find Him. Don't send someone else to find God for you. Go and find Him yourself. Prayer is how you find Him."

Wasn't prayer asking God for things? He never gave her the fine clothes, comfortable house, or heaps of food she'd prayed for. God hadn't kept papà from dying from bad humors. God didn't pay attention to her prayers or answer them, so she'd stopped asking.

Then she remembered the lace. It was long enough now. She knotted the lace, slipped it from the lucet, and handed it to the penitent.

"Grazie." The youth turned the lace over in his hand. "This will bind the straw to its handle. Then I can use the broom the way I wish. Prayer is a lace that binds you to God. When you pray, He can use you however He wishes."

"God doesn't use me," Elisa smugly said.

"God uses everyone." The penitent's eyes sparkled as he smiled at Elisa. Oh, he was handsome! "God has used you just now. Because of you, I can reconstruct this broom. We'll use it to sweep churches. Booths. Homes. When we sweep, Fra Francesco speaks of Our Lord and His Kingdom. He reminds people that God is near. We must seek Him, love Him, serve Him. We must prepare for when we die and stand before Him. All this your lace enables us to do."

One little lace could enable that? One little lace she'd made?

"The Lord is greater than any emperor's treasure. If you pray, He'll show you how else He wishes to use you. He'll show you how He loves you. Will you start to pray today?"

His beguiling eyes were fixed on her. "I'll try," she said. Now she would have to do it. She couldn't lie again to this magnificent man.

NOTES

Francesco's exhortation in this chapter is from the *Earlier Rule* (chapter XVII).

Egidio's likening of prayer to treasure is similar to an example he used with a secular man (*Life of Brother Giles*, 24Gen, section 94).

The fictional Elisa and her family demonstrate various reactions to the friars' early missions.

Although this first mission was in the direction of Ancona, we don't know if Francesco and Egidio reached that city before returning to Assisi. Fabriano has a plaque commemorating their visit in 1208.

55

Sabbatino

Hospital of San Rufino, Assisi (July 1208)

Morning sunlight was pouring through the cracks in the wooden shutters covering the windows of Sabbatino's room attached to the Hospital of San Rufino. His head was pounding. Maybe he should be in the sick ward.

Cold water. Yes, he needed cold water. The basin by his bedside was easy to see in the light. How long had he slept?

Sabbatino splashed lukewarm water over his face. Bah! If he wanted cool water in this sweltering July, he'd have to plunge into a fountain. He'd better rally himself. He was supposed to be tending the patients.

Near the window, Morico was sprawled on the floor, his diminutive, dozing body flooded with sunlight. After last night's revelry, Morico had been too drunk to walk home. So Sabbatino had let him come into his room and sleep off the wine. This had happened twice before.

Sabbatino bent down to rouse his friend. The smell of Morico's sweat, mingled with soured wine and fresh hay, assaulted him. Sabbatino shook the little body. "Morico, you need a bath. Aren't you supposed to be at work?"

Morico stirred and groaned. He sat up and shook his head. "My head hurts."

"Mine, too," Sabbatino said. "Wash up." Sabbatino pointed to the basin. "It must be past Terce."

Morico groaned. "Why are we doing this?"

"You're supposed to be in the fields. I'm supposed to be in the hospital."

Morico raised his open hands and shook them back and forth in rhythm with his words. "No. Why—are—we—doing—THIS?"

"What do you mean? You're drunk." Sabbatino dunked a towel into the basin, wrung it out, and gave it to Morico. "Wash up. You need to get going."

Obediently, Morico swabbed his face, neck, hands. He handed the towel back to Sabbatino. "Why—are—we—doing—THIS?"

Finally, Sabbatino understood. The familiar question. Again. He and Morico had several times discussed the "Why are we doing this?" question. Why are we working during the day, reveling at night, and sleeping off our drink? What are we looking for? This is not the way to impress a bride, if either of them ever made a move to find one. This was not the way to prepare for work, if either of them had a commitment to that. They were like two saplings, blown about by the wind. Why were they planted where they were planted? What was the point?

Morico shook his head and pushed himself to his feet. "I'm not going to the fields today. I'm going to see Francesco."

Sabbatino held his pounding head. Francesco! In their "Why are we doing this?" discussions, Francesco always seemed to come up. It happened more than ever since that shepherd from Mandria had joined his band of followers. What was the man's name? Filippo? Morico worked in the fields, too, but he'd never talked much about that idealistic boy shepherd who joined Francesco early on. They'd seen him around now and then. Egidio. Just a youth. What did he know? But this Filippo. A tall, muscled, confident shepherd, about Morico's age, whose assurance intrigued vacillating Morico.

"Francesco's away," Sabbatino noted.

"He's back. Ghita told me he'd come begging."

Ghita. Last night, Morico had spent quite a bit of time with Ghita.

Francesco was like a leaf in the wind. He was here now, but for how long? Who knew when he might blow somewhere else?

"If you're going to see Francesco," Sabbatino said, "I'll go with you."

NOTES

AP (chapter III) lists Sabbatino, Morico the Short, and Brother John (identified as John [Giovanni] di Capella in L3C, chapter IX) as joining Francesco upon the return from the 1208 mission. What are the backgrounds of these men? Why did they join? We don't know. This chapter is a hypothetical exploration of some possibilities.

56

Messer Angelo di Tancredi

Rieti (November 1208)

Attired in glittering armor, Messer Angelo di Tancredi guided his powerful charger through the Rieti streets. He was on his way to his lord's palazzo. He'd been invited there to a banquet for a duke with whom his lord hoped to make an alliance. As he rode leisurely along, the recently knighted youth smiled courteously at his fellow citizens, who gazed at him with adulation.

I wonder if I'll get used to this, Angelo mused. *I hope not!*

A commotion near the piazza's fountain drew his attention. Trouble? Knights were supposed to address trouble.

With his hand on the hilt of his sword, he nervously rode into the small crowd that parted for him. In the center stood two scruffy penitents, one tall and good-looking like Angelo himself, although not nearly as burly, and the other short and homely.

Angelo breathed more easily. No trouble here. He nodded courteously to the penitents, who returned his nod.

The short, homely man leaped onto the rim of the fountain and called out, "Pace e bene!" Peace and all good!

"Do you feel secure? Comfortable? A good thing, sì?" The penitent was calling out to the crowd like a podestà haranguing his town. "No! As Messer

Knight here knows,"—the penitent was gesturing toward Angelo and everyone was looking at him—"when one is too secure," the speaker continued, "one is less wary of the enemy. Isn't that correct, Messer Knight?"

Of course. Angelo nodded.

"If the devil can hold on to one hair of a person—"the speaker said, gesturing toward a long-haired laborer standing to the right. The laborer laughed. The penitent smiled. "If the devil can hold on to one hair of a person, he will soon make it grow into a plank! And if for many years," he nodded toward an elderly, stooped butcher to his left, "he cannot pull down the one he's tempting, he doesn't complain about the delay," he paused, looking from one face to the other, "as long as that one gives in to him in the end." Another pause. "This is his work." He was pacing the rim of the fountain, his head bowed as if in deep thought, "Day and night, this is his work." Then he looked up and scanned the crowd. "He isn't concerned about anything else." He paused and then called out, "So be not alarmed if you are tempted. No one should consider himself a servant of God until he has passed through temptations and tribulations. A temptation overcome is like a ring," he mimicked plucking a ring from the air, "with which the Lord betroths the soul of His servant." He bent toward a young woman standing nearby and, bowing to her, courteously presented to her the imaginary ring. "Many flatter themselves over their many years of merit and rejoice at never having suffered any temptations. But sheer fright would knock them out before a battle even started. So they should know that the Lord has kept in mind their weakness of spirit. As Messer Knight knows," he gestured toward Angelo, "hard fights are rarely fought except by those with the greatest strength." The speaker paused. "Therefore, let us all love the Lord God," his arms extended over the crowd, "Who has given and gives to each one of us our whole body, our whole soul, and our whole life, Who has created, redeemed and will save us by His mercy alone," he lifted his eyes heavenward, "Who did and does everything good for us," he pointed to himself, "miserable and wretched, rotten and foul, ungrateful and evil ones. Amen."

The penitent jumped off the fountain and joined the other penitent in walking among the people, speaking quietly to each.

Angelo had better get to that banquet.

Suddenly the speaker was beside Angelo's charger, stroking the animal's powerful neck.

"A magnificent animal, Messer. One sees God's glory and power in him."

Angelo nodded thoughtfully. He'd never recognized God's glory and power in his horse.

"Messer Knight," the man was smiling broadly, "armor, sword, and spurs are empty glamor. Would you not like to wear a coarse rope instead of the girdle, the cross of Christ instead of a sword, and the dust and dirt of the road instead of the spurs? Follow me. I shall make you a knight of Christ."

What? Unexpectedly heat welled up within him and Angelo felt unbearably hot. He removed his helmet. A thin breeze ruffled his thick, black curls and cooled him.

"Wish I had your head of hair!" called a bald tanner walking past.

Angelo laughed. "Wish I could share it with you."

The tanner bellowed and kept walking. The crowd was dispersing. The penitents were walking toward the mercato. Angelo squeezed his legs against his charger's ribcage. Obediently the horse moved forward and caught up to the men.

"What are your names?" he asked, his charger walking alongside them.

"Fra Francesco," said the homely one.

"Fra Filippo," said the handsome one.

"Where are you from?"

"Assisi," Filippo answered.

"I'm Angelo. I must go to my lord's banquet. Pray for me."

"We will pray for you to come someday to the greatest banquet." Francesco smiled.

Assisi. The greatest banquet.

The words became a refrain, overriding the ballads sung at his lord's feast, where the finery seemed shabbier than the penitents' tunics. After a night of feasting and song, then sleeping in his lord's stable near his charger, Angelo returned to Rieti, the word "Assisi" still ringing in his mind.

He always wanted to be his best. Wasn't a knight the noblest and best profession?

A knight of Christ? Christ was his lord's Lord.

Assisi. Assisi. The greatest banquet.

As he undid his armor in his palatial home, he wondered if he would ever don it again. As he brushed his matted hair, he wondered if Satan were trying to make his vanity and hesitation into a plank to cage Angelo in his lord's service when God was inviting him into His own.

Slipping into a nondescript tunic and wrapping himself in his reddish-gray fox-fur mantle and matching cap, Angelo left his house to find the two brothers. Two weeks later, he, clothed in undyed gray wool, left Rieti with Francesco and Filippo. As they strode out of the city on their way to Assisi, they nodded to a beggar clothed in a reddish-gray fox-fur mantle. Sitting next to him, a beggar child was wearing a matching fox-fur cap.

NOTES

Franciscan histories mention Angelo di Tancredi, Angelo of Assisi, and Angelo of Rieti. His identity is controversial (see *Early Documents II*, p. 67, footnote). Many modern scholars believe that these are the same individual. In Rieti, the house of Angelo di Tancredi later became a Poor Clare convent. Angelo was the first knight to follow Francesco and became one of his closest companions. Angelo's remains, buried in the Basilica of Saint Francis, indicate that he was a tall, robust man.

This chapter is based on Father Luke Wadding's recounting of Angelo's conversion (*Annales Minorum*) and recounted by Lodouico Iacobilli da Foligno (*Vite de' santi, e beati dell'Umbria, e di quelli, i corpi de' quali riposano in essa prouincia*, 1656, I, 243). Francesco's words about the devil are from 2C (second book, chapter LXXIX), about temptations from 2C (second book, chapter LXXXIII), and prayer from the *Regula non Bullata* of 1221 (*Earlier Rule*, chapter XXIII).

57

Morico

Rivo Torto (Early December 1208)

In the frosty December night, little Morico tugged his mantle tighter around his tunic-covered body. On his straw bed at Rivo Torto, he cuddled himself into as tight a ball of human flesh as possible, but he still was shivering. How much colder would he have been in his leaf-and-branch hut at the Porziuncula if Francesco hadn't relocated everyone to these warmer turf sheds? Despite his shaking and hunger pains, Morico wouldn't give in. Going hungry would conquer his gluttony.

When he and Sabbatino had first joined Francesco, Morico discovered that wine of the grape was tame compared to wine of this new beginning. Possessing God alone was exhilarating. Freeing!

Wine. If he had wine, he'd feel warmer. But all they had were begged turnips.

Turnips. Yummy!

Morico shook his head. *No! Think of something else.*

Yesterday. God loves you, Francesco said. He's counted the hairs of your heads and values you more than sparrows, whom He feeds. You're more valuable than sparrows.

Whom He feeds.

Trust God. Live like Jesus. Walk in His footprints.

Jesus was sometimes hungry. He multiplied loaves and fish.

He feeds the sparrows.

No food. Think of the brothers.

Filippo di Lungo. Morico emulated his bravery and decorum. He made the best savory soup of wild herbs and nuts.

Argh! The brothers!

Giovanni della Capella, one of the lesser nobles of Assisi. Handsome. Educated. His work was teaching youngsters to read. Their parents paid him in mutton and hen. Delicious!

Herbs. Nuts. Mutton. Hen.

Morico moaned.

The mission. Remember the mission. Eight men. They had prostrated themselves before Francesco, as knights promising him their obedience. "Go, my dear brothers, two by two through different parts of the world," Francesco said, "announcing peace to the people and penance for the remission of sins. Be patient in trials, confident that the Lord will fulfill His plan and promise. Respond humbly to those who question you. Bless those who persecute you. Give thanks to those who harm you and bring false charges against you, for because of these things, an eternal kingdom is being prepared for us. Cast your cares upon the Lord and He will sustain you."

Morico had accompanied Francesco, who begged but who gave most of the food to Morico. *He's fasting in reparation for his sins*, Morico thought. Then, in Poggio Bustone, Francesco confided that the Lord had just assured him that his sins were forgiven. However, he kept on fasting. Shortly after they returned to the Porziuncula, the other brothers also arrived, saying, "The Holy Spirit beckoned us back." Francesco exclaimed that the Lord had answered his prayer to see all the brothers again.

Morico had noticed that Francesco was still fasting. *My sins are at least as bad as his. I'd better fast more*, Morico thought. So, he had begun.

I'm dying. Like Pietro.

Even the ripe grapes Francesco had shared with Pietro couldn't cure him. In September, Pietro had died in Bernardo's arms. The brothers had buried his old, faithful body at the Porziuncula, not far from the grape arbor.

Grapes. Morico was disgusted. He'd think of the last mission.

Bernardo and Egidio—north to Santiago di Compostela, to pray for Pietro's soul.

Morico and Sabbatino—east where, in one small town, Morico had begged a pear and a gigantic thug had grabbed Morico's hood and swung him over his back like a trussed sheep. Carrying him through the mercato, he'd displayed Morico to a group of equally huge friends working at a forge. Morico, having eaten the pear, had called out to the youths, "I'm small, but God's love for you is great. You can carry that love around with you more easily than you carry me. God bless you. And you. And you." One of the amused smiths had offered Morico a loaf. "It'll help you grow!"

Grow? He was growing hungrier.

The mission. The mission.

Francesco and Filippo—south where, in Poggio Bustone, Francesco had a vision or dream. "Be strong, dear brothers, and rejoice in the Lord. Do not be sad, because you seem so few, and do not let my simplicity or yours discourage you. The Lord has shown me that God will make us grow into a great multitude and will spread us to the ends of the earth." In his vision, men of all nations were running to join the brothers. This joy would eventually turn bitter until the Lord, like a good fisherman, would be forced to sort through the catch and save the good while discarding the bad.

Fish. Sweet, tender fish.

Next to Morico, Barbaro, a simple, diligent leather worker, twitched. Had Morico disturbed him? Barbaro was the newest brother, along with Giovanni di San Costanzo, whose villa was a short gallop from the Porziuncula. Good men. Not bad fish to discard.

Fish. Bread. Grapes. Pears. Soups. Mutton.

"I'm dying!" Morico blurted out.

Oh, no!

"Brothers, get up and light a lamp!" Francesco.

Fumbling. Scrambling. Light from a burning taper flooding the room.

"Who was it who said, 'I'm dying'?" Francesco. Tender.

"Me," Morico confessed.

"What's the matter, brother? Why are you dying?"

"I'm dying of hunger."

"Let's set the table and have something to eat with our brother," Francesco said.

Shuffling. Trampling. A strong arm around Morico's shoulder.

"Lean on me." Sabbatino was already pulling him up. "I told you to fast less."

The brothers filed into the fire room and huddled around the flames. Sabbatino wrapped his own mantle around Morico. He was shivering less when Egidio took a pot off the fire and placed it on a narrow table. The brothers moved to the benches and, by firelight, offered a prayer of thanks.

Wooden bowls were passed around. Egidio ladled a scoop from the pot into each bowl.

Turnips. Never had they tasted so scrumptious.

"My brothers," Francesco said quietly, "I say that each of you must consider his own constitution. Although one of you may be sustained with less food than another, I do not want one who needs more food to try imitating him in this. Rather, considering his constitution, he should provide his body with what it needs. Just as we must beware of overindulgence in eating, which harms body and soul, so we must beware of excessive abstinence even more, because the Lord desires mercy and not sacrifice."

Francesco's voice was soothing. "But I tell you, in the future I do not wish to act this way because it wouldn't be religious or decent." Morico felt his face aflame. His outcry had caused the brothers to break both their Rule and their fast.

"Then what do you wish?" Sabbatino asked.

"Let each one provide his body with what it *needs*, as our poverty will allow. This is what I wish and command you."

Morico understood Sabbatino's nudge even before his friend whispered, "Don't be pig-headed, Morico. Do what he says."

NOTES

People believed that more spiritual people needed less food, so fasting was considered a spiritual discipline and a way to holiness. The stricter the fast, the more quickly one could become holier because fasting conquered the self. (See Caroline Walker Bynum, *Holy Feast, Holy Fast*, chapter 6).

AP (chapter V) mentions that an unnamed early brother was "carried by the capuche across someone's back for as long as he pleased." The capuche was the pointed hood worn by the brothers as part of their habit. Morico the Short is possibly that brother.

If the first Pietro was not Pietro di Catanio, then the first Pietro died early.

1C (first book, chapter XII) records Francesco's words as he sent the brothers on mission. AC records the incidents of Francesco eating grapes with an unnamed elderly, sick brother (section 53) and initiating a nighttime meal with an unnamed brother who said he was dying (section 50), which inspired his words on fasting, reproduced in this chapter. 1C (first book, chapter XI) records his words about the growth of the brotherhood and the good and bad fish. *Early Documents* (p. 205, footnote b) says that this incident probably took place in Poggio Bustone.

1C (first book, chapter XVI) records that during the winter at Rivo Torto, the brothers often had only turnips to eat.

58

Giovanni di San Costanzo

Assisi (January 1209)

Giovanni di San Costanzo practically danced through the Assisi streets, so joyful was he on this exceptionally warm day. Brilliant sunlight was drawing rivulets of sparkling water from the melting snow. After sweeping the Cathedral of San Rufino, Giovanni had used snowmelt and a rag to polish the floor. Now, before returning to Rivo Torto, he was begging.

The sunshine brightened Giovanni's dark, smiling eyes. Him, a noble, begging! Imagine! But here he was, knocking at doors, offering his benefactors something worth more than a hundred silver pieces in exchange for a penny, Francesco taught.

A young boy opened the door. "Could you give alms for the love of the Lord God?" Giovanni asked.

"Wait." The boy bowed and closed the door.

In a few moments, the door reopened and a man appeared. The house steward, judging by his dress.

"Could you give alms for the love of the Lord God?" Giovanni asked. "Compared to God's love, heaven and earth are nothing!" He had spoken the words Francesco had taught the brothers.

"Wait." The steward closed the door.

Initially Giovanni and many other brothers had been ashamed to beg. Thus, when the food they'd received in exchange for working was insufficient, Francesco had begged for them. However, the day after Christmas, Francesco had gathered the brothers around the fire.

"My dearest brothers and sons, don't be ashamed to go for alms, because the Lord for our sake made Himself poor in this world. Therefore, because of His example, we have chosen the way of the most genuine poverty and that of His most holy Mother. This is our inheritance, which the Lord Jesus Christ acquired. He bequeathed it to us and to all who want to live in holy poverty according to His example."

Giovanni had considered that. The world was celebrating God's birth into human poverty. To embrace poverty, Giovanni had joined Francesco. But poverty of spirit exceeded poverty of possessions. Humility should replace pride. Discomfiture should replace vanity. Littleness should replace greatness. Jesus embraced both poverty of spirit and poverty of possessions.

"I tell you the truth: many of the noblest and wisest of this world will come to this congregation and they will consider it a great honor to go for alms," Francesco had assured them.

Giovanni smiled at the memory as he stood waiting. He was not the only one begging. Somewhere Messer Bernardo di Vigilante di Bernardo di Bellettone, an Assisi nobleman who had just joined the brotherhood, was begging, too.

The door opened and the steward gave Giovanni two turnips. Giovanni smiled. "Grazie. God bless you." When he returned to his brothers and they compared who collected more alms, he would lose the contest today. They'd been eating turnips all winter. Maybe someone else had begged meat.

NOTES

According to Fortini (p. 286), Giovanni di San Costanzo had lived in a villa, which meant that he was a man of wealth. Bernardo di Vigilante di Bernardo di Bellettone was an Assisi noble. Other than this, we know no more about these men.

AC (section 51) describes how Francesco begged for the brothers who were too ashamed to beg themselves, then taught them how to beg in the words Giovanni uses in this chapter. AC (section 51) also describes how the brothers compared alms to see who collected the most.

59

Bishop Guido

Hospital of San Salvatore della Pareti, Plain below Assisi (February 1209)

Bishop Guido swung his bulky body onto his steed. Then he nodded a solemn farewell to the priest assigned to the lepers at the Hospital of San Salvatore della Pareti. The winter had been particularly harsh and snowy, and Guido had been waiting for a mild but overcast day to make his yearly visit. Today the sun, whose warmth drew out the contagion and stench of the lepers, was hiding behind cloud cover, while the nasty night wind had decreased to a breeze. The day was almost perfect for visiting a leper colony.

The inspection had been routine. Since last year, three lepers had died and three had been admitted. The brothers of penance continued to help tend the lepers, beg alms for them, tidy the hospital, and plant the gardens. Francesco's gentle touch had mellowed an irascible leper, who would allow only Francesco to bathe him. However, Francesco wasn't at the hospital today. The brothers said he was at Rivo Torto.

After riding through the forest and crossing the frigid stream, Guido and his squire stopped at the hovel on the opposite bank. Guido dismounted and handed the reins to his squire. When the weather warmed, the brothers would likely start traveling again. Guido needed to speak to Francesco before that happened.

Guido peered into the hut's narrow, left-hand room. Empty except for the circle of rocks that contained the fire and one cooking pot. In the prayer space, Morico and Sabbatino were kneeling beside the large wooden cross thrust into the ground. Guido glanced into the right hut. Empty but for mashed piles of straw and names written in chalk on the beams. Sabbatino. Morico. Filippo. Giovanni. No point in reading all the names.

Guido walked around the hovel to the back where Francesco had a cell of evergreen branches. Guido knocked at the door and entered. Inside the cell was another, smaller cell made of mats. Guido glanced into the second cell. Empty.

Finding this man is like finding a mouse in a parsnip patch, Guido thought.

He exited the cell. Now where? Then he spied Egidio coming from the forest, his arms laden with firewood. "Egidio, where is Francesco?"

"He said he was going to the leper hospital, Messer Bishop."

"They said he was here."

Egidio shrugged.

"When you see him, tell him that I need to see him."

"Sì, Messer Bishop."

Nodding, Guido mounted his palfrey and pointed him in the direction of Fontanelle. He had to visit that leper hospital, also. Maybe he'd meet Francesco there.

The mild weather lasted a day. The following day was bitter with wind and swirling snow. Guido was in his study, bundled in one of his fox-fur cloaks, reading the sermons of Saint Augustine and appreciating the barely perceptible warmth of the candles, when his secretary ushered in Francesco. Guido's gaze went from the man's snow-covered hood to his bare feet.

"Your life's too hard," Guido blurted out.

"Did you summon me to tell me that, Messer Bishop?" Francesco was smiling. He certainly didn't look cold.

"No. How many times have I told you that, but have you ever changed how you live?" Guido threw up his arms in mock despair. "I didn't summon you to have a useless conversation. Sit down."

Francesco plopped, cross-legged, to the floor.

"In that chair!"

Grinning, Francesco leaped to his feet and settled into a wooden chair opposite Guido.

"You look like you have flaming logs under your feet while I'm freezing." Guido waved his arm. "Never mind. It won't always be winter. Spring is coming. And when it does," Guido pointed his finger directly at Francesco, "you and your brothers must stay in my territory, not go elsewhere as you did last year."

Francesco looked confused. "We're doing nothing different than other hermits and penitents."

"You're no longer an isolated hermit or penitent, Francesco. You have brothers who dress like you, think like you, live like you. Your brotherhood looks like a religio."

"We're only following the Gospel, Messer Bishop."

"So say the heretics. They, too, look like a religio. I can protect you here, where I'm bishop. But I'm not bishop everywhere."

"Our Lord Jesus Christ protects us."

"That's not what I mean. Wherever you go, the bishop needs to know who you are and what you believe. He needs to be aware that you're speaking to his people."

"Do we need the bishop's permission to talk about penance?"

"No." Pope Innocenzo III had clarified that eight years ago. He had permitted lay penitents of the Humiliati in Milan to speak to the people about repentance and moral living. However, he hadn't extended that permission to laity preaching doctrine. How could uneducated laity correctly preach doctrine?

"You've heard me preach about heresy. You've heard me ask the faithful to report anyone who seems heretical."

"Sì, Messer. Many times."

"The Lord Pope has instructed all bishops to preach this. He wants to eliminate heresy. We bishops are to find and excommunicate heretics and their supporters. When you and your brothers go outside Assisi, people who don't know you may suspect you of heresy. They could tell their bishop. Word could get back to me. Or it could get back to Rome. Then Lord Pope would call me in, and I would be in trouble, and so would you and your brothers."

"What should we do? Jesus sent His followers throughout the world to tell others to turn to God."

"Lord Pope is God's representative. You'll have to get his permission."

Francesco jumped up. "Then we'll go to see Lord Pope!"

"You can't just go to see Lord Pope. You need a Rule of Life. You need a plan. Organization. You need to show him something."

"Our Rule is the Gospel. Our plan is to follow our Lord Jesus Christ."

"The heretics say the same. You need a written Rule of Life. One that shows that you're faithful to the Church. One that tells what you do. That shows your foresight and organization."

Francesco looked puzzled. Of course. He wasn't one to write things down. He'd always been spontaneous.

"This is getting too big, Francesco. When you first came to me, you alone asked to do penance. I gave you permission. Then you asked to speak with the people. I agreed. Then others came. I gave them permission, too. But now you have more men. How many are with you? Nine? Ten?"

"About that, Messer. Let me count them. Egidio, Bernardo, Sabbatino—"

Guido interrupted him. "You don't even know. You have to count them. Likely more will come. Lord Pope must understand you and your brothers before he hears misinformation and misunderstands. You need to write down your Rule of Life and share it with him."

Guido took a scrap of parchment from his desk. "I've written down the beginning." Guido began to read slowly so that Francesco could understand the Latin, "Brother Francis—and whoever is head of this religion—promises obedience and reverence to the Lord Pope Innocent and his successors. The rule and life of the brothers is this, namely: 'to live in obedience, in chastity, and without anything of their own.'"

Guido glanced up. "This shows your obedience to Lord Pope and contains words that he has approved for another group. Be sure these words are in your Rule."

"We're penitents, not a religio."

"You are a religio. There are too many of you to be anything else."

Francesco looked unsure.

"Francesco, if you wish to spread the message of conversion outside of my territory, the Lord Pope must permit it. Pray about it. In May, I'll be in Rome. Come to me then if you wish, with a written Rule to share with Lord Pope. Ask a cleric or a priest to help you write it. And give your group a name." He offered the parchment to Francesco, who hesitantly took it.

"Remember, Francesco. You and your brothers may spread your message only in my territory unless Lord Pope agrees to have you spread it elsewhere."

NOTES

Fortini (p. 206, footnote) lists the leper hospitals around Assisi.

The decretal and bull of Pope Lucius III (November 1184) decreed that bishops were to seek out heretics and excommunicate them. They were to re-announce this excommunication on all feasts and holy days. Heretics included those in recognized heretical sects and those who, without Church authorization, preached privately or publicly.

Although Francesco and his brothers were not preaching doctrine, their clothing and lifestyle resembled those of the heretics, particularly the Cathars.

Francesco never wanted papal privileges (see AC, section 20). At this time, he considered his men to be not a religious order, but rather penitents calling others to repentance. He had probably never considered problems that could arise from the brothers going into other bishops' territories.

Guido would have had the concerns that he states in this chapter. He would have wanted Francesco to write down his way of life to present to the pope for approval. This chapter postulates that Guido gave Francesco the juridical wording, in Latin, to begin his Rule. The words "to live in obedience, in chastity, and without anything of their own" is a phrase in the Trinitarian Rule approved by Innocent III in 1198. These words, as well as the others which Guido shares with Francesco in this chapter, are found in the first preserved Rule for the brothers, the *Regula non Bullata* of 1221 (*Earlier Rule*). Many historians believe that these words were in the proto-Rule that Francesco presented to Innocent III in 1209. There is no existing copy of that Rule.

Part Nine

"And I Had This Written Down Simply and in a Few Words and the Lord Pope Confirmed This for Me"

60

Messer Pietro di Catanio di Guiduccio

Piazza Santa Maria Maggiore, Assisi (February 1209)

The young cleric Pietro di Catanio di Guiduccio had long relinquished pride about impressive names. He was now dangerously close to relinquishing his few comforts. He had come to the piazza to distribute to the poor the alms given to him daily by his rector. For Pietro, distribution meant not just handing someone a coin but also sitting with each person, inquiring how they were feeling, and praying with them.

Smudgy-faced, shapely Yoconda now claimed Pietro's attention as he sought to persuade her from becoming a prostitute like her mother. "You could become a servant in a wealthy household," Pietro was telling her. "Visit my brother, Messer Tebaldo, and ask him to hire you as his wife's handmaid. Tell him that I sent you." Yoconda was skeptical. Pietro tried gentle reasoning while his heart beseeched God for her soul.

Pietro's tenderness was reflected in the soft features of his beardless face and in his delicate, almost feminine, long-fingered hands. Hardly taller than a youth of fourteen winters, he had, nevertheless, earned his law degree at the University of Bologna as the Church required of a cleric.

When Yoconda excused herself with a swish of her grimy skirt and a curt "I'll think about it," Pietro stood and brushed off his black cleric's robe. But he could not brush off the thought that had been plaguing him for nearly a year. On a day much like this one, Bernardo di Quintavalle and his old servant had given to the poor all their wealth and had joined Francesco. Their courage made Pietro, with his tidy room, ample food, and steady work, feel inadequate. Other than marriage, what had he relinquished?

He had convinced himself that Bernardo's folly had been a whim that his old servant foolishly embraced. Within months, they would leave Francesco. However, they stayed. Others had come and stayed. Folly? Whim?

Pietro's resistance was wearing down. God was prodding him, but was he, like Yoconda, brushing Him off?

That afternoon Pietro searched for Francesco and found him teaching the lepers at San Lazzaro d'Arce. That night he found himself squeezed into Rivo Torto under a beam that Francesco had marked with his name. His body was totally uncomfortable, but his mind was at ease. He awoke in the morning, having slept well.

Within days, Pietro was listening to Francesco and the brothers speak about their way of life, which Francesco said they must present to Lord Pope. On begged parchment, Pietro took notes, writing down the results of the discussions and adding Scripture passages that Francesco had memorized. Then, to check accuracy—for the brothers possessed no expensive book of Scripture—Pietro consulted the Scriptures kept at the Cathedral of San Rufino.

"God has sent you to us," Francesco assured Pietro. "Because of you, the Lord Pope will come to know our life."

NOTES

The opening quotation for Part Nine is from Francis' *Testament*, 15.

If Pietro di Catanio wasn't the second follower of Francesco, he would have joined Francesco a short time later. See Chapter Notes (no. 48, pp. 182–183) for references to Pietro di Catanio's background. Francesco needed to take a written copy of his Rule to the pope. Of the early brothers, the one most educated in Scripture and Latin would have been Pietro di Catanio. Presumably, he recorded the proto-Rule that Francesco dictated.

61

Bishop Guido

Rome (Mid-May 1209)

Bishop Guido was walking past the Trastevere fountain near the Church of Santa Maria in Rome. Just then he spotted a gray-robed penitent filling a pail of water while a young mother watched, balancing one toddler on her hip and holding another by the hand. Just another Roman scene except—

"Fra Egidio?"

The startled penitent put down the pail, knelt, and kissed Guido's hand.

"What are you doing here?" Guido couldn't imagine why Egidio would be here. Unless— was Francesco upset with Guido? Had he decided to move the brothers to Rome? Guido loved the brothers. They'd done much good in his territory. He didn't want to lose them.

"We came to see Lord Pope."

"We? Are you all here?"

"Sì."

"Where's Francesco?"

"With the lepers at San Lazzaro al Trionfale."

Of course.

"I'm staying at the Monastery of San Paolo Fuori le Mura. Have him come to me there."

"Sì, Messer Bishop."

"Are you helping this mother?"

"Sì. The pail is heavy."

Guido nodded. "Would you like a blessing, you and your children?"

Still holding the younger child and pushing the standing toddler into a kneeling position, the woman knelt for Guido's blessing.

Having been summoned from the monastery garden where he had been sitting on a stone bench, enjoying the sunshine, Guido followed a lay Benedictine brother to the parlor. There a penitent knelt to kiss his hand.

"Francesco, stand up. Why are you here?"

"Because you sent for me, Messer Bishop."

"I mean, why are you here in Rome?"

"You told us to meet you here."

Guido remembered now.

"Did you write your Rule? Do you have it with you?"

"Sì," Francesco pulled a small parchment from a pocket sewn into the chest of his tunic. He handed the document to Guido.

Guido scrutinized it. Yes, here were the juridical passages he had told Francesco to include. Then directives for the brothers' way of life, bolstered by Gospel passages, all of which Francesco had discussed with Guido. The Latin was meticulously correct.

"Who wrote this?"

"Fra Pietro di Catanio."

Guido stopped himself from gasping. FRA Pietro? He'd not known.

"Have you shared this with Lord Pope?"

"He didn't have time to see me yesterday in the consistory."

Pope Innocenzo was holding public consistories three times a week. Anyone could present a proposal. Francesco might wait months until obtaining a hearing.

"You need someone to present this to Lord Pope. May I keep it?"

"Certainly."

"He'll ask the name of your brotherhood."
"We've agreed on the name 'Poor Minors.'"

NOTES

History doesn't record the particulars of how Guido and Francesco met in Rome. 1C (first book, chapter XIII) records Guido's concerns that the brothers might be leaving his territory and recounts how he offered to help Francesco meet the pope. *Early Documents II* (p. 548, footnote) states that Jerome of Ascoli recorded that Francesco was found by the pope's servants at Saint Anthony's hospice near the Lateran. This was San Lazzaro al Trionfale (https://sv.wikipedia.org/wiki/San_Lazzaro_al_Trionfale).

At some point before their trip to Rome, the brothers began to call themselves Poor Minors (see *Early Documents I*, p. 594).

62

Pope Innocenzo III

Bedroom, Apostolic Palace of the Lateran, Rome (Mid-May 1209)

Innocenzo opened his eyes and stared up into the pale white canopy of his bed. In the candlelight, a dark pebble bobbed against the milky silk—a small, spinning spider. In the morning, he'd tell his chamberlain. Tomorrow night, the spider would be gone.

Innocenzo groaned. If only getting a dream out of his head were as easy as removing a spider from his bedchamber!

Two days ago, preoccupied with unconcerned clergy within the Church and heretics and infidels without, he'd been walking through the Hall of the Mirror to the public consistory. Then a man with bushy black eyebrows and ears that stuck out approached him, knelt and kissed his hand, then asked him to approve a Rule of Life. One glance at the patched gray tunic told Innocenzo everything. "Go pray with your pigs, then come and talk to me," he had barked at the swineherd, or maybe heretic or religious fanatic. *Why does the Church attract these kinds of people?* Innocenzo wondered.

The man stood, bowed, and left.

The consistory was well into the afternoon session, listening to a Roman matron requesting aid for the poor around her palazzo, when a stench wafted through the room.

The swineherd.

"What are you doing here?" Innocenzo had demanded.

"I've prayed with the pigs and returned. Will you consider the Rule for me and my brothers?"

Innocenzo was incredulous. "Come back when you and your tunic are clean."

The man bowed and left.

Late in the afternoon, Innocenzo had noticed him return, minus the stench. But the consistory was soon completed, and the man disappeared with the crowd.

In his eleven years as pope, Innocenzo had dismissed many deranged religious fanatics. Yet just now he'd dreamt of the swineherd as a tall, sturdy, capable man propping up with his shoulder the crumbling Lateran. That was as impossible as that spider holding up Innocenzo's bed.

NOTHING IS IMPOSSIBLE WITH GOD.

Innocenzo's eyes widened. He knew exactly where that was from, in the beginning of the Gospel of Luke. And similar passages in Matthew and later on in Luke.

YOU'VE REMEMBERED THE PASSAGES, the inner thought came. BELIEVE THEM.

NOTES

L3C (chapter XII) records the pope's dream. Roger of Wendover recounted how the pope dismissed Francesco, telling him to pray with swine before returning (*Early Documents I*, pp. 598–599). *Early Documents* (p. 548, footnote) states that Francesco first met the pope in the Hall of the Mirror.

"Nothing is impossible with God" is found in Luke 1:37 and 18:27, as well as Matthew 19:26.

63

Cardinal Giovanni di San Paolo

Monastery of San Paolo Fuori le Mura, Rome (Mid-May 1209)

Cardinal Giovanni di San Paolo strolled with his guests through the cloister garden of the Benedictine Monastery of San Paolo Fuori le Mura. His black Benedictine tunic was the single dark shade amid a profusion of brilliance.

"Here are Star of Bethlehem," he said, stopping at a small, contained bed of tiny, star-shaped white flowers peeking through a plethora of slender leaves. "They get their own plot because, if we plant them with anything else, they still get their own plot."

"Invasive. Like heretics!" Bishop Guido bellowed with laughter at his own joke.

Giovanni smiled, not so much at Guido's joke as at Guido himself. Standing next to a bed edged with *garofano*, in his crimson tunic and white mantle, Guido looked like a human version of the small flower. Fra Francesco beside him resembled the soil itself.

Giovanni loved this garden. Early in his monastic life, when he'd been elected abbot of this monastery, he'd come here to cultivate the roses and momentarily forget his other obligations. Lilies didn't question kitchen management. Peppers cared not a whit about privy maintenance. Violets were oblivious to his being Pope Celestino III's nephew. Here Giovanni was simply a gardener—his long, thin arms wielding a spade; his long, strong fingers planting cucumbers; his creative mind imagining new beds of poppies.

Then, in 1193, when he had been appointed cardinal-deacon, administrative work for the Church had totally swallowed his time. Under Pope Innocenzo III, whose election he'd helped achieve, he'd undertaken political and religious missions that had consumed months. Being home delighted him. Having his long-time friend Guido lodge here, while on business with the Curia, was an added joy.

Giovanni had planned their garden tour to end at a cluster of benches under a spreading fig tree, where the three sat.

"So, Fra Francesco, what do you think of our gardens?"

Spontaneously, it seemed, Francesco began to sing a *lauda*. His voice was strong, beautiful, cresting with every cadence of the Umbrian words. "Be praised, my Lord, for Sister Earth, our Mother, who nourishes us and sustains us, bringing forth fruits and vegetables of many kinds and flowers of many colors."

When the brief melody faded, Giovanni grinned. "If you sing like that for Lord Pope, he will grant whatever you ask. To approve your Rule, eh?"

"Sì."

"I've read your Rule, which Bishop Guido shared with me. Why don't you live by an already approved Rule? The Rule of Saint Benedict? Saint Augustine? Saint Anthony of the Desert?"

"Messer Cardinal, our Rule is the Gospel."

Living the Gospel! The cry of every new movement. What better Rule exists? But were the reformers living it?

"Fra Francesco, your Rule is too difficult." He extracted a parchment from a wide pocket sewn into the chest of his tunic and began to read aloud the impeccable Latin.

"In the name of the Father and of the Son and of the Holy Spirit. Brother Francis—and whoever is head of this religion—promises obedience and reverence to the Lord Pope Innocent and his successors."

He nodded. "Good."

"The rule and life of these brothers is this, namely: 'to live in obedience, in chastity, and without anything of their own,'"—Giovanni glanced at Guido, who was nodding in approval—"and to follow the teaching and footprints of our Lord Jesus Christ, Who says: 'If you wish to be perfect, go, sell everything you have and give it to the poor, and you will have treasure in heaven; and come, follow me.' And: 'If anyone wishes to come after me, let him deny himself and take up his cross and follow me.' Again: 'If anyone wishes to come to me and does not hate father and mother and wife and children and brothers and sisters, and even his own life, he cannot be my disciple.' And: 'Everyone who has left father or mother, brothers or sisters, wife or children, houses or lands because of me, will receive a hundredfold and will possess eternal life.'"

Giovanni caught Francesco's gaze. "All Scripture passages."

"The Lord gave us these passages when we prayed about how to follow Him."

"What do you mean?" Giovanni asked.

Francesco explained how he and his first followers asked God what to do, then prayerfully opened the Scriptures at random to these passages.

Skeptical, Giovanni went on reading. "Let the brothers who know how to work do so and exercise that trade they have learned, provided it is not contrary to the good of their souls and can be performed honestly. For the prophet says: 'You shall eat the fruit of your labors; you are blessed, and it shall be well for you.' The Apostle says: 'Whoever does not wish to work shall not eat . . .' and 'Let everyone remain in that trade and office in which he has been called.'"

More Scripture passages.

"And for their work they can receive whatever is necessary, excepting money. And when it is necessary, they may seek alms like other poor people. And it is lawful for them to have the tools and instruments suitable for their trades."

"It's good to propose working," Giovanni said, "but how can you survive without money?"

"Working and begging give us all we need," Francesco replied.

Really? Giovanni read on. "When the brothers go through the world, let them 'take nothing for the journey, neither knapsack, nor purse, nor bread, nor money, nor walking stick.' Whatever house they enter, let them first say: 'Peace to this house.' They may eat and drink what is placed before them for as long as they stay in that house. 'Let them not resist anyone evil, but whoever strikes them on one cheek, let them offer him the other as well.' 'Whoever takes their cloak, let them not withhold their tunic. Let them give to all who ask of them and whoever takes what is theirs, let them not seek to take it back.'"

More Gospel passages. Difficult. Yet Guido had assured him that the brothers did, indeed, journey with nothing other than their tunics and, if accosted, they allowed robbers to take even their garments. Men lived this? The man before him lived this?

"Let all the brothers be, live, and speak as Catholics. If someone has strayed in word or in deed from Catholic faith and life and has not amended his ways, let him be expelled from our brotherhood.

"Let us consider all clerics and religious as our masters in all that pertains to the salvation of our soul and does not deviate from our religion, and let us respect their order, office, and administration in the Lord."

Juridically astute passages, especially considering rampant heresy and criticism of the Church. "Very wise to include these, Fra Francesco."

"Grazie. I will tell Fra Pietro. He's a cleric and suggested this wording."

"Sagacious man," Giovanni said.

He read on, "Whenever it pleases them, all my brothers can announce this or similar exhortation and praise among all peoples with the blessing of God:

Fear and honor,
praise and bless,
give thanks and adore
the Lord God Almighty in Trinity and in Unity,
Father, Son, and Holy Spirit,
the Creator of all.
Do penance,
performing worthy fruits of penance
because we shall soon die.
Give and it will be given to you.
Forgive and you shall be forgiven.
If you do not forgive people their sins,
the Lord will not forgive you yours.
Confess all your sins.
Blessed are those who die in penance,

for they shall be in the kingdom of heaven.
Woe to those who do not die in penance,
for they shall be children of the devil
whose works they do
and they shall go into everlasting fire.
Beware of and abstain from every evil
and persevere in good till the end.
Glory be to the Father, and to the Son, and to the Holy Spirit.
As it was in the beginning, is now, and will be forever. Amen."

"Is this what you preach?"

"Sì."

Good moral exhortation. But the Rule? Benedictines wisely lived in monasteries with gardens and farms to supply their needs.

"Dogs have more stability than your men."

"Dogs sleep wherever their Master takes them. They eat the food He provides."

The man's faith discomfited him.

"Brother, I have many questions. Can you meet with me over the next several days and enlighten me?"

Over the next days, Giovanni plied Francesco with questions until Francesco's answers satisfied him. "I'll present your Rule to Lord Pope and let you know his response."

NOTES

According to Fortini (p. 293, footnote), Cardinal Giovanni di San Paolo and Bishop Guido were close personal friends. If this is so, then it seems likely that, when Guido came to Rome, he would stay with his friend at the Monastery of San Paolo Fuori le Mura (St. Paul Outside the Walls). The initial meeting between Giovanni, Guido, and Francesco took place in an unspecified location. 1C (first book, chapter XIII) records Giovanni's questions about Francesco's life and motives and his suggestions that he take another rule. The Rule shared in this chapter is composed of parts of the *Regula non Bullata* of 1221 (*Earlier Rule*) and, according to historian John R. H. Moorman (*The*

Sources for the Life of Saint Francis of Assisi, pp. 38–54), is a plausible recreation of the Rule that Francesco presented to the pope.

The scripture passages quoted in the rule are as follows: Matthew 19:21, Matthew 16:24, Luke 14:26, Matthew 19:29, Psalm 128:2, 2 Thessalonians 3:10, 1 Corinthians 7:20, Luke 9:3, Matthew 5:39, Luke 6:29–30.

Francesco's lauda on Sister Mother Earth is one verse of his *Canticle of Creation*.

64

Pope Innocenzo III

Corridor, Apostolic Palace of the Lateran, Rome (Mid-May 1209)

Like an actor in an eternal drama, Pope Innocenzo III walked thoughtfully down a long corridor in the Apostolic Palace of the Lateran. A slight, permanent smile on his bearded, youthful face greeted every cardinal, priest, and servant he passed. Each bowed to his nod of acknowledgment.

In the past twelve years, he had gone from being the aristocratic Cardinal Lotario dei Conti dei Segni to being Pope Innocenzo III. Forming alliances, keeping peace, and centralizing Church administration consumed his pontificate. Nevertheless, in his fifty years of life, his overriding passion persisted: to crush heresy. He and others had offered countless prayers and sacrifices to end this scourge. Could God now be answering those prayers through a man he'd mistaken for a swineherd?

Several days ago, Cardinal Giovanni di San Paolo had presented Innocenzo an astonishing Rule of Life and twelve men who were living it. Innocenzo had questioned the nervous, awestruck, awkward men, including the swineherd—no, Francesco—until he was convinced that they were sane and genuine, if idealistic.

"Your life is too hard and severe," he had told them, "if you wish to found a congregation possessing nothing in this world. From where will you obtain the necessities of life?"

"I trust in my Lord Jesus Christ," Francesco, the swineherd leader, had answered. "Since He has promised to give us life and glory in heaven, He will not deprive us of our bodily necessities when we need them on earth."

"What you say is true, son," Innocenzo had told him, "but human nature is weak and never remains in the same state. But, go and pray to the Lord with all your heart, so that He may show you what is better and more beneficial for your souls. Come back and tell me and I will then grant it."

Today the men were to return. They would be waiting here, in the Ten Commandments Room. Innocenzo opened the door, and twelve gray-clad men, Cardinal Giovanni, and Bishop Guido dropped to their knees before him. Innocenzo walked by them, allowing them to kiss his hand, then sat in his papal chair, his red and gold robes spreading around his knees.

"Be seated," he said.

They obeyed.

He nodded at Cardinal Giovanni and at Bishop Guido, then surveyed the twelve expectant, timid faces.

"Have you prayed about your life?" he asked.

"Sì, Lord Pope," Francesco answered.

"And what has the Lord showed you?"

"A tale. There was a little, poor, and beautiful woman in a desert, whose beauty fascinated a great king."

The tale was turning into a tune, accented with gestures and dance.

"He wanted to take her as his wife, because he thought that, from her, he would have handsome sons. After the marriage was celebrated and consummated, there were many sons born and raised. Their mother spoke to them in this way."

The singing slowed, became plaintive.

"'My sons, do not be ashamed, for you are sons of the king. Therefore, go to his court and he will provide for all your needs.'"

The singing, dancing, and gesturing resumed in a livelier manner.

"When they went to see the king, he was struck by their good looks, and noticing a resemblance to himself in them, he asked them: 'Whose sons are you?' When they answered that they were the sons of the poor little woman living in the desert, the king embraced them with great joy."

The song now swelled, and the dance intensified.

"'Do not be afraid,' he said, 'for you are my sons. If strangers are fed at my table, how much more will you, who are my lawful sons.' He then ordered the woman to send to his court all of the children she had borne to be fed."

The song died and Francesco spoke, his gaze penetrating. "Lord Pope, I am that little poor woman whom the loving Lord, in his mercy, has adorned, and through whom He has been pleased to give birth to legitimate sons. The King of kings had told me that He will nourish all the sons born to me, because, if He feeds strangers, He must provide for His own. For if God gives temporal goods to sinful men out of love for providing for His children, how much more will He give to Gospel men who deserve these things out of merit?"

In Innocenzo's dream, a little man had supported the Lateran and grown tall. A little man now pleaded before him. Cardinal Giovanni and Bishop Guido had assured him that these men, while living austere lives as did many heretics, were in total conformity with the Church. Better they, than heretics, inspire popular piety.

This is indeed that holy and religious man through whom the Church of God will be sustained and supported, Innocenzo realized. Words from the prophet Isaiah came to mind.

For my thoughts are not your thoughts,
neither are your ways my ways, says the LORD.
For as the heavens are higher than the earth,
so are my ways higher than your ways
and my thoughts than your thoughts.

And then a stronger conviction from the First Book of Samuel: "For the LORD sees not as man sees; man looks on the outward appearance, but the LORD looks on the heart." Should these Poor Minors grow numerous, they could become a powerful force supporting the Church.

"I approve your Rule," he said. "Go and preach everywhere as you propose."

"Grazie, my Lord Jesus!" Francesco exclaimed. He knelt before Innocenzo. "And grazie, Lord Pope. I promise you my reverence and obedience."

"Rise, Fra Francesco. Now you, his brothers, kneel before your leader and promise him your reverence and obedience as he has promised me."

With awkward, barely controlled joy, the eleven men knelt before Francesco who blessed them. Then Innocenzo raised his hand and blessed them all, including the bishop and the cardinal. "I will secure approval for you in the consistory," Innocenzo said. "Go. Live your life and preach penance. May God be with you."

The following day, in this last Roman consistory before his May 25 journey to Viterbo, Innocenzo was bombarded with objections that once had been his.

Cardinal Pietro Capuano di San Marcello: "The Rule is too difficult."

Cardinal Cencio, nearly sixty years old, vigorous and sharp-minded: "How can these Poor Minors live without possessions and money?"

Pietro: "Once their idealism wears off, will they abandon their harsh lifestyle?"

Cardinal Giovanni di San Paolo: "These men, loyal to the Church, are living what Christ preached in the Gospel, as heretics also claim to do. If we don't approve their way of life, are we saying that only heretics can live the Gospel?"

Cencio: "Who's going to oversee these men to confirm that they're living the way they propose? Who's going to examine their preaching to determine if it follows our guidelines?"

Giovanni: "I request to be made their protector. Their bishop and I will consult periodically about these men. I'll keep you abreast of developments."

Cencio: "Innocenzo, have you composed the bull approving them?"

Innocenzo: "I'll issue no bull. They're a religio. They can preach and request alms. Once we see how they prosper, we'll consider sturdier support."

Pietro: "How will people know that these men aren't heretics?"

Giovanni: "Suppose I give them a clerical tonsure?"

Cencio: "One, a cleric, already has a tonsure."

Pietro: "Sì. And he's promised obedience to a layman."

Cencio: "Their leader is a layman?"

Giovanni: "I'll tonsure him as a deacon."

Cencio: "Did he ask to become a deacon?"

Innocenzo: "It's a matter of obedience, not request."

Pietro: "He'll agree?"

Giovanni: "Sì. He's obedient."

Innocenzo: "Are we agreed? We tonsure the Poor Minors as clerics and their leader as deacon. We grant them verbal permission to exhort the people to penance."

Eyebrows arched. The cardinals looked from one to the other.

Giovanni raised his hand. "Agreed."

Cencio. "Agreed."

Pietro. "Agreed."

Others followed. Not all. But enough.

"Agreed," Innocenzo declared.

NOTES

This chapter closely follows the historical record (see 1C, first book, chapter XIII; AP, chapter VII; L3C, chapter XII; 2C, first book, chapter XI). L2C (Chapter XIII) relates Francesco's parable of the woman in the desert and her sons fathered by the king. The names of the cardinals in the consistory are accurate (see https://cardinals.fiu.edu/consistories-xii.htm), although no one knows their individual feelings or questions regarding Francesco's brotherhood.

At some point, the brothers were tonsured (AP, chapter VII), and Francesco was ordained a deacon (*Early Documents I*, p. 256, footnote). For the reasons discussed in the imagined consistory meeting and following AP (chapter VII), the author of this book postulates that both of these things happened after meeting with the pope in 1209.

The Scripture texts used are Isaiah 55:8–9 and 1 Samuel 16:7.

65

Fra Morico

Road to Assisi (Early June 1209)

Morico and his eleven brothers were walking back to Assisi. Little dust clouds rose around their jubilant feet.

Francesco's recent dream of him growing as tall as an exceedingly high, thick, and beautiful tree that he easily bent to earth had come true in the tree of the Church bending to approve their way of life. Cardinal Giovanni's tonsure, which indicated that approval, had changed everything. Morico, a cleric? Francesco, a deacon? He imagined that he looked as odd as they did with that small, shaved circle on the top of the head. Although he had studied his reflection in a basin of water, he could not see the tonsure but only his deep brown curls framing his face, as round as an orange.

The tonsure became a credential, fostering immediate acceptance among the people. Instead of shunning the brothers, people now nodded to them. When they begged, they nearly always received something, and not just bones with shreds of meat clinging to them. Two days ago, a Roman matron with two small sons had given them a whole roasted chicken. Imagine! When they spoke at a fountain or on the steps of a church, people stopped to listen instead of scurrying by. When they asked for lodging, they were welcomed into a courtyard or even a house. No brother was forced to sleep in an oven or on a doorstep as had

Bernardo and Egidio in Florence. And priests? Not one told them, "The church is open all night. Sleep there." Now it was, "Lodge with me."

For a few days after the approval, the brothers had remained in Rome to pray, preach, and beg. Then they visited Saint Peter's tomb, where they pleaded for guidance from the leader of the Apostles. This morning they had left for Assisi, marveling at God's abundant gifts and discussing among themselves how to live virtuously and carry out their mission. Now night was falling, the blooming countryside darkening with shadow, and the joyous birdsong dying. Here they were, in open country, not a home in sight. Nor had they passed any dwellings for hours. Where could they beg food? Morico resigned himself to going to bed hungry. He was exhausted enough to fall asleep on an empty stomach.

Nevertheless, Bernardo, the journey's leader, whom they had chosen before leaving Assisi, gave no sign of stopping, so on they walked. As they crested a knoll, they saw a man approaching carrying a thick loaf of bread. Without a word, he handed it to them and kept walking. "Grazie! Grazie!" the brothers called after him. Without turning around, the man waved his hand in the air to acknowledge their gratitude and disappeared out of sight as he descended the knoll.

"Let us thank the Lord for His mercy," Bernardo said. Bowing their heads, the men offered thanks, sat down where they were, divided the loaf and ate. After Sabbatino and Morico built a fire to ward off wolves, the men sat around it and prayed Compline as Pietro read from their single breviary. Wrapped in his mantle and praising God, Morico fell asleep under the stars.

In the morning, they set out. Near dusk, within sight of a city, they came upon a low, vine-covered, stone tomb of three rooms. Dry bones in disarray lay on ledges built into the walls, and bones and shards of pottery littered the floor.

"We'll stay here and pray for these souls and for the grave robbers who desecrated them," Bernardo said. Pietro, Egidio, Angelo, and Filippo ventured to the city to beg. Sabbatino and Morico built a fire at the tomb's entrance. The others tidied up the tomb, which Francesco swept. When the four returned, the men divided the food among themselves, stored the leftovers on a ledge, prayed Compline, and then fell asleep on the floor.

The city was Orte, whose inhabitants joyously welcomed Sabbatino and Morico when they took their turn begging the next day. "Lodge with us," a tanner invited, but Bernardo declined the offer. "We'll stay in the tomb God has given us."

The tomb was quiet and private, perfect for poor, prayerful living. No one knew them here. No one expected anything of them. Perhaps they should remain here where they felt as free as birds, enveloped in God's love.

After two weeks of bliss, they realized that they could not remain in seclusion. Around a campfire, Francesco voiced their thoughts. "Lord Pope has given us a mission to preach penance wherever God takes us. Yet this tomb has made us realize that we also need solitude. Assisi has a place where we can be alone with our Lord. Our prayer there will strengthen us for our mission."

NOTES

By comparing stories of how people treated the brothers before 1209 and thereafter, it becomes obvious that papal approval made the populace more favorable. How would people know that the brothers were in good standing with the Church unless there were a visible sign? The tonsure, by indicating Church approval, was a visible sign.

This chapter closely follows the account in 1C (first book, chapters XIII and XIV).

Part Ten

"To All Christian Religious People: Clergy and Laity, Men and Women, and to All Who Live in the Whole World"

66

Fra Angelo di Tancredi

Rivo Torto, Assisi (June 1209)

Ah! They were home. Seeing the two adjacent stone huts near the meandering Rivo Torto, Angelo di Tancredi felt a surge of joy. How he loved this place!

Goodness, how untidy it had become! A rabbit scampered out of the left hut and a squirrel out of the right. Carefully plucking a fat spider from the web it had spun across the cross in the prayer space, Angelo deposited it on a twig in the forest. Francesco and Egidio swept the cooking hut. Sabbatino and Barbaro fluffed up the straw in the sleeping hut.

The days advanced, each better than the day before. The tonsures changed Assisi's attitude. Overnight, the people regarded the brothers with respect. Francesco and other brothers began preaching inside the churches instead of outside. Others, including Angelo, helped in the fields, gardens, and vineyards while telling the workers of God's love and encouraging them in their faith. They took turns visiting the lepers, cleansing their sores, sharing Scripture, and assisting in their gardens. Angelo and Giovanni di Costanzo sometimes walked the roads just to speak to travelers. Always they tried to make their lives conform to their message. God is real. God made you. God loves you. God will take you to Himself. Let Him have you. There is no better lord.

NOTES

The opening quotation for Part Ten is from Francis' *Later Admonition and Exhortation to the Brothers and Sisters of Penance (Second Version of the Letter to the Faithful)*, 1.

This chapter postulates what life for the brothers must have been like at this time.

67

Fra Filippo di Lungo

Chapel, Rivo Torto, Assisi (September 1209)

In the rear of the prayer space at Rivo Torto, nineteen-year-old Filippo di Lungo was sitting on his haunches. His eyes focused on the barely visible, rude, wooden cross thrust into the ground between the two huts. Two hours ago, the brothers, as usual, had sung the Our Father, then entered into silent contemplation for the night.

To protect himself against mosquitoes, Filippo had pulled his hood over his head. Then he brought his long, slender legs up to his chest, and draped his tunic over all his exposed flesh. After assuming the same pose in Mandria while tending sheep, he'd lean against a boulder and gaze across a moonlit meadow or into a star-studded sky. Now he gazed above the dark forms of his brothers to the cross almost lost in the blackness. He needed no light to adore the God of meadow, boulder, and star; the God of man and sheep and mosquito.

The chirping of innumerable crickets, the distant hooting of an owl, and the occasional buzz of a mosquito punctuated the stillness. The peaceful breathing and gentle snoring of his brothers were lulling Filippo to sleep.

What? There! A glow against the bare earth. Scuttling. Stopping. Changing direction. A brother gasped. Another shrieked. The low, fiery orb kept darting between the dark forms of men shying away from it. The glow raced here, there, side to side, then rushed past Filippo where it disappeared into the night.

"What was that?" Morico's high pitched voice.

A greater glow appeared. Pietro di Catanio coming from the fire room with a lighted lamp. He set the small clay lamp on the ground at the base of the cross. In its glow, the faces of the brothers gleamed.

"It's gone," Pietro said softly.

"Francesco isn't here to tell us what it means," Barbaro offered. Francesco had gone to stay with the canons at the Cathedral of San Rufino, for he was preaching there early in the morning. He'd left Pietro in charge.

"Perhaps God will tell us what it means," Pietro suggested. He knelt to pray, and the brothers joined him. After a time, Pietro said, "Has God revealed anything to you?"

"Only that I shouldn't be sleeping at prayer." Sabbatino.

"He'd definitely tell you that!" Morico.

"He'd definitely tell you to trust Him more and not be so scared." Sabbatino.

"How do you know what he told me?" Morico.

Sabbatino shrugged.

Silence.

"I bet He told you not to be so enamored of this place." Giovanni di San Costanzo was looking at Angelo.

Angelo nodded. "Sì. But I bet He told you not to hold it in contempt."

Giovanni bowed his head. "Sì."

"God's miracles can happen anywhere. Even here." Barbaro.

"To you, everything is a miracle." Bernardo di Vigilante.

"Because—" Egidio.

"—everything is." Bernardo di Quintavalle finished the sentence for him.

Egidio looked askance at him and nodded.

Silence.

"Maybe that's how our soul appears to God. Like a glowing orb in the darkness of sin," Pietro suggested.

"Why would God send an orb on a little chariot?" Egidio.

"Chariot! You have knights and battles in your blood." Bernardo laughed.

"It moved like a chariot, didn't it, Angelo?" Egidio.

"Sì. But how do you know that I'd know?" Angelo.

Egidio grinned.

"Maybe it was Francesco, coming to show us that he's with us even when he's away." Barbaro.

"Perhaps we'll never know." Giovanni della Capella.

"Some things even you can't figure out, Giovanni." Sabbatino.

"Maybe I should stop trying." Giovanni.

"I never saw anything like this." Filippo.

"Nor did I."

"Or I."

"Or I."

"Elijah was taken to heaven in a fiery chariot." Pietro.

"That would have been a lot bigger than what we saw." Morico.

"Do you think someone's going to die?" Barbaro.

"Someone's always dying." Giovanni di San Costanzo.

"The practical one would say that." Egidio.

Giovanni smiled.

"Let's pray for those who are dying," Bernardo di Quintavalle concluded.

Filippo had been thinking the same thing.

The brothers knelt while Pietro led them in prayer for the dying. "Most High God, have mercy on souls who are coming to You tonight. Grant them the grace of final repentance. Holy Angels, take these repentant sinners into the sight of the Most High."

"Amen," the brothers replied in unison.

"My brothers," Pietro said, "let's resume our prayers. When Francesco comes, perhaps he can give more meaning to what we've seen."

The brothers settled into prayer, their faces soft in the lamplight. Filippo thought of his brothers in Mandria—Biagio, Giovanni, and the others. He thought of his sisters. His family members were so close that they could guess one another's thoughts. So could these men. The brothers had become family.

NOTES

Fortini (pp. 279–280) describes Filippo di Lungo's probable background and family members.

Without giving details on what was said or what the chariot was, 1C (first book, chapter XVIII) describes the fiery chariot and how, in discussing it, each brother's conscience was revealed to the others.

What the brothers saw is not known, although there is a scorpion native to the area that glows in ultraviolet light. Possibly, with a bright moon, a scorpion could have been seen to be glowing as it moved around them.

68

Siffredo

Forest along Rivo Torto, Assisi (Spring 1210)

"Move, stupid donkey!" Siffredo cursed at his obstinate beast. No. Messer Vasilios' obstinate beast. The donkey was no longer his. If the thing would only move, they could both get out of this rain. But no. On the Via della Spina, the animal refused to budge.

Drenched to the skin, seventeen-year-old Siffredo sagged under defeat and inescapable misery. Since his wide-set, squinty eyes and bulbous nose made it impossible to offer a woman his good looks, he strove to offer her stability instead. For three years his small plot of land had provided ongoing sustenance, and he had begun to seek a bride. However, last summer's paltry harvest, followed by a harsh winter, had broken him. With food and funds depleted, he, like a few others, had turned his land and himself over to Messer Vasilios, in exchange for the lord's sustenance and protection.

Vasilios was delighted with Siffredo's small farm but not with the tipsy hut in which Siffredo lived on one side and the donkey on the other. Yesterday, atop his sleek, black steed, with his crimson cape billowing about him, he had commanded, "Tomorrow, take my donkey and go live in the turf huts I have near Rivo Torto. Where the river intersects with the Via della Spina, follow it toward Assisi and you will see the huts on its bank. Then demolish this pigsty of a house and plow everything up. Three times. In the fall, you'll be planting grape vines here."

Tomorrow, take my donkey to Rivo Torto. Siffredo grumbled mentally. *Take my donkey to Rivo Torto. In the rain. Did you ever try to lead a donkey in the rain? Do you know anything about donkeys? Bah!*

"Move, stupid donkey!" Wonder of wonders, the animal put one foot before the other and began to move.

They plodded on until coming to a meandering stream that intersected with the road. Siffredo led the donkey along the tree-lined bank until he spied two turf huts ahead. Goodness, those would work for him and his beast! Humph! His lord would probably have him bring other beasts here. No matter. So long as he had a warm, dry place to live, he could tolerate donkeys nearby. Maybe he could fix this place up so that a wife would like it.

Hmm. Smoke wafting from the left hut. Someone living here? Cooking, likely.

Then he heard chanting. Praying. Siffredo groaned. Religious people? Well, they were going to have company. Sounded like they were in the left hut. He'd use the right one.

Siffredo squared his dripping shoulders and barked to the donkey. "Go inside! We shall do well in this place!" The beast plodded in, shook itself dry, and began to nibble at the matted straw littering the floor. Siffredo loosely tethered the animal to a beam on which some writing was scratched.

Hungry, Siffredo shoved past the nibbling donkey and followed his nose into the left hut. On a hearth in the middle of the floor, a fire burned, its smoke wafting upward and exiting through vents in the walls below the ceiling. Something luscious was simmering in a black kettle.

"Got anything to eat?" he blurted out.

The chanting stopped as the kneeling, gray-robed men glanced at one another.

A short, homely man, probably their servant, stood and plucked a wooden bowl and ladle from a shelf. Then he dished up a portion and handed Siffredo a bowl of thick soup. The servant fished in a pouch hanging on the wall and pulled out a trencher, soppy with juices.

"Would you like to pray with us while you eat?" the servant asked.

"Nope. I'll go join my donkey." *HIS donkey.*

The servant bowed.

"Borrow yer mantle til I warm up?"

The servant quickly slipped it from his shoulders and handed it to Siffredo.

Hmm. Threadbare and patched. "Good for dryin' the donkey," he said. He pointed to a princely-looking man, whose mantle appeared to be almost new. "Yours?" he asked.

The prince gave it to Siffredo.

Siffredo patted himself as dry as he could with the new mantle and wrapped it around himself. Then he darted out into the rain with his meal and the servant's ragged mantle, with which he quickly dried the donkey. The chanting resumed.

Settling on the straw, Siffredo ate heartily. The trencher was delicious, the soup bland, the chanting soothing. He imagined himself a king being serenaded while he ate.

He finished his meal and dozed. When he woke, the room was dark, and the men were filing in, checking the beams and settling down here and there under them. The last one was the servant. Siffredo pointed to the mantle, in a soggy heap near the donkey. The man took it, glanced at the beams, and settled himself under one.

"We're gonna do just fine together," Siffredo assured the awkward men. "I kin help you add on ta this place. When my lord's other work is done, that is. Come summer, this'll be even more cozy."

"We're happy to have helped you today," the servant said, bowing to Siffredo. Then he turned to the others. "But I know, my brothers, that God did not call us to prepare a lodging for a donkey, nor to have dealings with men. While we are preaching the way of salvation to people and are giving them wise counsel, we should dedicate ourselves most of all to prayer and thanksgiving." Then he smiled at Siffredo. "Since you and your beast need this place, we will look for another. For now, we will sleep together."

Siffredo grinned.

Must be God's Will that he be here. Him and a wife and his children in this room. Donkeys in the middle area. He'd put a roof on there to keep 'em dry. Cooking in the fire room.

Yep. He'd do fine here.

NOTES

1C (first book, chapter XVI) relates how an unnamed rustic moved his donkey into Rivo Torto. No other details are given.

Francesco's words to the brothers are in L3C (chapter XIII).

69

Fra Angelo di Tancredi

Rivo Torto, Assisi (Spring 1210)

Francesco's words were like a punch to Angelo di Tancredi's gut. Leave this place? Just like that?

Just like that, he'd left his palazzo, his only home since birth, to come here where Messer Angelo di Tancredi had been reborn as Fra Angelo.

Here, eating begged leftovers helped conquer the concupiscence of sumptuous banquets.

Here, wearing woolen capes and mantles conquered the vanity of fox fur, silk, and leather.

Here, instead of vying to see Emperor Otto IV when he rode by, the brothers purposely stayed away, all except Pietro, whom Francesco had sent to exhort Otto to repentance. Pietro told them that Otto and his retinue had ridden past Pietro without so much as a nod to acknowledge that they'd heard him.

Here, instead of hosting overnight lords and ladies who left after visiting, the brothers welcomed new men who stayed. Tebaldo. Agostino. Illuminato. Masseo. Francesco had chalked their names on the beams, just like the others. More brothers. More crowding. More laughter. More personalities. More love.

The memory of the glowing chariot darted through his mind. It had raced out of Rivo Torto as quickly as it had raced in. Had God intended to show the brothers that their time here was beautiful but brief? How had they missed that message?

Days passed while Francesco searched for another place. Meanwhile, the brothers remained at Rivo Torto with Siffredo and the donkey, who were gone by day but back each night, bringing with them the world the brothers had left. Charitably, the brothers listened to Siffredo's endless gossip, but, although they asked him to share less, he didn't understand. He needed a family. Angelo prayed for him to find a good wife. What relief when Francesco announced that, although neither the bishop nor the sympathetic churches could offer the brothers a place to stay, the abbot of San Benedetto on Monte Subasio was happy to welcome the brothers back to the Porziuncula. Because there were more of them now and their numbers were growing, Francesco insisted on paying rent. The abbot agreed to a yearly basket of the tasty fish *lasca*. On a brilliant June morning, the brothers bid farewell to Siffredo and walked to the little church.

As Angelo knelt and gazed at the tabernacle on the altar at the Porziuncula, a thought intruded. BIRDS OF THE AIR HAVE NESTS AND FOXES HAVE DENS, BUT THE SON OF MAN HAS NOWHERE TO LAY HIS HEAD. Home was not a place you went to. Home was your soul where God lived. Your soul, like that glowing orb on the chariot the brothers had seen, you carried always with you. No matter where your feet took you, you were always home.

NOTES

1C (first book, chapter XVI) mentions Otto's retinue passing by Rivo Torto, but without naming the brother who preached to them. The author of this work suggests Pietro di Catanio, as he was, at this time, the most theologically educated among the brothers.

For the new brothers who joined, mentioned in this chapter, see Fortini (p. 324, footnotes f and g, and p. 396, footnote b).

The brothers moved to the Porziuncula, "renting" it in exchange for a basket of *lasca* fish paid yearly to the abbot of the Benedictine Monastery on Mount Subasio (1MP, section 27).

70

Dom Silvestro

Cathedral of San Rufino, Assisi (Mid-Summer 1210)

Dom Silvestro was doing something he hadn't done for many years. This early, even before Prime, he was prostrate before the altar in the Cathedral of San Rufino, praying intensely for God's guidance. All because of a dream.

He had become a priest because his family had expected it of one of their sons. More than his siblings, he seemed to love God. His sharp mind learned quickly, and he wanted to benefit others. As he had slid into his priestly vocation without proper discernment, property and wealth continued to infatuate him even while his compassion for the poor swelled.

Sì, he was greedy. Ever since he'd taken that money from Messer Bernardo, he'd been troubled. Those coins were the poor's, not his.

Am I not miserable? he often thought. *Old as I am, don't I still covet and desire the things of this world? And doesn't this youth Francesco despise and scorn them for the love of God?*

Why did Francesco trouble him? He hardly knew him. He'd never spoken to him except for selling him stones. Business deals. But now Francesco had followers—fanatics, Silvestro had originally thought—and more men were joining. Most he didn't know. But he knew Pietro di Catanio. Generous. Caring.

Sensible. Before joining Francesco a year ago, Pietro had sometimes consulted Silvestro on how to best help the poor.

Now Pietro was no longer the only cleric among the brothers. Some cardinal in Rome had tonsured them all as clerics and had made Francesco a deacon. Unbelievable! Many of them couldn't read! But now they were all preaching, some more than others, Francesco most of all. Every Sunday he was in one church or another. Silvestro had heard him a few times. His animated, colloquial style and simple call to personal reform were invigorating.

Whenever the brothers went God knows where, Silvestro secretly wished they'd never return. Then he could put them out of his mind. But they always came back. Now they seemed here to stay, not only in Assisi but also in the hospital, where two came daily to help with the patients.

Earlier this morning, Silvestro had had a dream. He'd seen an immense cross, whose top reached to the heavens and whose arms stretched across the world. The base of the cross was planted in the mouth of the stubbly bearded, hooded, penitent Francesco.

What does it mean, my Lord? he begged. *What do you want me to do?*

As he prayed in the early morning silence before the Eucharistic presence of God, an awareness swelled. That unlikely young wastrel was God's friend and servant. The cross of Christ that he and the brothers preached and lived would spread across the world.

Silvestro knew. He, too, had to do penance. Eat less. Pray more. Give greater alms. Try harder to see Jesus in everyone. He'd start by giving Bernardo's coins to the poor.

Another thought came to him, however. YOU'LL BEGIN BY DOING PENANCE ON YOUR OWN. BUT YOU'LL END BY DOING PENANCE WITH FRANCESCO.

Silvestro ground his fingernails against the cathedral's floor. *I'm not ready, my Lord.*

SOON YOU WILL BE.

NOTES

Dom Silvestro's words and dream are recorded in AP (chapter IX). Silvestro joined the brothers shortly after their return from Rome.

71

Messer Monaldo di Offreduccio

Monaldo's House, Assisi (Late Summer 1210)

Disgusted that he had to call this meeting, Messer Monaldo di Offreduccio stood at the head of the sturdy, oval table in his family's meeting room. He swept his gaze over his younger brothers seated around it. In the early morning sunlight flooding into the room through the open windows, each knight in his family appeared in sharp relief. Round-faced Favarone on his left, squinting up at him. Paolo next to Favarone, almost too broad to balance on the bench. Ugolino, across from Paolo, who, even though seated, towered above the others. Ruddy Scipione on Monaldo's right, looking redder than usual.

Stifling his urge to pounce on Scipione, Monaldo forced himself to sit in the elaborately carved chair reserved for the head of the family. "We know why we're here," he said in measured tones. "What are we going to do about it?"

"Rufino is Scipione's son," Ugolino ventured. "He should decide."

"Rufino is an Offreduccio," Monaldo reminded him. "When an Offreduccio offends the family, we all decide."

"He's an adult. And he's trying to follow God," Favarone offered. "We shouldn't get in God's way."

"God wouldn't have an Offreduccio follow Francesco and his pious vagabonds," Ugolino barked. "Our family belongs in respectable monasteries like San Benedetto."

"This isn't from God," Monaldo said in a measured voice. "This is rebellion."

Scipione rose to his feet. "My sons aren't rebellious."

"This proves that one of them is," Ugolino shot back.

"Whether he's a rebel or not, he's disgraced the family," Paolo stated the obvious.

"And we have an obligation to the family to get him back," Monaldo reminded them.

"I say we go to the Porziuncula today and bring him back," Ugolino declared.

"No!" Scipione banged his hand on the table. "He's my son. Leave him where he's chosen to go."

Monaldo grabbed Scipione by the neck of his plum-colored tunic. "*Your* son has disgraced *this* family."

Favarone was on his feet. He grabbed Monaldo's wrist. "Leave him alone! Rufino has been gone only a day. The novelty will wear off, and he'll return home."

Paolo sneered. "Sì. Rufino is the soft one in this family. He'll not long endure the penances of Francesco and his men."

Ugolino agreed.

Monaldo released his grip on Scipione's tunic, but his gaze pierced his brother. "What does his papà think?"

"His papà has already told you," Scipione retorted. "Leave him where he's chosen to go."

NOTES

The histories don't record this meeting, but it likely took place. While we don't know the appearance or the personalities of the Offreduccio brothers, we do know their names (Fortini, p. 329).

Rufino joined Francesco shortly after his return from Rome.

72

Madonna Chiara di Favarone di Offreduccio

Favarone's House Chapel, Assisi (Late Autumn 1210)

Madonna Chiara di Favarone di Offreduccio was kneeling on the cool floor of her parent's house chapel, the flickering light of a single candle illuminating the room against the darkness. Nothing but the distant barking of a dog broke the stillness. Other than the watchmen, only she was awake in the household.

Against the chill of this third-floor room, Chiara pulled a forest-green mantle tighter about her shoulders. Her gaze was fixed on the crucifix, almost lost in shadow above the altar. She no longer needed a crucifix to remind her of God's love. He had burned His love into her heart.

Wordlessly she knelt, her heart speaking. Tomorrow, as arranged by her cousin Rufino, she would meet Fra Francesco for the first time. He was living what she, even as a child, had known, namely that what one has in this world means nothing. What matters is what one has in the next.

Now that she was sixteen, her family increasingly pressured her to marry. But she had already chosen a Spouse Who beckoned her to join Him on the marriage bed of His Cross. Never would He abandon or disappoint her. She had only to run to Him and give Him her all. Oh, that Fra Francesco might show her how to do it!

NOTES

The young noblewoman Chiara di Favarone di Offreduccio was renowned for her holiness. Francesco gave her direction in how to bring about her desires (see Nugent, *Chiara*, chapters 8 and 10).

Part Eleven

"Do Not Look at the Life Without, for That of the Spirit Is Better"

73

Madonna Ortulana di Favarone di Offreduccio

Bedroom, Offreduccio House (Monday of Holy Week, March 19, 1212)

Madonna Ortulana di Favarone di Offreduccio sat on her bed, clutching her daughters, fourteen-year-old Madonna Catarina and thirteen-year-old Madonna Beatrice, and wanting to weep, scream, and laugh all at the same time.

Her oldest daughter, eighteen-year-old Chiara, was gone. Gone through the door of the dead. Gone to join Francesco and his brothers.

Yesterday had been Palm Sunday, the day of Jesus' triumphal entrance into Jerusalem. Today began the holiest week of the year, leading to His passion, death, and resurrection. Christ's sacrifice, Chiara's sacrifice, her own sacrifice—everything was scrambled in Ortulana's mind.

She held close her two sobbing daughters, trying to offer them comfort while wondering if they all should run to join Chiara on her reckless adventure of love.

Isn't love always reckless? Ortulana thought. She had loved Favarone, had borne him three daughters, and then watched him die after a hunting accident with a boar. Who knows where love will take you? Who knows what will try to pull you away?

Monaldo had taken the family knights to fetch Chiara home.

Ortulana was weeping because she missed Chiara.

She was laughing because Chiara had chosen the greatest Lover of all.

She was screaming because, knowing Monaldo, she feared for Chiara's safety.

Lord, she prayed, *protect your new bride*.

NOTES

The opening quotation for Part Eleven is from Francesco's *The Canticle of Exhortation for the Ladies of San Damiano*, line 3.

For details of Chiara's escape, see Nugent (*Chiara*, chapter 11).

74

Fra Egidio

Amphitheater, Salona, Slavonia (Summer 1212)

Egidio was sitting on a stone bench in the old Roman amphitheater in Salona, watching Francesco stroll meditatively through the arena.

Like many cities, Assisi also had an amphitheater, but this one was holy. Sailors had shared that the emperor Diocletian had martyred Christians here. Egidio was sitting where long-dead people had watched Christians being attacked by beasts down there where Francesco was walking. Egidio was gazing out over the open circular space where those Christians who had survived the mauling were led out to be dispatched by the sword, while people sitting where he was sitting cheered.

Egidio and Francesco had gone to be martyred. After Madonna Chiara, Madonna Agnese, and Madonna Pacifica had been securely housed at San Damiano in May, he and Francesco had walked to Brindisi. There, just last week, they had boarded a ship bound for Syria. There they had planned to preach to the Saracens, who would almost certainly kill them for blasphemy. But God had foiled their plans. High winds, arriving earlier than usual, had blown the ship to Spalatum, where sailors had anchored it in the city's ample harbor. That had been one of the last ships to sail to Syria this year. To sail again, they would have to wait until next year, when the prevailing winds shifted direction.

Francesco and he might as well go home.

The amphitheater was not far from the Spalatum docks. They'd come here to pray, to meditate, to mourn. In two days, the next ship would leave for Ancona. From Ancona, they'd walk back to Assisi.

A red-bearded sailor with red curls spilling out of his cap sat at a small wooden table at the foot of the gangplank. He opened his palm toward a middle-aged merchant in a mauve tunic who dropped a few coins into the hand. The sailor glanced at them, put them into a box on the table, and motioned the man aboard. The next merchant, intimidating in his height, dropped coins into the outstretched hand and was waved aboard. Francesco and Egidio were next. Into the open palm, Francesco traced a cross.

The sailor flicked his palm as if flicking off a fly and opened it again toward Francesco, who repeated the cross tracing.

The sailor's eyes flashed. He shouted something in a strange language. Francesco opened his empty hands wide and shrugged. Then he pointed to the ship, signed as if wishing to board, and bowed. The sailor grabbed him by the collar of his tunic and threw him aside like a sack of wheat. Before the sailor could manhandle Egidio, a nearby sailor grabbed the money collector by the chest and held him back.

Egidio and Francesco scampered away. They found a cluster of barrels and sat on them. *Lord, show us what to do.*

Francesco nudged Egidio. He was pointing to six blindfolded horses, tethered to a nearby pole, crates piled up around them. Tending them was a bearded groomsman in a deep blue tunic, wearing a pale gray headscarf bound to his head with a rope. An Arab.

"Egidio, we're becoming Arabs. Follow me." Francesco jumped off the barrel and nonchalantly strolled the beach. Then, abruptly, he ducked behind a fruit seller's booth, unclasped his mantle, and untied the rope around his waist. Draping the mantle over his head like a headscarf, he doubled up the rope and wrapped it around his head to hold the scarf in place. "Egidio, can you knot this behind my head?" Egidio did so deftly.

"Your turn." A bit incredulous, Egidio followed Francesco's lead, and Francesco knotted Egidio's rope around his headpiece.

"Did you ever tend horses?"

"Sì."

"Good. Now if we help him, perhaps he will help us."

Francesco led the way back to the horses and picked up a brush sitting on a nearby crate. He handed a second brush to Egidio. As they energetically began to brush down the horses, the Arab groomsman spotted them and opened his mouth to protest. Francesco smiled and put his finger to his lips. Then he pointed to the boat and put his finger to his lips again.

A look of comprehension came over the Arab's face. He looked at the boat and back at the two pretend Arabs, then grinned, shrugged, and let them get on with the work. Two more horses remained to be brushed when a clean-shaven man in a lemon tunic approached and motioned them forward. The three men untethered three horses and followed.

In the ship's hull, a door opened with a gangplank extending to the beach. While the man in the lemon tunic and the red-bearded sailor spoke and laughed together, the Arab, Francesco, and Egidio each led a horse up the ramp.

In the gently rocking belly of the ship hung twelve canvas slings fastened to the ceiling. The Arab unfastened one, draped it under his horse's chest and brought it up to refasten above the animal. Francesco and Egidio positioned their charges and followed the Arab's lead. Then they led the last three horses into the ship's hold.

When all six horses were secure in slings, the Arab dumped into each manger a cup of barley from a nearby crate while Francesco forked hay to each horse. Egidio filled a pail with water from one of many barrels. The animals drank heartily.

The last horse had just finished drinking when a short sailor with deep-set, dark eyes ran up the gangplank and spoke to the Arab. The Arab looked at Francesco and Egidio, dismissed them with a wave of his hand, then darted down the gangplank to the beach.

Francesco looked at Egidio. "Now we hide." Francesco pulled off his headpiece, unknotted the rope, and tied it about his waist. He shoved his mantle under a pile of old cloth. Egidio quickly did the same. Then Francesco and

Egidio burrowed into the hay piled around the hold. Egidio's prayers could barely keep pace with his beating heart.

NOTES

Without giving details, 1C (first book, chapter XX) relates this story of Francesco's and Egidio's aborted trip to Syria, probably in 1212.

75

Bogoslav

Dock, Spalatum, Slavonia (Summer 1212)

Bogoslav clapped his big hands together and whooped for joy. The horses were loaded, and the fine money he'd received for them he'd use to repair the stable.

He smoothed his lemon-colored tunic and, a bit irked, waited to pay the Arabs he'd hired to board the horses. Sly traders, those Arabs. He thought he'd hired one and three showed up. Well, he'd pay them all to keep peace, and he'd still have money left.

One Arab bounded off the gangplank and approached, hand outstretched. Into it, Bogoslav dropped a generous sum, and the Arab went off grinning.

He turned his attention to the ship. The gangplank into the hold was being hoisted shut. Where were the other two Arabs? The ones in the tattered tunics? Tattered like the tunics of the two clerics in front of him when he and the Christian ship captain had been waiting in line for the money collector. "My sailors will care well for your horses," the captain had assured him just as the money collector tossed aside the shorter cleric who couldn't pay passage.

As he stared at the ship battening down for departure, Bogoslav's mind was racing. Two poor clerics who couldn't pay passage. Two poor Arabian grooms-men boarding the ship. Whoa! Ingenious! But imprudent! He didn't see the

Arabian clerics carrying provisions. What would they eat? The captain was unsympathetic. They'd get nothing from him.

Bogoslav remembered something else. A stocky sailor in a short, russet tunic had grabbed the money collector after he'd thrown aside the short cleric. The captain had grabbed the sailor. "Aleksandar! You know the policy. No pay, no passage. Mind your own business if you intend to sail with my vessel."

Bogoslav's pouch was heavy with coins. He had intended to give some in alms. Why not do it now?

NOTES

1C (first book, chapter XX) states that, unable to pay their passage, Francesco and Egidio became stowaways on a ship bound for Ancona. How did they do this? Stealing aboard with horses is pure speculation.

76

Aleksandar

Deck of Ship, Spalatum, Slavonia (Summer 1212)

Aleksandar was standing on the ship's deck, waiting for orders to pull anchor. His sturdy, stocky body had developed on ships, so he could climb the rigging as easily as a child could climb a tree. His deep-set, brown eyes were always the first to spot a school of fish or a rising storm. Now the early morning fog had lifted, the vessel was loaded, and Mirko was folding his table and gathering his coins. All morning Aleksandar had been thanking God that the captain hadn't fired him for grabbing Mirko to protect the poor cleric. Aleksandar needed this voyage's pay to support his wife and infant son. He crossed himself, thanked God again, and asked Him to bless his family and to tame his temper. He whispered a prayer for a safe journey, then added a prayer for the clerics. To end his prayer, he crossed himself again.

A short time later, while Aleksandar was checking the rigging, a stranger in a lemon-colored tunic who was carrying a double-pouched sack approached him and gave him the sack. Then he said, "Take with you all these things, and in their time of need faithfully give them to those poor men hiding on your ship."

"Where?" he asked.

"With the horses." The man in the long, lemon tunic put a finger to his lips. Aleksandar understood.

Dumbfounded, he accepted the sack and, as the stranger descended the gangplank to the beach, Aleksandar descended the ladder into the hold. Ah, over there. That pile of hay was larger than he remembered. He strode over to it and pushed some straw aside, uncovering two tonsured heads. How did they get aboard?

He opened the pouches. They were filled with bread. Emptying one side of the sack, he handed the loaves to the two frightened men. Then he squeezed the emptied sack through the Y-shaped support of a beam bracing the deck, leaving the full side of the sack dangling. He then repacked the loaves into the empty side, nodded to the stowaways, and climbed the ladder to the deck. The crew were manning the oars to row the vessel out to sea. He found his place and heaved.

For the first two days, the sea was gentle. On the third day, the waves were choppy, and the breeze intensified. In the west, gray clouds cluttered the horizon above the steely water.

The storm hit on the fourth day. To keep from washing overboard, the crew tied themselves to the ship with lengths of rope. They lowered the sail, struck the mast, and lashed it to the deck. Day and night, the crew manned the oars, fighting to keep the vessel afloat. Those not sleeping or rowing bailed out the hold where skittish horses whinnied with fear. Meanwhile the two barefoot clerics waded through watery straw, spoke soothingly to the blindfolded beasts, and tried to calm them.

The clerics had the foresight to fork the hay from the floor into five unused slings, hoisting them as high off the flooded floor as possible. Into the sixth sling they'd poured the barley. With bridles made from rope, the clerics cinched the horses' necks so that they couldn't nibble at the water-logged straw at their feet nor drink the sea water sloshing about their ankles. The captain and sailors, who, when they had discovered the clerics aboard, had originally growled at the stowaways, now marveled at them. Without their attention, the horses would have drunk themselves to death on the saltwater.

The sailors' food ran out. Aleksandar remembered the clerics and the sacks. He descended to the hold and mimed the need of bread for the sailors. The clerics nodded graciously. Aleksandar removed three loaves and carried them up the ladder.

Finally, the storm abated. The sailors assessed the damage, hoisted the mast and the sail, and got their bearings. When they finally docked at Ancona, the clerics' pouches were as empty as everyone's stomachs. Yet they'd all survived.

With a quizzical look, Aleksandar bid the clerics farewell as they descended the gangplank. Did they know that, no matter how many loaves Aleksandar took from the pouches, there always remained plenty for the next day? He blessed himself, whispered a prayer of gratitude to God, and wondered if he'd been part of a miracle.

NOTES

Without giving names or backgrounds, 1C (first book, chapter XX) relates how a mysterious benefactor gave a God-fearing sailor bread for the stowaway brothers and how that bread sustained the entire crew during a violent storm at sea.

77

Guglielmo di Lisciano

Convent of San Salvatore di Colpersito, San Severino (Summer 1212)

Atop his shoulder-length raven locks, Guglielmo di Lisciano wore a crown of fresh red roses as befitted a poet laureate crowned by Federico, King of Sicily. Smiling broadly at his doting followers, Gulli flung open his amethyst-hued mantle, intentionally contrasting it with his new, lemon-yellow tunic. Having traveled to San Severino for a festival, Gulli had generously thought of bringing a little glamor to this dull cloister where his cousin and several other nuns dwelt. He rang the bell at the turn to summon them while his retinue stood waiting.

To entertain the holy women, Gulli had altered a popular song about a married woman and her knightly lover. But he changed the lover to her husband and replaced the lusty, suggestive words with moderate, flowery phrases. Gulli had spent most of his twenty-three years singing, writing, dancing, and rhyming. "You were born a poet," his loving mother had often told him. He missed her, dead these five years now.

A rustling at the grate interrupted his reminiscing. A wrinkle-faced nun in a black tunic had pushed aside the dark curtain. "I'm sorry, but we're assembling in the church to hear a preacher, Fra Francesco di Assisi. Please join us." The nun pulled the curtain closed before Gulli could reply.

Rude! Well, they'd come to visit his cousin. Might as well hear the preacher and then visit.

The troubadour and his fans sauntered into the small church, finding places between two nobles on horseback and behind the smattering of men, women, and children colorfully dressed for the festival. Taller and lankier than most people, Gulli scanned over their heads. Two penitent clerics in patched, gray tunics were kneeling before the altar.

Suddenly Gulli saw two gleaming swords, one vertical from the head of the short penitent to the floor and the other across his shoulders. The swords glittered and were gone. Sunbeams?

The taller penitent stood and walked off to the left. The sword-signed penitent stood, crossed himself, and walked toward the center of the sanctuary.

"Lord, God of my salvation, I cry day and night to you. Let my prayer enter into your sight; incline your ear to my prayer. Attend to my soul and free it."

Well, his sonorous voice could capture your attention. That had to be the preacher. What was his name? Fra Francesco di Assisi?

"Blessed are the clean of heart, for they will see God!"

Was the preacher, that Francesco, looking at him?

"The truly clean of heart are those who look down upon earthly things,"—he *was* looking at him—"seek those of heaven,"—why was he looking at him?—"and, with a clean heart and spirit."

Gulli groaned. Does he know? About Gulli's amorous trysts, his drinking, gambling, impure jokes and lyrics, flamboyant dress?

The preacher was repeating. "Blessed are the clean of heart, for they will see God!" Then he broke into a troubadour melody that rivaled any Gulli had ever written or sung.

"The truly clean of heart are those who look down upon earthly things,
seek those of heaven,
and, with a clean heart and spirit,
never cease adoring and seeing
the Lord God, living and true.
Therefore,
let us desire nothing else,
let us want nothing else,

let nothing else please us and cause us delight
except our Creator, Redeemer and Savior,
the only true God,
Who is the fullness of good,
all good, every good, the true and supreme good,
Who alone is good,
merciful, gentle, delightful, and sweet,
Who alone is holy,
Just, true, holy, and upright,

Who alone is kind, innocent, clean,
from Whom, through Whom and in Whom
Is all pardon, all grace, all glory
of all penitents and just ones,
of all the blessed rejoicing together in heaven."

As the song continued, Gulli felt like a snail without its shell that finds itself unexpectedly on a dark boulder under an intense July sun. He was melting. His face must be as red as the roses he wore. Would anyone notice?

That preacher was right. Gulli ought to change. *My Lord, I'll do better in the future*, he promised. He was still praying when the singing stopped. The church was hushed.

His friends stood silently around him. They expected certain songs, certain behaviors, a certain lifestyle from him.

I'll do better, he prayed again. *But how?*

The church was emptying except for two people chatting with the two clerics.

"Let's go," Gulli called to his friends.

They turned to leave, but Gulli felt a touch on his shoulder.

Fra Francesco.

"May I speak with you?"

"Sì." He probably wanted to speak to him about his music.

"You sing well," Gulli said. An understatement.

"You sing better." Francesco was smiling as he gently guided Gulli outside the church.

"You've heard of me?"

"Who hasn't heard of the 'King of Verses'?" They were outdoors and walking away from the church. "I've wanted to meet the poet whom the king crowned with roses. Now I have. You've heard me sing, Messer. I should like to hear you."

"For the nuns, I've composed a song. My cousin is in there."

"She's chosen wisely."

Gulli shrugged. He hardly thought so.

Francesco continued to meander down the road. "I used to be like you."

"Never!" Gulli stared incredulously at him.

"Sì." The holy preacher sang out a lusty ballad accompanied by a spirited, suggestive dance.

Unbelievable!

"One remembers what one has done for years."

"How did you change from that to . . . to . . . ?" Gulli stammered.

Francesco laughed. "This wasn't my idea. The Lord made me realize that all those who aren't living in penance—"

"Like you?"

"Like anyone who gives his or her life to God, wherever they be—they're living in penance. Have you done that? Given your life to God?"

Gulli felt like a snail melting. "Uh. No."

"Neither had I. Anyone who practices vice and sin and walks after evil concupiscence and wicked desires," Francesco was pointing to his own heart and nodding, "anyone who serves the world with their bodies, the desires of the flesh, the cares and anxieties of this world, and," he was tapping his chest, "the" (tap) "preoccupations" (tap) "of this life—" (tap) "all these are deceived by the devil, whose children they are and whose works they do."

The sun was oppressive. Gulli was perspiring.

Francesco pointed to the blazing orb. "They are blind because they do not see the true light, our Lord Jesus Christ." He pointed to his head. "They do not have spiritual wisdom because they do not possess the Son of God, the *true* wisdom of the Father, within them." He pointed again to his heart. "They see," he pointed to his eyes, "recognize, know," he pointed to his heart, "and do evil," his hands emphasized the word, "and, knowingly, they lose their souls." He plucked an imaginary something from his chest, threw the invisible soul to the ground, and trampled on it. He brushed his hands against his tunic as if cleaning them of dust, folded his arms, and looked Gulli squarely in the face.

Gulli stared back, the image of the plucked out and trampled upon soul vivid in his mind.

"What's the point of piling on any more words? Let's move on to deeds!" Gulli declared. "Take me away from people, and give me back to the Great Emperor!"

Francesco grinned. He twirled around in a short dance of joy, this time without the bawdy gestures. "Go back to your friends today and, if you still desire this tomorrow, return here at the same time as today and we will clothe you in the habit of penance."

Oh, he'd be back all right! He'd be back early!

However, how should he tell his friends that he was done with their life? They'd think he was judging them, acting holier than they were.

After speaking to and chastely entertaining his cousin and her fellow nuns, Gulli returned with his friends to San Severino and its nightlife of dice, feasting, and women. Gulli wanted no part of it. "I'm not feeling well," he confessed. Indeed, he was nauseous. Thinking about changing his lifestyle was making him ill. How do you relinquish all you've known?

In the room he was renting, he crept into bed next to two snoring men in their coifs and tried to sleep, but fear and desire battled in his soul. He needed to abandon his foolish lifestyle. But was he courageous enough to do it?

After his tossing and turning woke the man next to him, Gulli climbed out of bed. He donned his clothes and crept into a corner where he tried to doze. The fierce, internal attacks persisted.

What will your friends think?

What will the world think?

You've got talent. You want to throw it away?

You only know how to support yourself by singing. What will you do if you abandon that?

Do you think living in poverty is easy? You can't do it.

You're a hopeless sinner. What makes you think God would want you?

All right! Let me alone! I'll go to the festival. Let me alone!

The attacks stopped. Gulli felt nauseous.

No! I'm not going to the festival. I'm going to hell. God, help me! Mamma, help me!

Was his meeting Francesco the result of Mamma's prayers? "When opportunity comes," she'd often advised, "take it because it might not come again."

Meeting Francesco wasn't coincidental. Nothing is coincidental with God. Meeting Francesco was God giving him a way out of a destructive life. How would he manage that? Bah! Let God worry about it. It was time that the "King of Verses" became the servant of the King of kings.

At dawn, before his friends awoke, before he could change his mind, Gulli paid the innkeeper and was gone.

He arrived at the empty convent church, hours before the time Francesco had set. Pulling his amethyst mantle around his lemon tunic, he curled into a corner in the back of the church. He gazed above the altar at the wooden dove in which rested the Body of Christ.

I'm sorry, my Lord. From now on, help me to serve You, he prayed.

When he awoke, Francesco was sitting to his left and the taller penitent to his right. They were both gazing at the wooden dove.

"Are you at peace?" Francesco spoke softly.

Gulli felt tremendous, encompassing peace, the peace of a snail that's melted to a fragile sheen under the brilliant Son.

"I'm at peace."

"Then stand and Fra Egidio will cut your hair."

Cut his hair? Of course. What had Jesus said? "If your right hand causes you to sin, cut it off."

As if he were an onlooker, Gulli saw his raven locks falling about his feet in front of the altar. He felt lighter already.

"Perhaps the good nuns can make altar cloths and vestments from your tunic and mantle. Your hose and shoes we'll give to the poor," Francesco said.

He handed his sumptuous clothes to Fra Francesco, and then Fra Egidio slipped a scratchy gray tunic over Gulli's head.

Francesco was smiling at him. "Since you've been brought back to the peace of God, now give Him thanks, Fra Pacifico, 'man of peace.'"

NOTES

2C (second book, chapter LXXII) details Pacifico's conversion. Local authors in Italy identify Pacifico as the youth Guglielmo (William) of Lisciano (https://www.catholic.com/encyclopedia/pacificus). Pacifico joined Francesco sometime after his return from Rome and sometime before 1217, when Pacifico was sent to France.

2C also states that the emperor had crowned Guglielmo "King of Verses." The emperor referred to was likely Frederick II, who was emperor when 2C was completed in 1247 and who was a patron of poets and musicians. In 1212, Frederick was king of Sicily, and was crowned Holy Roman Emperor in 1220.

The author postulates that Francesco was at the convent to preach to the nuns. Francesco's opening prayer is in a prayer to be said at Matins from his *Office of the Passion*. His text on "blessed are the clean of heart" is Francesco's *Admonition XVI*. His song, "Therefore, let us desire nothing else" is found in chapter XXIII of the *Earlier Rule*. His words about "those who are not living in penance" are taken from his *Later Admonition and Exhortation to the Brothers and Sisters of Penance*, sentences 63–68.

78

Bishop Guido

Bishop's Palace, Assisi (Summer 1212)

Bishop Guido was about to climb into bed when he suddenly felt strangely unwell. A searing pain ripped through his chest and up his shoulder and, at the same time, his stomach heaved and he almost retched onto the floor. Collapsing under the pain and the nausea, he barely had a moment to silently cry out, "My God, receive my soul," before it left him for his Creator.

NOTES

Historians tend to agree that Guido became bishop of Assisi in 1204. Recent scholarship indicates that he died (we do not know how) in 1212. He was succeeded by Bishop Guido II who governed Assisi until his death in 1228 (see Nicolangelo D'Acunto, "*Il Vescovo Guido Oppure I Vescovi Guido?*").

79

Madonna Jacopa dei Settesoli

Church of San Biagio, Rome (Summer 1212)

Her flushed cheeks taut in her oval face, Madonna Jacopa dei Settesoli walked dazedly out of the Church of San Biagio in the Trastevere section of Rome. It was not far from the languid Tiber that was strewn with sailing vessels, not far from the crowded mercato that clogged the river's docks. Almost as tall as her massive husband Graziano Frangipani, but slender and carrying herself regally like a queen, she had one arm linked in Graziano's. Her other hand clasped the hand of five-year-old Giovanni, who had begged to hear the novel preacher.

Jacopa had heard him, all right. She had heard him all too clearly.

The little family had walked to San Biagio to hear Fra Francesco preach. Friends at the Lateran had said that he, who had founded a religio up north, had come to tell Pope Innocenzo about a new group of enclosed women who were living the same way. "Come with us to hear him," her friends encouraged her. "When he preached to the pope, he danced and mimed!"

Indeed, his style was entertaining. Giovanni had been mesmerized. So had Jacopa.

Her friends had told her about what Fra Francesco had given up, but he didn't speak of that. He spoke of his brothers in the religio and the new group of sisters and how they had exchanged living in the world for living for God. Worldly attachments, he said, impede us from praising, loving, and serving our loving Creator and Redeemer. His words seared her soul: "Therefore, let nothing hinder us, nothing separate us, nothing come between us."

As the little family walked to their nearby palazzo, Jacopa became more and more convicted of her hypocrisy. She pretended to be holy, but what challenged her holiness? What sacrifices did she make? What possessions had she relinquished?

She had innumerable gowns to wear, like the favorite maroon velvet she was wearing now, with ermine at the collar and cuffs, no less. Would she appear so regal if she were a house servant?

Her perfectly arched eyebrows framed her deep brown, languid eyes, her nose was fine and long, her lips small and refined. She turned heads wherever she went. Suppose she had been born with a crooked nose or oversized, protruding teeth. Would she then have admirers?

Plump in all the right places, Jacopa's shapely figure delighted Graziano and attested to her having all the food she desired. Suppose she were a beggar. How enticing would she then look?

And Graziano—he was a noble, wealthy, sturdy, loving husband and Giovanni, a gentle, intelligent, thoughtful son. Neither brought a single suffering into her life. Servants came and went at her bidding. Rome was her mercato, playground, and social circle. She lacked nothing.

She had come to hear the preacher, not thinking about all she had. Now, for the first time in her twenty-two years of life, she realized how pampered she was. She had always wanted to love God above all things, but she now realized that she loved all things above God.

Therefore, let nothing hinder us, nothing separate us, nothing come between us.

Everything had come between her and God. She knew what she had to do, and her resolve was tearing her heart.

"You're quiet," Graziano said as they neared their palazzo.

"Papà, did you see how he danced out the story of the dying rich man?" Giovanni did a little dance, pulling at Jacopa's hand. She smiled weakly at him.

"I meant your mother," Graziano said. "Are you all right, my lady?"

How should she answer? "I'd like to speak to him about my soul."

"Invite him for dinner!" Graziano laughed. "Him and the other one. They're skinny. They'll come!"

"Grazie," she said.

"Can I sit by them?" Giovanni asked.

"Certainly!" Graziano laughed again.

The next evening, after a dinner of roasted venison, dressed in truffles and figs, after cheese and apples and wine, after the prayer of thanksgiving at the end of the meal, while a servant took Giovanni to bed and other servants cleared the board of food, Graziano asked the penitents, "Could my wife speak with you?"

In the fire room they sat, Graziano and Jacopa on one side of the hearth, and Francesco and the skinny brother on the other.

Jacopa wished she could speak to Francesco alone, but what would be the point? Eventually Graziano would have to know. Tears stung her eyes with love for him, for Giovanni, for her family and even for her servants. *Love doesn't die, even if one is absent from the beloved,* she told herself. But she had to love God more than anything or anyone else. She would throw all her loves into the fire of God's love. She would give Him herself.

"Brother, you said there are convents of Poor Ladies?" she said, her voice shaky.

"Sì."

"And married women have entered?"

"Sì."

Graziano jumped to his feet. "My lady, what are you thinking?"

"I am thinking I need to save my soul," Jacopa said weakly.

"So, you shall," Francesco said, "but here, my lady. A convent is not for you."

"Certainly not," Graziano said, sitting down.

"I have everything here. I have given God nothing."

"You can give Him everything here," Francesco said.

He must have read the question on her face. "His Father's will was such that His blessed and glorious Son, Whom He gave to us and Who was born for us, should offer Himself through His own blood as a sacrifice and oblation on the altar of the cross: not for Himself through Whom all things were made, but for our sins, leaving us an example that we might follow His footprints. Your life here is your altar, my lady. Giving up your own will for others is your cross. You offer yourself upon this altar, upon this cross, for your own sins and for the sins of others. This is how you follow in His footprints. He wishes *all* of us to be saved through Him and receive Him with our heart pure and our body chaste. Can you not do this here?"

Tangled thoughts pulled at Jacopa's heart. She had been sure that God wanted her to relinquish everything she loved to become a Poor Sister. Now Fra Francesco was telling her to keep everything and be holy here. "How?"

"Christ said, 'Blessed are the poor in spirit, for theirs is the kingdom of heaven.' Heaven is your goal, isn't it?"

"Of course," Jacopa and Graziano said together.

"In heaven, we see God, don't we?" Francesco asked.

"Sì." They spoke together again.

"Our Lord Jesus said, 'Blessed are the clean of heart, for they will see God.' Who are the clean of heart?"

"Those whose thoughts are pure?" Graziano ventured.

"Sì. But there is more. The truly clean of heart are those who look down upon earthly things, seek those of heaven, and, with a clean heart and spirit, never cease adoring and seeing our Lord God, living and true."

"But how? How do we do that?" Jacopa blurted out.

Francesco, the skinny brother, and even Graziano were staring at her oddly. Couldn't they understand?

Jacopa felt flustered. "I need more direction. Something written. Details."

"Aren't the Gospels enough?" Francesco smiled.

Jacopa fumbled for words. "Our Lord asks us to pray. To fast. To give what we don't need. The Poor Ladies and Lesser Brothers do this. You have a way to pray. To eat. To give. You don't have to determine the details. But for me . . ."

"You're seeking a detailed way to do what God asks?" Francesco said.

"Sì. I'm not good at details. How often should I pray? What should I pray? How often should I eat? What should I eat? What should I wear? How many clothes should I have?"

Graziano was staring at her, as if seeing her for the first time. "Messer, you know I'm not good at these things," she said to her husband. "I'm not disciplined. The Poor Ladies, and the Lesser Brothers have a detailed way of life to live."

"They don't look at their trencher and wonder if they should have another serving," Graziano said.

He understood. "Sì," she said.

Francesco nodded. "Perhaps you also need a Rule of Life."

"Exactly." She and Graziano spoke together. Had he just agreed with her?

"You're not the first to request this. What do you think, Brother? Would a Rule of Life be good for people like my lord and my lady?"

"Who ever heard of such a thing?" the skinny brother asked.

"Not every good thing is something we've already heard of," Francesco said. "Be patient and I'll give you a Rule of Life. In the meantime, live as if you already have one."

"We can write out something, my lady," Graziano said. "We'll pray together morning and evening."

Jacopa's excitement mounted. "Only one trencher of food at meals."

"Maybe two for me?"

Jacopa laughed. "For you, two. For me, one!"

Graziano looked stern. "I don't want you skinny like him." He pointed to the skinny brother.

"I'll never be skinny like him, Messer," Jacopa chuckled.

"And no more than ten gowns," Graziano said.

"Ten?" That seemed stark. "Ten tunics for you, too, then, Messer."

"The poor can always use gowns and tunics," Francesco said.

"Certainly!" Jacopa and Graziano said together. They looked at each other and giggled.

NOTES

For the background of Madonna Jacopa and her family members, see:

— http://www.sanfrancescoassisi.org/en/st-francis/important-persons/jacopa-dei-settesoli,

— 3C (chapter VI),

— https://www.ewtn.com/catholicism/library/st-francis-of-assisi-5317.

We don't know the exact year in which Jacopa was married or Giovanni was born. Some sources believe that Jacopa first met Francesco in 1212, but history records no date or circumstances of that original encounter.

Simone Martini's erroneously named portrait (1315) of Saint Clare is believed to be that of Jacopa. Her description in this chapter reflects that portrait and the description of her bodily remains from her tomb near that of Saint Francis.

Following the death of Bishop Guido I, Francesco may have journeyed to Rome to tell the pope of the new group of sisters housed in San Damiano. If this were the case, he would likely have preached while in Rome, possibly in several different churches. The Church of San Biagio (now the Church of San Francesco a Ripa) is in the Trastevere section of Rome where Jacopa and her family likely lived. The phrase "Therefore, let nothing hinder us" is in Francesco's *Earlier Rule* (chapter XXIII).

Historians generally agree that Jacopa may have been one of the first to request from Francesco a lay Rule of Life.

History doesn't record whether Graziano ever met or supported Francesco, although his powerful family, the Frangipani, engaged in charitable works as well as political intrigues.

Francesco's conversation with Jacopa and Graziano is taken from his *Later Admonition and Exhortation to the Brothers and Sisters of Penance (Second Version of the Letter to the Faithful)* and the *Admonitions (XVI: Cleanness of Heart)*. We do not know if Jacopa ever considered becoming a nun.

80

Arrigo

Field in Ottiano, outside of Assisi (Late September 1212)

Eight-year-old Arrigo scampered barefoot through the upturned furrows, looking for newly exposed rocks. When he saw one, he'd pluck it and carry it to the edge of the field where he tossed it atop an accumulating pile. If the stone were too heavy, he'd call eleven-year-old Belvender to help. If the two brothers together couldn't manage the weight, they'd call their oldest brother Giovanni. Giovanni was big and strong. He'd move anything.

Giovanni was plowing in the middle of the field, preparing it for spring planting. The family's two white oxen, Avena and Traviata, were straining to pull the plow through seedling shrubs and tangled grass that threatened to turn this fallow field into forest. Tomorrow, when Giovanni finished plowing, Arrigo, Belvender, and their older brothers Adalberto and Guilio, would spread dried dung from the family's oxen, fowl, and themselves over the upturned clumps in preparation for spring planting. Arrigo liked that job better than picking stones. He could run through the furrows, throwing dung to left and right without having to look out for anything except vipers.

"Giovanni!" Adalberto's shout startled Arrigo. He was supposed to be working today with their neighbor Andrea. "Fra Francesco is back! He's going to speak in the church at Sext!"

"Grazie!" Giovanni shouted.

"Bye!" Adalberto called back. "I'll tell papà." He sprinted down the road.

Arrigo had heard of Fra Francesco. He had big ears. Sometimes he came to Ottiano to sing and dance about Jesus Christ. Arrigo wanted to see him. He hopped across the furrows to Giovanni. "Can we go?"

"Please?" Belvender asked.

"Please?" echoed Arrigo.

"Sì." Giovanni grinned. "But work hard until the bells ring."

And they did, the work easier because it would end at noon. After what seemed forever, the church bells rang.

"Giovanni!" Arrigo called.

Giovanni was shoving the plow into the earth. He unhitched Avena and Traviata and gave each a smack on her rump. They plodded a short distance before stopping to nibble at the unplowed grass.

Giovanni leaped across the furrows toward the road, Arrigo and Belvender following.

"Race you!" Belvender challenged.

The boys took off in a fierce run.

The Church of San Michele Arcangelo was just down the road. From inside the church came a *swish, swish, swishing*. Puzzled, Arrigo peeked in while Giovanni strode right past him into the church, gently took a broom from a gray-robed penitent, and began to sweep. The penitent, who had been sweeping, knelt and prayed.

The penitent had big ears. Fra Francesco?

No one else had yet arrived. "Race you!" Belvender challenged. Arrigo bolted after him down the road.

The race brought them face-to-face with neighbors coming to hear the penitent. Another penitent, big like Giovanni, came along with their neighbor Andrea and his workers, including Adalberto and Guilio. Arrigo and Belvender joined their brothers and arrived at the church about the same time as mamma holding baby Humiliana and papà holding the hands of Biona and Annah.

The family sat together on the floor, Arrigo next to Belvender. He could not help fidgeting until Fra Francesco began to talk. Then the penitent's hand gestures, songs, and little dances kept Arrigo wondering what would come next. Fra

Francesco sang about doing good and praising God. He said some scary things about how the devil comes to take away a dying, greedy soul. He made the devil so real that Arrigo cuddled closer to Belvender, who shoved him away. Then Fra Francesco acted out how God welcomes a soul who shares, and Arrigo resolved to do better at sharing. After ending with, "Now, good people, go and do what you have heard," Fra Francesco blessed them. Then everyone left the church, Arrigo and Belvender being two of the first. Mamma, papà, and the girls started off in the direction of home. Adalberto, Guilio, and the big penitent went off with Andrea. Arrigo and Belvender began to run around the church. When they exhausted themselves, they rolled in the grass under a large oak to catch their breath.

At last, Giovanni came out of the church. They caught his glance and followed him back to the field. Arrigo thought he would resume plowing but, instead, he took the rope which held the oxen to the plow and quickly made a halter which he slipped around Avena's head. Then he unhitched her and Traviata from the yoke and began to walk off with Avena.

"Where are you taking Avena?" Arrigo asked.

"You'll see," Giovanni said.

Arrigo looked questioningly at Belvender, who shrugged. The boys trotted behind Avena and soon returned to the church.

Giovanni went into the church and brought Fra Francesco out. "Brother, I have served my papà and everyone in my household for many years. Although my portion of the inheritance is small, I want to take this ox as my share and give it to the poor, as you think best according to God."

"No!" Arrigo shouted. "You can't give away Avena!" He pressed his head against her wide white cheek and began to wail. "You can't give away Avena! I'm getting mamma and papà!" He raced home, Belvender following.

"Giovanni is giving Avena to Fra Francesco!" he wailed.

"Sì! He's giving away Avena!" Belvender cried.

Mamma and papà stared at each other. "Where?" papà asked.

"At the church," Belvender said.

Papà ran off, Arrigo and Belvender racing after him.

Fra Francesco and Giovanni were still standing in front of the church, Avena between them.

"What's this about your giving away Avena?" papà demanded.

"What's this?" mamma repeated, coming up behind. She was carrying Humiliana and holding the hand of Biona, who was holding Annah's hand.

"You can't have Avena," Arrigo wailed. He flung himself against the ox's front leg and held on tightly. The beast turned her head and licked the side of his face with her huge black tongue.

Belvender and Biona joined in.

"Avena is ours."

"Don't take Avena."

"We need Avena."

"Traviata will miss her."

"Hush," Francesco said loudly. "Prepare and serve a meal so we can all eat together, and don't cry, because I'll make you happy."

The preparations distracted everyone. Giovanni brought Avena and Traviata in from the field and put them in the meadow near the house, where they happily grazed. Arrigo lugged a pail of water from the well for them. Belvender ran to see if the hens had laid eggs. Mother found flour and quickly made pan bread cooked over the hearth. Papà brought green beans, cabbage, garlic, onions, and squash from the garden. Mamma chopped the vegetables and put them all into a big pot over the fire. Annah and Biona took turns stirring. Belvender cracked four eggs into the cooking vegetables. Whoever was near Humiliana's cradle rocked it and kept the baby dozing. Fra Francesco sang troubadour tunes with verses from the Psalms. Soon everyone was sitting joyfully around the table while Fra Francesco blessed the food.

Amid banter and laughter, the meal continued until no food was left. Then Fra Francesco blessed them all again. "This son of yours," he said, "wants to serve God, and you should be glad and not sad about this. This will be counted an honor and advantage to your souls and bodies, not only according to God but also according to the world, because God will be honored by your own flesh and blood, and," he looked at mamma and papà, "all our brothers will be your sons." He smiled at the children. "And our brothers will be your brothers."

Francesco continued. "And because he is a creature of God and wishes to serve his Creator, and to serve Him is to reign, I cannot and should not return him to you."

Arrigo was finally beginning to understand. “You can have Giovanni but not Avena!” he cried.

“Hush,” papà commanded. “Giovanni was to have Avena as his inheritance.”

“When you promised him Avena, he talked about marrying and settling here.” Mama looked as if she might cry. “We would share Avena.”

“God wants our son,” papà declared. “We will work with one ox.”

“Giovanni wasn’t going to take Avena with him,” Francesco explained. “I had told him, ‘Brother, if you wish to belong to our life and company, you must rid yourself of all your things that you can get without scandal and give them to the poor according to the counsel of the holy Gospel, because my brothers who were able to do so have done this.’”

Francesco paused. “I see that taking your ox seems scandalous and irresponsible.”

“Not Avena!” Biona shrieked in her high-pitched voice.

All around the table, the crying resumed.

Fra Francesco’s voice rose over the din. “Hush. In order that you receive and keep some consolation from all this, I want Giovanni to rid himself of this ox by giving it to you, although, according to the counsel of the holy Gospel, it ought to be given to other poor people.”

Arrigo jumped up from the bench. “We get to keep Avena?”

“Sì,” Francesco said. “You get to keep Avena.”

“We get to keep Avena!” Arrigo began to dance around the table. “We get to keep Avena!”

Belvender and Biona joined him, dancing and chanting, “We get to keep Avena!”

Laughing and clapping, Annah joined in, repeating, “Uh-Bee-Nuh! Uh-Bee-Nuh!”

Fra Francesco stood and began to strum the air as if he were holding a lute. He began to sing in time to the children’s chants.

“Sing a new song to Him
Sing to the Lord all the earth.
Because the Lord is great and highly to be praised,

awesome beyond all gods.
Give to the Lord, you families of nations,
Give to the Lord glory and honor
Give to the Lord the glory due His name."

The children collapsed, laughing and exhausted.

"Fra Giovanni will return to Ottiano from time to time to preach and minister here," Fra Francesco assured them. "Now, before we return to Assisi, we must find Fra Egidio. He's working for a farmer today."

"Andrea!" Arrigo shouted. "My brothers are working for him today, too!"

"Can you take us to Andrea?" Fra Francesco asked with a smile.

Arrigo felt important. "Sì!"

Fra Francesco rested his hand on Giovanni's shoulder. "Fra Giovanni, bid your family farewell."

NOTES

AC (section 61) records this incident while giving no information about Giovanni's age, siblings, or oxen. This chapter presents a recurring scenario—friars rang the church bells, gathered the people, and then offered them brief exhortations on the Gospel and on repentance.

The themes of Francesco's talk are in his writings. His song is from his *Office of the Passion* for Vespers, verses 5 to 7.

81

Fra Leone

Road to Montefeltro (May 7, 1213)

In the gathering dusk, Francesco pointed up a steep hill toward the walled town of Montefeltro.

"Race you!" Like a rabbit, Francesco darted up the hill.

Leone was tall, sturdy, and younger than Francesco. But the older, shorter man was more agile and energetic. He was already at the town's gate when Leone arrived.

The gate was closed. They knocked and pounded.

"Come back tomorrow," a voice shouted from the other side. "No one enters once the gates are closed."

Francesco shrugged. "Our good God must want us to speak to others tonight."

Turning away, the men quickened their pace down the road away from the town. Since they were on a mission of evangelization through the Romagna, they would walk until finding someone with whom to share the Gospel. Only if night overcame them would they sleep in seclusion.

Leone had been a priest in Assisi where he had lived an ordered life of praying the Hours, offering Mass, visiting his congregation, and studying. Over a year ago, he had realized that his life was as organized as a book, with God penning notes in the margins. Francesco and his brothers had ceased trying to write the books of their lives. They gave God a blank parchment on which the Spirit could write. What would He write tonight?

"Look!" Francesco was pointing to a thin ribbon of smoke trailing across the pink- and gray-streaked sky. How many times had they followed smoke to speak with the people who had kindled the fire?

As a new brother, Leone had accompanied Francesco to escort Madonna Chiara to the Porziuncula, where she had given her life to God. From that moment to this, life with Francesco had been a string of adventures laced with prayer. The freedom and joy of life on the hem of God's garment was so exhilarating that many desired it. Earlier this year when Francesco had preached in Ascoli, thirty brothers had joined. Every month, men arrived to relinquish their goods and receive the habit of penance.

People were listening. Changing. Turning to God. If Francesco were not sometimes prostrate with illness, if he were not occasionally peevish over worldliness, if he had not been a cocky cloth merchant, Leone might have wondered if he were more angel than man.

God spawned the graces that flowed through Francesco. He wasn't soliciting the hermitages and churches that people offered to him. He wasn't recruiting men to join him or women to join Madonna Chiara. God's Spirit was leading like a smoke trail to whatever God wanted. *The brotherhood*, Leone thought, *is part of something greater than we imagine. And so is everyone else, if only they would give God control. . . .*

The road had led through forested hills and now emerged from the woods. Across dark fields danced firelight.

"Grazie, my Lord!" Francesco whooped. The brothers struck off the road and directly across the fields toward the fire. After passing through a flock of sheep that skittered away from them, they came upon a cluster of shepherds' huts.

Of course, the brothers could have a bit of the shepherds' bread and cheese. Of course, they could sleep around the campfire.

The curious shepherds asked all the familiar questions.

"Who are you?"

"Where do you come from?"

"Why are you here?"

"How do you live?"

Leone and Francesco answered patiently, satisfying the questioners.

"Now, may we ask you the same questions?" Francesco smiled. He was sitting near the fire, the blaze lighting his face, deepening the age lines creeping along his cheeks and forehead.

Squatting next to Leone, a young shepherd—who might have seen fewer than ten summers—said, "That's a silly question. You can see that we're shepherds from these parts, and we live in those houses."

"Things aren't always what they seem," Francesco said.

"What does that mean?" asked a grizzled shepherd, sitting next to Francesco.

"You see yourselves as shepherds. God sees you as more." His gaze moved from face to face. "Consider, O human being, in what great excellence our Lord God has placed you."

"What excellence? We're poor here. Can't you see that?" The voice came from a dark hulk hunched over with his chin resting on his knees.

Francesco put his finger to his lips to ask for quiet. "Consider in what great excellence our Lord God has placed you, for He created and formed you," he looked at the grizzled man, "and you" to the shepherd boy, "and you" to the hulk, "and you" to a teen wrapped in a dark mantle. "He created and formed you in the image of His beloved Son according to the body." He paused. "And to his likeness according to the Spirit."

"You mean we look like God?" the boy asked.

"Sure is ugly if He looks like you!" the hulk grumbled.

"Don't call me ugly!" the boy shouted, jumping up.

Leone caught the boy's arm. "Wait. Listen," he admonished him.

Francesco looked at the hulk and then at the boy. "Blessed are the peacemakers, for they will be called children of God. This is what Jesus told us. Those people are truly peacemakers who, regardless of what they suffer in this world, preserve peace of spirit and body out of love of our Lord Jesus Christ."

"You mean I'm supposed to let him say that to me?" the boy demanded.

"Sì. Let him say whatever he wants. The Lord says to love your enemies and do good to those who hate you, and pray for those who persecute you and slander you."

The boy was staring at the hulk.

"Does He mean I have to love him?" he whispered to Leone.

Leone nodded. "That's what Jesus said to do," he whispered back.

The boy sat and moved closer to Leone, resting his head on Leone's arm.

Francesco was smiling at the boy. "That person truly loves his enemy who is not hurt by an injury done to himself, but, because of the love of God is stung by the sin of his enemy's soul." He turned his gaze to the hulk. "Let him show his enemy love by his deeds."

Francesco stood and brushed the seat of his tunic. His gaze swept the four shepherds clustered around the fire. Beginning to walk around the perimeter of the shepherds, he said, "There are many people who, when they sin or are injured, frequently blame their enemy or their neighbor." He poked the grizzled shepherd. "You made me sin. Or you . . ." He tapped the hulk. "Or you . . ." He tousled the boy's hair. "Or you . . ." He touched the teen's shoulder. "Or you . . ." He playfully punched Leone. "Or me!" He raised his hands. The shepherds laughed. Francesco looked from one to the other. "So, who is to blame for my sin? You, or you, or you, or you? No! Each one has the 'enemy' in his power—that is, his body through which he sins."

"You mean the enemy is me?" the teen asked.

"Sì!" Francesco grinned. He mimed wrestling with an invisible enemy and pinning him to the ground. Then he leaped up and pretended to plant his foot on the enemy's chest. In an exultant voice, he proclaimed, "Blessed is that servant, then, who always holds captive the enemy delivered into his power and wisely safeguards himself from him; because, as long as he does this, no other enemy visible or invisible will be able to harm him."

He then walked over to the hulk and whispered something to him. The hulk waved his fist at Francesco, who backed away.

"You're shepherds," Francesco said, "so consider the Good Shepherd Who bore the suffering of the cross to save His sheep. Your sheep can remind you of the sheep of the Lord who followed Him in tribulation and persecution, in shame and hunger, in weakness and temptation, and in other ways; and for these things they received eternal life from God. Be good shepherds then, to your sheep, and to one another. Be good sheep who follow your Good Shepherd."

"You know who needs to hear you talk like that?" the hulk muttered. "Them lords and ladies coming to the festivities tomorrow."

"Sì," the boy sighed. "Knighting two lords."

"Big celebration in Montefeltro," the teen said.

"All show for the well-off," grumbled the grizzled shepherd.

"Leone, what do you think?" Francesco asked. "Tomorrow, let us go up to that festival, for with God's help we will gather some good spiritual fruit."

NOTES

According to Fortini (p. 547, footnote), "the castello (castle and walled village) of Montefeltro . . . is today known as San Leo, in Romagna, a short distance from San Marino." Today, the name Montefeltro refers to the region.

Bernard of Besse (*A Book of the Praises of Saint Francis*, chapter I) states that Leone was Francesco's confessor. Fortini (p. 324, footnote f) notes that the only Leone in Assisi was a *Domino* Leone, possibly indicating that Leone was a priest. As Francesco's confessor, one would assume that he was a priest and able to offer daily Mass for the brothers. 24Gen (section 65) provides more information on Leone's background. His physical description is interpolated from his remains buried in the Basilica of Saint Francis in Assisi.

C1 (chapter XXII) mentions that, in Ascoli, thirty men wanted to join the brotherhood.

Thomas of Celano, in *The Life of Saint Clare Virgin*, details her flight from her family.

An oral tradition in San Leo states that Leone and Francesco came to Montefeltro (now called San Leo) when the gates were closed. But they followed a fire to shepherds with whom they stayed the night and who told them about the following day's knighting (http://www.diocesi-sanmarino-montefeltro.it/portfolio/la-pietra-di-consacrazione-del-1244-del-convento-di-santigne/).

Francesco's exhortation to the shepherds is taken from his *Admonitions* (sections V, VI, IX, X, XV). His words about going to Montefeltro to gain some spiritual fruit are in *Fioretti* ("Considerations on the Holy Stigmata: The First Consideration").

82

Count Orlando dei Catani

Hall in the Palazzo, Montefeltro (Late Evening, May 8, 1213)

As if he were going into battle, Count Orlando dei Catani could not still his pounding heart. He was peering out a second-story window in a palazzo in the castello of Montefeltro. The night breeze was blowing his auburn locks around his beardless face. How many times had he tucked his wind-blown hair under his gold trimmed cap? The last thing any knight wants is obstructed vision!

His quick, dark eyes, bright as a weasel's, were scanning the piazza below and the five streets leading into it. Still, no figure approached through the breeze-shivered torchlight.

In his twenty-nine years of life, Orlando had never experienced anything quite like this. The now empty, banner-festooned banquet hall, where he'd been pacing for the past several minutes, seemed suffocating. He looked out a window again and took a deep breath.

Why is he taking so long?

There stood the Pieve di Santa Maria Assunta where, early this morning, Bishop Feretrano Alberto had knighted the brothers Messer Montefeltrano II and Messer Taddeo. Midway from the church to here stood the towering elm surrounded by a low wall on which . . .

Why is he taking so long?

Orlando himself should have been exhausted after the two-day journey from his castle in Chiusi; this morning's festivities; the prolonged, sumptuous meal that had swollen his trim waist, followed by cavorting and caroling entertainers well into the night. Like everyone else, he should have stumbled to bed and fallen into a deep sleep. Instead, he was wide awake.

Why is he taking so long?

This morning, the piazza had hosted a festive tournament that had followed the knighting. The now vacant square had reverberated with pounding hooves, clashing lances, and exultant cheers. Astride his chestnut steed, Orlando had awaited his turn to joust when an awed hush swept the crowd. Turning to see its cause, Orlando had spied two dusty minstrels, dressed as barefoot clerics, cavorting and leaping up the street straight into the crowd. They were dancing to a familiar love song made more plaintive by their resonant voices. "So great the good I have in sight that every pain I count delight."

The familiar song recounted the deeds of a knight who travels the world, bearing in his heart the image of his mistress. To the brave knight, pierced by love, every pain, risk, and hardship is sweet because happiness in the arms of his beloved awaits him at his journey's end.

The shorter minstrel had jumped up on that wall surrounding the city's elm tree and continued singing to the vast audience, ending the love song with an added verse: "'Your grief will be turned into joy,' Jesus said. Thus it will be for those who serve others for the love of Christ and bear this world's pains in imitation of our Lord."

Then Orlando had known. The troubadours dressed as clerics were clerics preaching like troubadours. He had heard of Francesco di Assisi and his style. Now this audience was experiencing him.

"And the Spirit of the Lord will rest upon all those men and women who have done and persevered in these things and It will make a home and dwelling place in them. And they will be children of the heavenly Father, Whose works they do." In mime and dance, Francesco described deeds of saints and martyrs who had relinquished their all to the great All.

Then the song and dance took a sinister turn as Francesco mimed the end of an unrepentant sinner's life. Wanting his family to have his inheritance, the wretched man puts all his possessions into the hands of his relatives, and thus when a priest is called to his deathbed, he has no alms to give to the poor. "But let everyone know that whenever and however someone dies in mortal sin without making amends when he could have and did not, the devil snatches his soul from his body with such anguish and distress that no one can know except the person experiencing it."

Sitting in his saddle in full sunlight, Orlando had shuddered with a sudden chill. *If I die right now, where will my soul go?*

Before Francesco's exhortation, Orlando had thought little about his life. He was a knight. Killing or maiming his enemies was his duty. Today he had imagined his son, still an infant, someday being knighted as were Messer Montefeltrano and Messer Taddeo. He'd imagined him jousting before a cheering crowd, pictured him embracing nobility, purity, and fearless courage for the love of God.

Until Francesco, he had never considered that his son would be someone else's enemy.

Until Francesco, he had never considered that his enemies were someone else's sons.

Orlando's sword had ended the lives of others' sons.

God, have mercy.

He needed to talk to Francesco.

Why is he taking so long?

Everyone had heard how Francesco had been a wealthy merchant-become-knight and how he had relinquished everything to live in poverty as Jesus did. Francesco had been a holy myth. Today he had become a flesh-and-blood reality. Fra Francesco and that other brother (Fra Leone?) gave God their all. What had Orlando given Him?

Immediately after the exhortation, before his turn to joust, Orlando had approached Francesco, who had stroked the steed's sleek neck as Orlando said, "I would like to speak to you about the salvation of my soul."

"I am glad," Francesco had said. "But this morning, go and honor your friends, since they invited you to the festival, and have dinner with them, and after dinner we will talk together as much as you wish. I will meet you in the banquet hall."

This was the banquet hall.

Why is he taking so long?

Was Orlando on the way to hell? He had money, wealth, power, honor. He ought to give them up as did those two men. Yet he also had a wife and an infant son. He had tenants who relied on him for sustenance and protection. He had elderly parents who lived in his castle and who depended on his care. Did God want him to leave all these others for the salvation of his own soul? To drop upon these innocents the burden of caring for themselves because Orlando wanted to care for himself? Such abandonment seemed wrong.

Orlando's mind imagined the scene Francesco had described. Dying man. Weeping relatives. Priest unable to absolve a man who, even in death, is robbing the poor. Satan crouching in a dark corner, waiting to snatch a soul to hell.

God, what was Orlando clutching that he needed to give to the poor? He gave alms. He could give more. His castle. His lands. He needed those to sustain and protect the many who relied on him.

LA VERNA.

The name of the rocky, wild crag that loomed above his castle popped into his mind.

No. Not La Verna.

SÌ. LA VERNA.

Orlando moaned. He loved La Verna. Not only did he hunt there but, more often, he rode there to be alone, to leave behind his too busy life and to find himself again in the vast, benevolent wilderness of rock, tree, and gully. No one knew La Verna better than he, except perhaps the robbers who inhabited it. Unarmed and carrying no money, he had sought them out on his first trip up the mountain. Sure enough, the robbers had found him, bringing him to their leader, Lupo, with whom he made a pact. "As long as you trouble no one from my estate, you may stay here unmolested." The men had shaken hands, and Orlando had thenceforth been able to visit La Verna without fear.

Lord, I love La Verna! his mind shouted.

PRECISELY. YOU SHALL HAVE NO OTHER GODS BUT ME.

Orlando moaned. Had La Verna become like a god to him? No! He was going there to find God, to listen to the Spirit in the peaceful disarray of that solitary mount. Not La Verna. Any other possession but La Verna.

"Excuse me. I'm sorry that I'm late."

The voice startled Orlando. Turning away from the window, he fell to his knees, a sob catching in his throat. "Brother, I need to speak to you about the salvation of my soul."

"Certainly." Francesco knelt beside Orlando and wrapped his arm around the kneeling man's shoulders.

Francesco prayed.

". . . Send him true peace from heaven . . . ." Of all that Francesco prayed, those words reverberated in Orlando's soul. True peace from heaven—that's what he needed.

"Are you comfortable sitting here while we talk?"

Not since he was a child had Orlando sat on the floor. He needed to do penance. He needed to grow smaller.

"Sì."

So, there on the polished walnut floor, next to a man people thought might be a saint, Orlando babbled out his heart. All he had done. All he should have done. All he should not have done. All his possessions that he could not give up. All that he could relinquish.

"I cannot give you absolution. I'm not a priest."

"But you can give me direction."

"Be not hard on yourself. Blessed is that person who supports his neighbor in his weakness as he himself would want to be supported in a similar situation. It seems to me that you have done much of this."

Orlando thought over the support of those in his care.

"The good that you do comes from God's grace. Have you thought of this?"

Orlando had never considered the good he did as stemming from God's grace. He just did it. He became suddenly aware of how unaware he was. God didn't permeate his life as He did Francesco's. God was out there, somewhere, but Orlando had grown indifferent to Him. Only when he was in a place like La Verna, alone and surrounded by vast beauty, did his mind drift to the Creator.

"How can I make return to God for the good He has given me? I never think of Him."

"Possibly here's a way to begin. You travel much, don't you, through your estate?"

"Sì. Daily."

"The roads. Do they have crosses along them?"

"Sì."

"And your estate and the towns and cities you travel through—do they have churches?"

"Sì."

"Who resides in those churches and chapels?"

"The priests."

Francesco smiled. "Sì. The priests. Who else?"

"People visit and pray. But they don't reside there."

"Someone other than the priest resides there, Count."

"Our Lord?"

"Precisely. Our Lord. And should you see Messer Montefeltrano or Messer Taddeo on the road, what do you do?"

"I hail them and bow."

"Sì. And what do you do when you pass our Lord Jesus Christ?"

"Nothing."

Francesco's pause let the truth sink deep.

"Suppose you hailed our Lord Jesus as you do an earthly lord. Suppose, when you pass a cross or church, you bow. Suppose you pray this prayer with devotion: 'We adore You, Lord Jesus Christ, and we bless You in all Your churches throughout the whole world, because, by Your holy cross, You have redeemed the world.'"

Orlando repeated the words. "This is a beautiful thing to do."

"Remember that our Lord offers Himself to us as His children."

Orlando's head was bowed. "He's given me much, but I've been an ungrateful child."

"It's always the right time to begin. Let us bless our Lord God living and true! Let us always render Him praise, glory, honor, blessing, and every good."

"Amen," Orlando whispered. "Amen."

La Verna.

Orlando raised his head and gazed into the gentle eyes gazing at him. "Fra Francesco, I have a mountain in Tuscany which is very solitary and wild," Orlando's voice trembled with memory, "and perfectly suited for someone who wants to do penance in a place far from people or who wants to live a solitary life. It is called Monte La Verna." He could barely speak, for love for that place was clogging his voice. "If that mountain should please you and your companions, I would gladly give it to you for the salvation of my soul."

Francesco broke into a grin. "Grazie, Count Orlando! We had wanted a place suitable for contemplation. Grazie, my Lord Jesus! When you go home, I will send two of my companions to you, and you can show them that mountain. And if it seems suitable for prayer and penance, I will very gladly accept your charitable offer."

Orlando took Francesco's hand and brought it reverently to his lips. "Grazie."

Grazie for instructing my heart and accepting its gift.

NOTES

According to tradition, this incident took place in the castello (castle and walled city) then called Montefeltro but now named San Leo. It occurred in a second-floor hall in the palace in the castello on May 8, 1213, following a knighting ceremony after which Francesco preached on the theme "So Great Is the Good." Upon hearing this exhortation, Count Orlando orally gave La Verna to Francesco as alms toward the salvation of his soul. See *Fioretti* ("Considerations on the Holy Stigmata: The First Consideration"). A deed from Orlando's family, drawn up in 1274, records this event.

However, historian Luigi Pellegrini, in his book *I luoghi di frate Francesco* (pp. 107–119) states that the document of donation is false. Since Francesco and his friars definitely used La Verna as a hermitage, the author of this book has chosen to use the traditional story and date of the donation.

Francesco's words to the count are taken from his *Admonitions* (section XVIII), his *Second Version of the Letter to the Faithful*, and his *Office of the Passion*. According to *The Legend of the Three Companions* (chapter X), Francesco instructed his brothers to bow and pray when passing a cross or a church and to offer with devotion the prayer he shares with Orlando.

Part Twelve

"Promises Obedience and Reverence to the Lord Pope Innocent and His Successors"

83

Fra Bernardo di Quintavalle

Hermitage of San Bartolomé, Rocaforte, Spain (Spring 1214)

Fra Bernardo sat by a wooden pallet in the hermitage of San Bartolomé in Rocaforte. The hermitage had been built by King Pedro I of Aragon and Navarre for pilgrims on their way to the tomb of Santiago. Bernardo wiped the brow of his second feverish pilgrim. The first pilgrim, a man whom Francesco had left him to care for when they'd stayed here on their way to Compostela, had recovered and left a few days ago to return to his family. Then the second patient arrived—Francesco himself—returning from Compostela, shivering and barely able to walk.

"Did you thank him for bringing me here?" Francesco asked.

"Sì." A noble pilgrim, on his way back to Florence, had transported Francesco from Compostela to here by litter.

"He's a good man. We must pray for him. The Lord didn't heal his legs."

Bernardo dipped a cloth into a basin of water and squeezed it out, then began again to swab Francesco's forehead. "Before he left, he said, 'I've never been grateful for my poor legs, but if I could walk like other pilgrims, I wouldn't have ridden my palfrey.'"

"His palfrey pulled the litter which brought me here."

Bernardo nodded. "'The saint hasn't healed my legs,' your noble friend said, 'but he's healed my heart. He's used my cross to help another person.' He meant you, Francesco."

"I couldn't have gone anywhere without help."

Bernardo wiped Francesco's left arm. He could hear other pilgrims chatting in the corridor.

"Bernardo, at the tomb of Santiago, the Lord spoke to me. He said that the brotherhood must spread throughout the world. Do you think he blocked me from going to Morocco so that He might use me, a sinner, to do this?"

Bernardo slipped up Francesco's right tunic sleeve and began to swab his arm. "It seems so."

"The Lord doesn't want me to preach to the Saracens? To be martyred for love of Him?"

"Not now, it seems."

"Yet we made this journey for that reason."

Bernardo dipped the cloth into the basin and wrung it out again. "Sometimes the Lord has us do things for our reasons because that is how He gets us to do what He wants."

Francesco looked quizzically at him.

"Like when I asked you to dinner. Remember?"

"Sì."

"I was curious about what you were doing. I had no idea that God wanted me to do the same thing."

Francesco's eyes brightened. "So, we're here to spread elsewhere. Grazie, my Lord. Bernardo, you tell the good people here about our good God."

So, he did. The language which Bernardo had learned on his journey to Compostela years earlier now served him well. By spring, Francesco, accompanied by a new brother from Navarre, was strong enough to return to Assisi. Bernardo stayed behind to continue the Spanish mission.

NOTES

The opening quotation for Part Twelve is from the prologue of Francis' *Earlier Rule.*

1C (first book, chapter XX) relates Francesco and Bernardo's pilgrimage to Saint James of Compostela, sometime in late 1213. They intended to travel from Spain to Muslim lands in order to preach there. Later sources (*Fioretti*, chapter 4; 24Gen, section 38) state that, in Rocaforte, Spain, Francesco left Bernardo caring for an ill man. In Compostela, after receiving a message from God about expanding the brotherhood, Francesco fell ill (3C, chapter V) and had to return to Assisi. The sources mentioned above also state that he traveled to Spain with Bernardo and a few brothers and that he opened houses in Spain before returning to Assisi.

Francesco would have had to leave someone in charge of each house who already understood the way of life. Those would have been the other unnamed brothers who accompanied him and Bernardo.

In 1217, the brothers created the office of provincial minister, and it seems that Bernardo was named provincial minister of Spain (author's correspondence with Franciscan scholar Jean-François Godet-Calogeras, October 2014). 24Gen (section 38) mentions that Bernardo "remained in that place, at the command of Francis, in order to serve some poor and sick persons." He was also likely overseeing the new foundations in Spain. When the office of provincial minister was established in 1217, Bernardo was then officially given the title for a function that he was already fulfilling.

This chapter postulates that Francesco returned to Italy when he had a new Spanish brother with whom to travel. The Spanish brother could then return to Spain, having experienced how the brothers lived in the Italian foundations.

84

Dom Impuro

Priest's House, Pavia (Summer 1214)

Half asleep, Dom Impuro turned to the right and groped for Bina. She must have awakened, put out his breakfast, and left. Bina was lively in the night, but at dawn she scurried off like a mole. He forced his eyes open and groaned. Light was pouring through the shutters. He must have missed leading Matins. Again. No matter. Penitents often prayed without him. If Primerio, who could read, was absent, the others would pray their twelve Our Fathers and Hail Marys. They really didn't need Impuro.

Impuro pushed back the sheets, untied his sleeping cap, and ran his hands across his balding scalp. Ugh! The day was already warm. He pulled on his breeches and tunic, then breakfasted on the cheese and wine Bina had set on the table. Pretty, diminutive Bina. The fifteen-year-old had fallen into her mother's occupation as whore until Impuro had persuaded her to become his concubine. He could never persuade her mother. He smiled wryly. Bina might be his daughter, just as the child in Bina's swelling belly might be his. Might be. He couldn't be sure.

Impuro pulled on his auburn cap and ventured outdoors into the languid morning. San Teodoro was just up the street. Better make an appearance. He hurried toward the church, ignoring the ugly stare of the Manichean heretic fisherman Otello who was lugging a basket of fish from the river.

Too late. The penitents were exiting. Pious folks. Foolish to spend so much time in prayer. But good. They supported the church and him.

Hmm. Two unfamiliar, gray-robed clerics filed out with them. Impuro nodded politely. The clerics bowed, reached for his hands, and kissed them.

"Look, good men!" Otello's challenging voice was addressing the newcomers, "Should we believe what a priest says and reverence the sacraments he administers," he looked Impuro straight in the face, "when he maintains a concubine and his hands are polluted from sins of the flesh?"

Before Impuro could retort, the shorter cleric fell to his knees before him and took his hands into his own. "I do not know whether these hands are such as this man says they are," he spoke to the gaping penitents. "But even if they are, I know that they can in no way lessen the power and efficacy of the sacraments of God. These hands remain the means through which many of God's benefits and graces flow to the people. That is why I kiss them," and he kissed them again, "out of respect for the things they administer and out of reverence for Him by Whose authority they do so."

The cleric stood, nodded to Impuro, then turned to the crowd. He began singing a melody as lilting as a love song, his fingers strumming an imaginary lute, dancing reverently around the clustered church-goers. "Let everyone be struck with fear, let the whole world tremble, and let the heavens exult when Christ, the Son of the living God, is present on the altar in the hands of a priest!" As the song drifted across the street, a crowd gathered like curious children flocking to a minstrel.

"O wonderful loftiness and stupendous dignity!" the cleric sang. "O sublime humility! O humble sublimity! The Lord of the universe, God and the Son of God, so humbles Himself that for our salvation He hides Himself under an ordinary piece of bread!" The man's resonant voice throbbed with reverence. "Brothers, sisters, look at the humility of God, and pour out your hearts before Him! Humble yourselves that you may be exalted by Him! Hold back nothing for yourselves, that He Who gives Himself totally to you may receive you totally!" To the hushed crowd, he again sang, "Hold back nothing for yourselves, that He Who gives Himself totally to you may receive you totally!"

Impuro was as mesmerized as everyone else. Even Otello was struck dumb. The cleric spun around, firmly took Impuro's arm, and danced with him away from the crowd and around a corner to an empty section of street. With a pleading look, the cleric softly implored as he continued to walk, "My priest brother, remember what is written in the law of Moses: whoever committed a transgression against even externals died without mercy by a decree of God. How much greater and more severe will be the punishment of the one who tramples on the Son of God, and who treats the Bread of the Covenant in which he was sanctified as unclean, and who insults the Spirit of grace?"

Impuro was being led along, turning another corner and leaving the crowd on the church steps. They were listening to the other cleric, whose preaching was fading with distance. However, the voice at his shoulder was clear. "For a person looks down upon, defiles, and tramples the Lamb of God," the cleric said, smashing a clump of horse dung with his bare foot, "when, as the Apostle says, not distinguishing and discerning the holy bread of Christ from other foods or actions, he either unworthily or, even if he is worthy, eats It in vain and unworthily, since the Lord says through the prophet: the person is cursed who does the work of the Lord deceitfully. He will, in truth, condemn priests who do not wish to take this to heart, saying: 'I will curse your blessings.'"

"'I will curse your blessings!'" The quote from the prophet Malachi caught Impuro off guard. How did this simple-minded cleric know this obscure verse?

The cleric looked Impuro squarely in the eye as Otello had done. "See your dignity, my priest brother, and be holy because He is holy. As the Lord has honored you above all others because of this ministry, for your part love, revere, and honor Him above all others. It is a great misery and a miserable weakness that when you have Him present in this way, you are concerned with anything else in the whole world!"

The cleric knelt at Impuro's feet and said softly, "I cannot absolve you of your sins, but I ask you to absolve me of mine. Would you hear my confession?"

Impuro was flustered, confused. When had he last heard anyone's confession? Did he remember how to absolve?

Right there at his feet, the cleric, with his head bowed, began to confess. Impatience. Anger. Lack of faith. Lustful feelings. Gluttony. Greed. Vanity. Envy. Indifference. Sloth. Avarice. The cleric had temptations toward these things and sometimes fell, but, when he did, he had submitted himself to unique penances. Because he felt possessive toward a pelt that covered him when he slept, he cast it into a fire. Because, on an abstinence day, he had followed doctor's orders by eating chicken to help cure a painful stomach ailment, he had a brother lead him through the streets with a rope about his neck, announcing to everyone, "See the hypocrite! Fra Francesco ate chicken on an abstinence day!" When, while crossing the Alps, he had been greatly troubled by longing for a wife and family, he had pulled off his tunic, rolled in snow, and made himself a snow wife and children, ordering himself to find employment to feed and clothe them.

Before Francesco had finished his confession, Impuro's knees seemed to soften, and he had to fight the compulsion to kneel as well. This poor brother had performed great penances for minor sins. Impuro had sinned greatly without a second thought. Even as he, his heart pounding, absolved the cleric, Impuro faced a choice: either change his life and return wholeheartedly to his faith, or continue living as he was and admit he was living as if God did not exist.

Did God exist? Where did creation come from? The trees, the sky, the earth, Bina, himself. Maybe creation always existed, and the book of Genesis was as nonsensical as God becoming a human being and that human being becoming present in the form of bread consecrated through Impuro's sinful hands. Being a priest was his occupation. He could still administer the sacraments even though he no longer believed in them.

NOTES

Noted medieval preacher Stephen of Bourbon (*Early Documents II*, pp. 787–788) used in a sermon aid the example of Francesco reverencing an unnamed, impure priest in Lombardy. Neither the city nor date is given. The meeting of the priest, heretic, and Francesco, including Francesco's words to the people, follows Stephen's narration. Francesco's song about the Eucharist and his words spoken privately to Impuro are taken from Francesco's *Letter to the Entire Order*.

The tonsures cause Impuro to clump Francesco and his fellow friars into the Church category of clerics. Impuro, who rejects repentance as an ordained priest, would be incredulous that laity (the brothers were laity at this time) were voluntarily embracing a stricter lifestyle than ordained clergy.

85

Fra Masseo di Marignano

Rome (November 14, 1215)

Tall and swarthy, with a head of thick, black hair, Fra Masseo di Marignano could have passed for an alluring gypsy if he were wearing colorful breeches and a short vest. Nevertheless, despite his tonsure and tattered tunic, he felt like a gypsy walking through Rome while leaving Francesco with the lepers at San Lazzaro al Trionfale. Tonight, they'd lodge there. Tomorrow, they'd attend the Council at the Lateran. Then, they'd return to Assisi to deliver the Council's decisions to the brothers and to Madonna Chiara and her sisters.

Ahead loomed the Colosseum. He'd heard of this place. He could almost hear spectators cheering as early martyrs died, mauled by leopards or gored by bulls.

Lord, have mercy on the souls of those who died here, and on their killers and spectators, and on those who devised these torments.

Reverently Masseo stroked the curved wall of the massive ruin. How proud he'd been when he first joined Francesco! How holy Masseo had thought he'd become! The Christians who died here were holy. Not Masseo. Why, Francesco had assigned him to beg and haul firewood and rocks while the other brothers prayed! Only when some of them offered to relieve Masseo of his burden could he sit with Jesus. But by then he'd learned that holiness is fostered not in doing what one wants, but in doing one's duty with love and patience, for God's glory. Wasn't that what the martyrs did?

Masseo walked on, wandering where the Spirit took him. Francesco had taught him that lesson, too, when they'd been on a preaching mission and reached a triple fork in the road. "Spin around like a playing child, and don't stop until I tell you," Francesco had ordered. Feeling like a simpleton, enduring the stares of other travelers, Masseo had twirled until he was about to collapse from dizziness and Francesco commanded, "Stop!" He was facing the road to Siena, so to Siena they had gone.

Masseo was walking among towering monuments to war victories. That time they had arrived in Siena, two men had just been killed during a skirmish. When Francesco's preaching restored harmony, the grateful bishop offered them lodging for the night. But the next morning, before the bishop could honor them, Francesco and Masseo had slipped out of his house and left. Masseo had thought that rude until he realized that the way to honor peace was not with accolades or monuments but with living in harmony.

Lord, bring peace to all those warring with one another, in this city, and elsewhere.

Masseo came upon what appeared to be a ruined temple. Was this to a pagan god or to a ruler who claimed to be a god?

Lord, let us not make gods of ourselves but give You lordship of our lives.

When Masseo returned to the lepers, he paused at the door to ponder the city behind him. Centuries ago, the Romans had not known Christ.

Lord, have mercy on those who still don't know You.

NOTES

Fra Masseo was from Marignano, a town in the Assisi contrada (Fortini, p. 324, footnote). His mortal remains, buried in the Basilica di San Francesco in Assisi, indicate that he was tall and robust. 24Gen (sections 119–120) attests to his prayerful spirit.

The histories don't name the brother who would have accompanied Francesco to Rome in 1215, nor do they mention where Francesco stayed. The incidents that Masseo reflects on during his prayer pilgrimage are found in *The Life of Brother Masseo* (24Gen). Section numbers are as follows: Francesco assigning him work while the other brothers prayed (section 115), Masseo twirling (section 116), and civil strife in Siena (sections 116–117).

86

Messer Elia di Bonbarone

Assisi (Late December 1215)

Messer Elia di Bonbarone was staring into the flames dancing in the night darkness of his home's warming room. The servants had retired to bed. He was alone.

How the flames of time had consumed his life! His parents, dead in their elder years. His wife, dead from an untreatable wasting disease that had taken her life before Guiduccio married. Between Elia's involvement in city politics and his mattress business, life went on, but life had lost its zest.

Last week he had happened to meet Francesco, so he'd invited him home to talk. Francesco's life was fuller than full. He'd been to the Council at the Lateran, where the pope requested that religious orders gather their members together yearly, so he was planning how to conform to this request. He also wanted to stipulate that the brothers must be Catholics, and must confess their sins and receive the Body and Blood of Christ with great humility and respect.

While Elia had been listening to Francesco, a thought had broken in.

JOIN HIM. IT'S TIME.

He gazed at the fire again. His well-planned life had burned to ashes.

I AM THE RESURRECTION AND THE LIFE. I MAKE ALL THINGS NEW.

NOTES

Elia seems to have joined Francesco sometime after Francesco's visit to the pope.

87

Madonna Jacopa dei Settesoli

Frangipani House, Rome (August 31, 1216)

Madonna Jacopa dei Settesoli was sitting on the lush grass in her garden. A sheep, which Francesco had given her as a lamb, was asleep with its head on her thigh. Her belly was big with another child and her heart was just as swollen with grief. Absently she watched Giovanni cavorting as he tried to catch butterflies, dragonflies, and frogs. If he happened to be successful, which was rare, he would race to her with his prey, waiting for her to ooh and ahh over it before releasing it. Butterflies and frogs would be the highlight of her day, not attending the crowning of Pope Onorio. Her household had gone to the solemnities. She would have gone, too—with Graziano.

But Graziano was dead. Dead these past months, dying even before Pope Innocenzo had died in July. Sudden deaths, both: Innocenzo in Perugia on his way to arbitrate a dispute between Pisa and Genoa; Graziano here in Rome, in one of those familial political vendettas. Innocenzo had died from something bursting within his body. Graziano had been murdered. Power, no matter how much one held, was powerless over death.

She stroked her stomach where her baby was arching and kicking. Life was power. Death was power only in that it ushered in eternal life for those who loved the God of Life. She prayed that Graziano and Innocenzo were enjoying that life now. She smiled to think of them getting along in heaven when, in this life, the Frangipani family and the papacy had often been at odds.

Now the years stretched out before her, filled with everything she wanted but Graziano. Once she had thought of relinquishing everything to follow God, but Francesco had told her "no." He knew her better than she knew herself, she realized. God had removed one joy from her life, leaving her the rest. Losing that one had thrown her into a dark pit. How would she ever climb out?

The sheep stirred against her thigh, and she stroked its head. While a lamb, the sheep had been on its way to slaughter when Francesco intercepted the farmer and offered his mantle in exchange. Lambs reminded him of the innocent Lamb of God, he said. He'd carried the lamb to their palazzo and asked Graziano if he would care for it. Graziano had burst out laughing. His family kept a tame leopard at home. He'd be a man of peace and keep a lamb. Jacopa had woven a length of cloth from its spun wool and made Graziano an undyed tunic. The first time he wore it, he had strutted around her like an emperor to make her laugh. Now, along with more undyed cloth she'd spun from the lamb's wool, Graziano's tunic was folded alongside her wedding veil in a chest in their bedroom.

Giovanni bounded toward her with something clutched in his hand.

He opened his chubby fingers and a small toad blinked in the light, its eyes bright and unafraid. She reached out a finger to stroke it, and it leaped away, landing on the sheep's shoulder. The sheep flicked her shoulder, and the toad hopped down into the grass and then away without a backward glance.

"I'm going to find another!" Giovanni said, running off.

Jacopa looked after the toad, but it had disappeared. Just because she couldn't see it didn't mean that it wasn't alive. She stroked her stomach again. She couldn't see this baby, but he or she was surely here. She couldn't see God, but He was surely here in all His creation. She couldn't see Graziano, but she could feel his presence in her heart. Death didn't mean someone's destruction. It meant only that they were hidden by the impenetrable grass of eternity.

NOTES

Jacopa's husband Graziano died sometime before 1217, apparently in a familial skirmish. History doesn't record if their second child was born before or after his death. Pope Innocent III died on July 16, 1216, and Pope Honorius III was elected two days later, with his crowning in Rome on August 31.

A local tradition in Rome states that Francesco gave Jacopa a lamb that he redeemed from slaughter (*Early Documents II*; LMj, chapter 8), and that she made his burial tunic from its wool. Fortini (pp. 528–529) states that at one time the Frangipani family kept a leopard that roamed through their palace as a "pet."

Part Thirteen

"Who Desires by Divine Inspiration to Go Among the Saracens and Other Nonbelievers"

88

Fra Elia di Bonbarone

Porziuncula (May 10, 1217)

Elia and Francesco were strolling through the woods near the Porziuncula. After today, would they ever see each other again?

The Pentecost Chapter of May 5 was over. Elia had calculated the number of brothers who attended. Perhaps a thousand. Imagine!

An undercurrent wanted to soften their way of life, reduce the labor to focus on preaching. Francesco had refused. Working with the people, the brothers preached by example, which often was more effective than words. The brothers must always work.

The brothers were commissioned to evangelize the world, so they had divided it into eleven provinces each with a brother, its custos, in charge, and other brothers to accompany him. Bernardo di Quintavalle was going to Spain to become its custos. Giovanni della Penna and sixty brothers to Germany. Francesco with Pacifico and Silvestro, to France. Elia to Syria. They were going with only the clothing they wore and the small books, shared among them, to pray the Divine Office. Most didn't know their destination's language or culture. They knew only a smattering of Latin and their faith. That, Francesco believed, would be enough.

After Sext today, Elia would be leaving with the brothers accompanying him. He and Francesco had stolen away from the others for this brief walk. They'd reminisced about their past together and discussed how God was leading them to a promising future. They'd walked perhaps an hour, and now the Porziuncula was again in sight. Francesco knelt on the soft spring earth. Elia knelt beside him.

"In farewell, brother, let's pray together the prayer at the end of the Praises." Elia knew it well. Francesco had written the Praises to be prayed before every hour of the Divine Office.

The brothers bowed their heads and prayed together. "All powerful, most holy, most high, supreme God: all good, supreme good, totally good, You Who alone are good, may we give You all praise, all glory, all thanks, all honor, all blessing, and all good. So be it! So be it! Amen."

NOTES

The opening quotation of Part Thirteen is from Francis' *The Early Rule (Regula non bullata)*, chapter XVI, 3.

The French edition of *Early Documents* (chronology for 1217) estimates that 1,000 brothers attended the Pentecost chapter. Details of this chapter and assignment of the brothers are in:

— General Information: AP (chapter XI)
— Giovanni della Penna and the German Mission: 13CC (*Chronicle of Jordan of Giano*, section 5)
— Bernardo and the Spanish Mission: author's correspondence with the Franciscan scholar Jean-François Godet-Calogeras, October 2014
— Francesco, Silvestro, Pacifico and the French Mission: AC (section 108)
— Elia and the Syrian Mission: 13CC (*Chronicle of Jordan of Giano*, section 9).

We have no historical record of a farewell between Francesco and Elia, although it likely happened. Francesco's prayer concludes *The Praises to Be Said at All Hours.*

89

Dom Silvestro

Arezzo (Summer 1217)

Dom Silvestro stood by the main city gate of Arezzo and wondered how Francesco thought that he, an old priest, had enough faith to cast demons out of the city.

Francesco, Pacifico, and he had arrived outside Arezzo intending to spend the night at a hospice, but sleep was impossible. Day and night, the streets clamored with beating hooves, shouts, threats, screams. Two rival factions had been warring for months. The hospice owner shrugged when asked what anyone was doing to stop the violence.

"Demons have taken over this city," Francesco noted. "They are inciting the people to destroy Arezzo with fire and war. Go in front of the city gate, and in a loud voice command all the devils to leave this city."

Refuse? He had pledged Francesco his obedience. So here he was. Through the arch of the city's main gate drifted the acrid smell of burning timber. He could hear a distant wailing.

Silvestro prayed for wisdom and the right words.

NAME THEM.

Name them?

"In the name of Jesus, I command you, demon of anger, to come out of this city and never more enter it," he called out. A well-dressed lord and his lady, riding into the city, looked quizzically at him.

"In the name of Jesus, I command you, demon of vengeance, to come out of this city and never more enter it!"

A knight on horseback paused.

"Demon of pride!"

"Demon of violence!"

"Rape!"

"Theft!"

"Avarice!"

"Lust!"

"Self-interest!"

As he cast each demon out, another thought suggested itself.

"Demon of self-indulgence . . . indifference . . . hatred!"

A crowd had gathered around him, listening, watching.

"Demon of greed . . . gluttony . . . murder . . . profane speech . . . envy . . . !"

He went on, naming the demons until he could think of no more. Then he called out to the crowd.

"The demons will return if you permit them entry. Resist them, and they will take flight. Give your souls to Jesus Christ and do whatever He tells you. Then peace will come to your city."

NOTES

AC (section 108) records this incident and Francesco's words to Silvestro. How Silvestro cast out the demons is speculation by the author of this book.

90

Cardinal Ugolino dei Conti di Segni

Bishop's Residence, Florence (Summer 1217)

Cardinal Ugolino dei Conti di Segni was sitting near a window in a second-floor bedroom in the Bishop's Residence in Florence. Absentmindedly, he stroked his square-trimmed, silvery beard, which concealed his cheeks, gaunt from fasting. Both the beard and his flowing scarlet robe helped keep hidden the voluntary penances that he was offering as bodily prayers for the Church and its people.

He gazed down into the bustle of the street. How might he, as papal legate to these regions, most effectively promote the pope's crusade? Florence was an enormous hub of trade, finance, and wealth. Perhaps he'd best exhort its citizens to finance the crusade. He'd urge other, more military cities to send knights. He could base his exhortation on Jesus' words in the Gospel of Matthew: "You cannot serve both God and money."

A knock at the door scrambled his thoughts.

"Messer Cardinal," a servant bowed, "Messer Bishop requests your presence, if you have a moment."

As lodger and guest in the bishop's palace, Ugo would make a moment.

The servant led him to the bishop's moderately sized but well-stocked library. Casually dressed in a red tunic and zuchetto, the bishop was seated at a table across from a penitent cleric who was wearing an excessively patched gray tunic. Both stood and bowed as Ugo entered. In a habitual gesture, Ugo extended his right hand, and both dutifully kissed it.

"Cardinal," the bishop said, "have you met Deacon Francesco di Assisi? He has preached before Lord Pope, who has approved his new religio."

No, he had never met him or heard him preach. But when Ugo returned to Rome after his frequent journeys on papal business, other cardinals had much to say about this controversial man who claimed to live in total reliance on God. Was he genuine? A charlatan? Lunatic?

Curious, Ugo began to question the small, rather unattractive deacon until he became convinced of the man's sincerity.

"What brings you to Florence?" Ugo asked.

"We've had our chapter gathering and the brothers have been sent on mission. Some to Germany. Some to Spain. Fra Pacifico and I to France. Our bishop has asked us to visit every bishop whose territory we pass through, explain our mission, and seek his permission."

Ugo glanced at the bishop.

"He's obtained my permission to preach here."

Ugo nodded. "You're going to France?"

"Sì."

"Do you know the dangers of your going?"

"I'm not afraid of danger. May I willingly die for my God!"

"I don't mean danger for you, Brother. I mean for your religio."

"Pope Onorio approves of it. He has granted an indulgence to all who pray at our house in Assisi, the Porziuncula," the brother answered with great confidence.

"Sì." Ugo nodded. "The indulgence is similar to the Crusade indulgence. Many cardinals fear that it will dissuade people from going on Crusade."

"Do you think so?"

"No. It's a beautiful indulgence for women and children, for those too old, too young, or too frail to fight. But how I feel doesn't matter." Ugo paused while bringing the discussion back on track. "Brother, I do not want you to go beyond the mountains, because there are many prelates and others in the Roman Curia who would willingly block the religio's interests. The other cardinals and I, who love your religio, can protect and help it more willingly if you stay within the confines of this region."

Ugo caught the dismay and surprise on Francesco's expressive face.

"We're only trying to follow the footsteps of our Lord Jesus Christ."

"I understand. Cardinal Giovanni di San Paolo thoroughly explained your way of life to me. We had many conversations about it before he died."

"Messer Cardinal, it is a great shame to me, if I remain in these regions when I send my brothers to regions that are remote and far away."

"Do they know the languages?"

"No. But the Lord will help them."

"How can they beg or find shelter, or protect themselves from being deemed heretics, if they don't speak the language? Why did you send your brothers so far away to die of hunger, and to so many other trials?"

"Messer Cardinal, do you think or believe that the Lord sent the brothers only for these regions? But I tell you in truth that the Lord chose and sent the brothers for the benefit and salvation of the souls of all people in the whole world, and they should be received not only in the land of believers, but also in that of nonbelievers. As long as they observe what they have promised, the Lord will minister to them in the lands of nonbelievers as well as in the countries of believers."

Ugo sighed.

"Brother, you have spoken the truth. But so have I. For the sake of your brothers, you must remain in these regions where the other cardinals and I can protect you. I promise you my help and offer you my assistance should you have any need to speak with me."

Francesco's face was a mixture of joy and disappointment. "Grazie, Messer Cardinal. At your request, I will send Fra Pacifico and some other brothers to France while I remain behind. Grazie for your offer of help."

"You know," the bishop said, "God has a way of working out His Will. You, Cardinal, didn't expect to be His instrument in this way, and you, Brother, didn't expect to be foiled in your mission. Yet God sees the complete picture. Today He has used my house to facilitate His Will."

NOTES

As Francesco traveled through Florence on his way to France, he called on the bishop of each province through which he passed. Cardinal Ugolino was in Florence to preach the crusade and met Francesco, possibly through the bishop. AC (section 108) records the conversation between Francesco and Ugolino reproduced in this chapter.

The exhortation in the Gospel of Matthew that Cardinal Ugolino thinks about is from Matthew 6:24.

91

Ysidro

Porziuncola (Late May 1218)

Near this little church in the forest, the penitent Ysidro balanced his bulky body on a tree stump seat, just a bit too narrow for his broad behind. Nearby, Pablo, a huge, block-shaped priest whom only a fool would threaten, was precariously balanced on a log. Seated on the grass before them, the diminutive founder of the Poor Minors religio was explaining its way of life.

Both penitent and priest were on a pilgrimage from Navarre, Spain, to Rome. But they'd made a side trip to Assisi to meet Fra Francesco, having heard much about him from the brothers of his religio who were living at San Bartolomé. The brothers had received Pablo's permission to repair the roof of his church and to address the congregation.

"Are the brothers well?" Francesco asked.

"Sì. I sometimes take food to San Bartolomé for the pilgrims," Ysidro said. "When it is the brothers' turn to be servers instead of hermits, they take care of the pilgrims well."

"Servers?"

Surely their founder knew about servers. "They take turns living alone and waiting on one another."

Francesco seemed intrigued. "How do they do this?"

He didn't know? "Your brothers in our country stay in a poor hermitage. They have set up the following way of life for themselves: half of them take care of the household chores and half remain free for contemplation. In this manner each week the active half moves to the contemplative, and those contemplating return from repose to the toils of labor."

Francesco was attentive, so Ysidro went on to explain more. Once, when the brothers rang for their evening meal, one of the contemplating brothers did not come. When the other brothers went to his cell to call him, they found him facedown on the ground, deep in prayer, his arms stretched out in the shape of a cross, with candelabra burning at his head and feet. Reverently they had closed the door and gone to their meal. The brother arrived later and confessed his fault for being late.

"That's the kind of thing that happens in our country," Ysidro boasted.

Pablo grinned and nodded.

"Grazie for sharing that," Francesco said. Then he raised his gaze heavenward. "I give you thanks, Sanctifier and Guide of the poor, you who have gladdened me with that report about our brothers! Bless these brothers, I beg you, with a most generous blessing, and sanctify with a special gift all those who make their profession fragrant through good example!"

NOTES

2C (second book, chapter CXXXV) records the undated incident of an unnamed Spanish cleric telling Francesco how the brothers lived in an unnamed Spanish hermitage. This chapter quotes the cleric's words. At this time, the brothers were established at the hermitage of San Bartolomé. Historians speculate that this encounter inspired Francesco's *Rule for Hermitages*, composed between 1217 and 1221 (*Early Documents I*, pp. 61–62).

92

Fra Gregorio di Napoli

Porziuncula (May 26, 1219)

After the altar servers and Fra Francesco, the priest Fra Gregorio di Napoli was last in the procession. He had just offered the early morning Mass on a raised platform erected by Assisi men in a clearing near the Porziuncula. He removed his vestments, smoothed his gray tunic, and made his way through the brothers seated on the forest floor for this huge Pentecost gathering. He sat to the far right of the platform where his towering bulk would not block the view of brothers behind him, but where he could see and hear Francesco and anyone else who spoke.

Having joined the brotherhood three years ago while a student at the University of Bologna, Gregorio was trained in canon law. While younger than many of the brothers, he was more educated than most. As he settled into the out-of-the-way spot, he remembered Francesco's striking words about priests. *I do not want to consider any sin in them, because I discern the Son of God in them and they are my lords. And we must honor all theologians and those who minister the most holy divine words and respect them as those who minister to us spirit and life.*

Other brothers would have heard these or similar words from Francesco. They had seen Gregorio offering Mass. *Lord, I am nothing without You*, he reminded himself. How had Francesco put it? *By our own fault, we are disgusting, miserable, and opposed to good, yet prompt and inclined to evil, for, as the Lord says in the Gospel: "From the heart proceed and come evil thoughts, adultery, fornication, murder, theft, greed, malice, deceit, licentiousness, envy, false witness, blasphemy, foolishness. All these evils come from within, from a person's heart, and these are what defile a person."*

Lord, I am nothing without You, Gregorio reminded himself again, as if forcing himself to believe it. For some reason, he had been chosen to offer the Mass that opened this gathering. The old enemy, pride, welled up in his soul, and he tried to squash it flat as a beetle. Closing his eyes, he prayed against his sin.

The quiet chatter among the brothers ceased.

"My brothers, let us begin."

Francesco stood on the platform, his voice exultant and strong. "Let every creature in heaven, on earth, in the sea and in the depths, give praise, glory, honor and blessing to Him Who suffered so much, Who has given and will give in the future every good, for He is our power and strength, Who alone is good, Who alone is almighty, Who alone is omnipotent, wonderful, glorious, and Who alone is holy, worthy of praise and blessing through endless ages. Amen."

Was it a thousand voices? Two thousand? Three thousand? The forest resounded with "Amen!"

The meeting began. Brief reports from the custodes of the regions. Reports on the missions. Most missions had had some success, unlike the one to Germany. There, the custode reported, the brothers, not knowing the language, had been mistaken for heretics, robbed of their clothing, beaten, and almost killed. Understandably, they didn't want to return to Germany.

Francesco commended their bravery and zeal. "The Lord says in the Gospel: 'Whoever does not renounce all that he possesses cannot be my disciple'; and 'Whoever wishes to save his life must lose it.' This precept you, my brothers, have followed." He paused. "However, one need not go on mission to fulfill this precept." Francesco again paused. "That person who offers himself totally to obedience in the hands of his prelate leaves all that he possesses and loses his body." He looked from one friar to the other across the vast audience. "And whatever he does and says which he knows is not contrary to his prelate's will is true obedience, provided that what he does is good."

That prompted a question. Gregorio waved his hand and caught Francesco's attention. Francesco nodded to him.

"What if he can do some things better than the prelate?" Gregorio asked.

Francesco gazed out over the brothers. "And should a subject see that some things might be better and more useful for his soul than what a prelate commands, let him willingly offer such things to God as a sacrifice; and, instead, let him earnestly strive to fulfill the prelate's wishes."

Did Gregorio agree with that? In his nearly thirty years of life, he had, from time to time, known better than his superiors what ought to be done.

As if reading Gregorio's thoughts, Francesco continued, "For doing what a prelate wishes is loving obedience because it pleases God and neighbor."

That could not always be right. Gregorio waved his hand again. Francesco turned to him.

"What if what the prelate wishes is morally wrong?"

His voice strong, Francesco called out, "If the prelate, however, commands something contrary to his conscience, even though he may not obey him, let him not, however, abandon him. And if he then suffers persecution from others, let him love them all the more for the sake of God. For whoever chooses to suffer persecution rather than wish to be separated from his brothers truly remains in perfect obedience because he lays down his life for his brothers."

Was he saying that, while a brother should not do what opposes his conscience, he should, nevertheless, remain with the religio, even if doing so meant persecution from the prelate whom he could not obey? Was this prudent?

"In fact, there are many religious who, under the pretext of seeing things better than those which the prelate commands, look back, and return to the vomit of their own will. These people are murderers and, because of their bad example, cause many to lose their souls."

Was Francesco saying that laying down one's life extended even to being persecuted because one couldn't, in good conscience, follow orders? Imagine a brother possessing such great poverty of spirit that he'd remain in the religio and accept unjust punishment! Francesco was asking that? For the sake of others' faith? Admittedly, leaving would cause people to question not only the religio, but also faith: "Are religious people as holy as they appear? Was the religio really God's idea? Does God exist?"

People! Who could understand them? Why question a Church-approved religio because of one person's actions? Shouldn't people trust the judgment of the Church, which our Lord Jesus Christ had founded and to which He promised His guidance?

Gregorio had studied the Church and its teachings. He was a priest. He put his future into God's hands.

This year's missions were organizing. Spain. France. Hungary. Morocco. Brothers volunteered for the missions, came forward, and stood near that mission's custode. The custodes selected some and sent the others back to their places. Gregorio remained seated. He didn't feel the Spirit prompting him to volunteer. Before assignments to the loci of the brothers had begun, Francesco had announced that, since he would be going to Egypt, to the Crusade, two vicars would take his place. He'd pointed to one baby-faced brother sitting near Gregorio.

"Brother . . ."

"Matteo di Narni," the youth said.

"Fra Matteo, you'll stay here at the Porziuncula and receive into the brotherhood any new brothers who come to you."

Matteo stammered. "Brother, I'm new myself."

"Precisely. Therefore, you'll understand the zeal of those who come to you because their zeal is still yours."

Gregorio looked incredulously at Matteo.

"Sì. I accept."

"Fra Matteo, receive each who comes with kindness, encourage him and diligently explain the tenor of our life to him. When this has been done, let him, if he wishes and is capable of doing so spiritually without any difficulty, sell all his belongings and be conscientious in giving everything to the poor." Matteo was nodding. "But you, brother, be careful not to interfere in any way in his temporal affairs, nor to accept money. When he returns, having done this, clothe him as a brother in our way of life."

"Sì, Fra Francesco." The youth's voice was low and humbled.

"And you, Fra . . ."

Was Francesco looking at Gregorio?

"Fra . . . ?"

"Gregorio di Napoli."

"Fra Gregorio, you'll travel from locus to locus to offer Mass for the brothers. If the brothers share with you any difficulties, you'll notify their custode."

Gregorio felt unnerved. He would replace Francesco in visiting the loci? Francesco must know that he had a quick mind and thorough education.

"Grazie," he said. "I accept."

As the assignments of the brothers to the loci began, Gregorio's brain was running through the duties that he and this Matteo would have to assume. Vicars replacing Francesco. He felt heady with power and honor.

NOTES

While the histories record no specifics of the order of Masses, exhortations, and meetings at the friars' gatherings, this chapter recreates what likely happened at the 1219 Pentecost gathering of the brothers (see 13CC, "Chronicle of Jordan of Giano," sections 5, 9–11). Francesco's words about priests and theologians are from his *Testament*. His words about our inclination to evil are from the *Earlier Rule* (chapter XXII), and he quotes from chapter 15 of the Gospel of Matthew. His prayer at the beginning of the gathering is found in his *Later Admonition and Exhortation to the Brothers and Sisters of Penance (Second Version of the Letter to the Faithful).*

Francesco's words on obedience are in his *Admonitions* (section III). At the time, the term "prelate" referred not only to a bishop but to any religious superior; here it refers mainly to one's superior in the religio.

Francesco's instructions on how to accept new brothers are found in chapter II of the *Earlier Rule.*

The Scriptures Francesco quotes are from Luke 14:33 and Matthew 16:25.

The histories offer no background on Fra Matteo di Narni.

From his later escapades in the histories, Fra Gregorio di Napoli seems to have been a capable and educated priest with a streak of self-will. The histories do not indicate why Francesco selected these two men.

93

Cardinal Pelagius

Crusader Camp, Damietta, Egypt (September 8, 1219)

His pinched, gaunt face looking less severe than usual, Cardinal Pelagius stood in the burning sun. He shaded his eyes as he watched the two gray-robed monks-without-a-monastery disappear into the distance across the sand. He hoped they'd never return. Already he could feel peace descending. He could deal with the other half-dozen-or-so docile monks left behind. But those two! Especially one. That Francesco. Didn't he understand the word "no"?

What had he done to deserve these wolves hidden in sheep's clothing, who'd arrived in the summer? Oh, how peaceable and kind these monks had seemed! They would do as Pelagius asked, meekly and humbly like Jesus. They would inspire and exhort the knights to give up gaming, cursing, and whoring. God knows, he thought, this camp could use more order and morality.

They had, indeed, done that. The knights, bored with waiting to attack Damietta, were less apt to pull out the dice or pull in a woman while monks strolled among them.

But then that Francesco had begun to hound him to make peace. Peace? With the heathen Sultan Malik al-Kamil? The only peace with him would come from extermination.

The two gray-robed specks disappeared against the desert sands.

Good riddance.

Pelagius turned toward his tent, awaiting the arrival of spies whom he had sent to gauge the progress of the siege. The people in Damietta must be feeling anxious. Pelagius had the city surrounded. No one could leave for supplies. He and his troops, on the other hand, could receive supplies by boat. They could camp here for years. It would not take years for Damietta to starve.

He sat at a table in his tent and groaned. This should have ended two weeks ago. Whatever had happened on August 29? Maybe he had selected an ominous day to assault Damietta. The feast of the beheading of John the Baptist. Pelagius had asked the Baptist to bless their attack, picturing the beheading of the infidels following a victory. Instead, the Saracens had crushed the Christian armies. The Spanish knights had been all but exterminated. The loss was infuriating.

That Francesco had begged him not to attack, saying the attack would fail. What did a monk know?

The slaughter hadn't induced the monks to leave. It had caused Francesco to badger him even more. "Let us go to the sultan!" The prelate grew sick of hearing that repeated plea.

This morning Pelagius had lost his composure. "Against my advice, go," he had shouted. "Your deaths be on your own heads."

They were gone. Today. Forever.

About three weeks later, on a sweltering day just like every other one, Pelagius was riding through the camp, encouraging the knights, when he spied two gray robes walking through the desert. They were accompanied by two mounted Saracens, banners trailing from the spears each held aloft. Before Pelagius could analyze the sight, the Saracens whipped their horses around and galloped out of sight. The gray robes kept walking toward the camp.

NOTES

This chapter follows the historical record, well documented by Paul Moses in *The Saint and the Sultan* (chapters 11 and 12). See also 1C (first book, chapter XX) and 2C (second book, chapter IV). We do not know the exact date in September on which Francesco and Illuminato went to visit the sultan.

94

Fra Illuminato

Crusader Camp, Damietta, Egypt (Late September 1219)

As the two Saracen escorts wheeled away, Illuminato's bright, dark eyes spied another horseman in the distant Crusader camp. Red robe. Tri-pointed cap. Cardinal Pelagius.

He glanced at Francesco, who nodded. He'd also seen the cardinal.

How could they make the cardinal understand their experience? It would be as difficult as trying to make Illuminato's noble family understand the joy of the poor brotherhood.

Three weeks before, Illuminato and Francesco had gone to speak to the sultan about Jesus and about peace. Chances of converting the sultan were slim, but Illuminato and Francesco were eager to take the chance even if it meant martyrdom. When mounted Saracens had swarmed about them, their swords flashing, Illuminato thought his end had come. However, Francesco had called out, "Sultan! Sultan!" Crying, "Sufi? Sufi?" the horsemen had escorted the brothers to a tented campsite. There they were ushered into the presence of the black-bearded sultan, who appeared to be about their age.

The sultan fed them figs, cheese, and sumptuous dishes of ground beans seasoned with oil and herbs. He questioned them in Latin, asking if they were religious Sufi, if they proposed a truce, if they were deserters. They replied to him in Latin, as best they could. When he understood that they were none of these, he asked who they were. *"Angeli pacis Domini Jesu Christi Domini nostri,"* Francesco replied. "Messengers of peace of Our Lord Jesus Christ."

Thus began an unanticipated three-week dialogue on religion. They told the sultan of the life and teachings of our Lord Jesus Christ, and he told them of the teachings of Muhammad. They shared their prayers with him, and he shared with them the prayer of the Ninety-Nine Most Beautiful Names of God. While they continued to pray their Divine Office eight times daily, they heard the muezzin call out the adhan, summoning the army to prayer five times daily.

Francesco and the sultan even teased one another. One day, Francesco and Illuminato had walked across a carpet to sit at the sultan's table. He had asked them why, if they respected the cross of Christ, they had trod upon it. Sure enough, among many other decorations, the carpet over which they had walked was dotted with crosses. Francesco's eyes twinkled when he responded, "Those are the crosses of the thieves. The cross of Jesus Christ we carry in here," and he pointed to his heart. Understanding, the sultan smiled and nodded.

Another time, the sultan asked, "Since Jesus Christ said, 'if someone takes your cloak, give Him your mantle as well,' then why are the Christians trying to take back lands from the Saracens? Shouldn't they be giving them more land?" Graciously Francesco had replied that the Saracens were preventing the Christians from worshipping Jesus Christ on the lands where He'd walked. If the Saracens would acknowledge and adore the Creator and Redeemer of the world, which He made for everyone to use, the Christians would love them as brothers and sisters.

The sultan had promised to think about what Francesco proposed. He offered them many gifts, but Francesco accepted only one, a horn used to call the people to prayer. He carried that now. Would the cardinal allow him to use it?

NOTES

This chapter is based on what we know of the meeting between Francesco and Sultan Malik al-Kamil (*The Saint and the Sultan*, chapter 13).

95

Cardinal Pelagius

Damietta, Egypt (November 5, 1219)

His red mantle billowing behind him and his tri-pointed hat perched on his head, Cardinal Pelagius rode his chestnut-and-black courser through the streets of Damietta. Here and there, bodies littered the pavement, some guarded by one or two emaciated, wailing individuals. He passed Francesco and the other monks, who were trying to calm and comfort the living. Bishop Jacques di Vitry was baptizing a limp infant. Its mother, the cardinal assumed, was the crumpled, lifeless body at the bishop's feet. Perhaps Pelagius should seek other children and make them Christians so that they'd enter heaven when they died. First, he'd verify that his soldiers were rounding up the survivors as war prisoners.

He passed a huge mosque, its white marble columns supporting arch-covered passages through which he could see a large open courtyard. He rode his courser into the deserted building. In his mind, he saw a main altar and side ones as well. He would transform this into a cathedral to honor the Blessed Virgin.

The ringing of his courser's hooves against the colorful pavement portended the vitality that would return to this city of death. Thankfully, Pelagius had stuck to his original plan. Refusal of al-Kamil's offers of peace. Refusal of King

Jean de Brienne's entreaties to make peace. Refusal to the monks who begged for peace. His plan? Starve Damietta.

When spies told him that the city was ready to fall, he had sent his knights to capture the towers and storm the walls. Corpses littering the streets and the few emaciated people still alive offered no resistance.

Damietta was his. Now, maybe, the Crusade would capture other Saracen strongholds to glorify Christ, the Church, and perhaps even Pelagius.

NOTES

This chapter follows the historical record (*The Saint and the Sultan*, chapter 14).

Part Fourteen

"I Firmly Wish to Obey the General Minister of This Fraternity"

96

Fra Pietro di Catanio di Guiduccio

Cathedral of the Holy Virgin, Damietta, Egypt (February 2, 1220)

Fra Pietro di Catanio di Guiduccio, along with Francesco, Illuminato, Barbaro, Leonardo, Ceasario, and others, stood in the majestic mosque, awaiting its formal dedication as the Cathedral of the Holy Virgin. The massive central altar, dedicated to the Holy Virgin, was obscured from view by the throng of armor-clad Crusaders, colorfully dressed squires, respectably attired wanton women, and tidied-up cooks, armourers, and blacksmiths. A full-throated choir of strong, male voices announced the procession of Cardinal Pelagius, Bishop Jacques di Vitry, and numerous other bishops, priests, and attendants. Because of the bodies standing in front of him, Pietro could see only the cross lifted high above the heads of the throng while hearing the armor of these warriors for God clanking beneath their rich vestments.

Pietro's heart was weeping. Starvation had acquired this place. Baptizing the survivors had seemed a bitter mercy, for most of them could no longer eat and were dying. Perhaps God had looked with more favor on them than on the survivors who were being sold as slaves.

Holy Mass was beginning. Pietro should focus his attention on the holy words. But his mind heard, instead, the cursing and lustful calls that so often issued from the mouths of these attentive crusaders and these observant women. *My Lord, give me charity. You're their judge.*

There on the crucifix, Jesus in His risen glory gazed benevolently on every soul even as His image pleaded for repentance. Francesco's oft spoken words resonated in Pietro's heart. *Nothing should displease a servant of God but sin. And no matter how another person may sin, if a servant of God becomes disturbed and angry because of this and not because of charity, he is storing up guilt for himself. That servant of God who does not become angry or disturbed at anyone lives correctly without anything of his own. Blessed is the one for whom nothing remains except for him to return to Caesar what is Caesar's and to God what is God's.*

My Lord, Pietro prayed. *May the graces of this Mass fall on everyone here, especially those who most need them.*

A few days later, Pietro, Francesco, Illuminato, and Ceasario bade farewell to the few brothers who would remain in Damietta to lodge in a house and use a church that the Bologna and Lucca crusaders had allotted to them. Those leaving were going to Acre to visit Fra Elia. Then they would determine where to journey next.

NOTES

The opening quotation for Part Fourteen is from Francis' *Testament*, 27.

Most historians believe that Francesco and the brothers remained in Damietta until its mosque had been consecrated as the Cathedral of the Holy Virgin on February 2, 1220 (*The Saint and the Sultan*, pp. 148–151). Francesco's words are found in his *Admonitions* (section XI); he quotes Matthew 22:21.

97

Cardinal Ugolino dei Conti di Segni

Palazzo, Viterbo (Early May 1220)

The last person Cardinal Ugolino dei Conti di Segni expected to see in his palazzo in Viterbo was Fra Francesco. It was rumored that he had died in Egypt. Now here he was, sitting across from Ugo at the great table in the great hall. His red and tearing eyes were blinking in the morning light flooding through the windows. His customary smile was banished from his grayish face.

"What's wrong, Brother?"

Instead of discussing his health, Francesco spoke about the brotherhood. Messer Cardinal knew, didn't he, that five of the brothers had been martyred in Morocco? Also seeking martyrdom, Francesco had gone to Damietta. There he had shared his faith with the sultan and realized that the sultan wouldn't kill him as long as he didn't denigrate the sultan's faith nor insist on his conversion. What had the martyred brothers said or done to instigate their deaths?

"Francesco, perhaps your brothers need more instruction on dealing with non-believers. Teach them."

"There's more." A brother had found Francesco in Acre and told him that the brothers he had left in charge were changing the way of life. They'd established more days of fasting and stricter rules about it.

Ugo's eyebrows raised. Were these brothers trying to be as strict as the heretical, holy-looking Cathars who considered meat sinful?

Francesco was rambling. The ministers he had put in charge had allowed Fra Giovanni di Campello to begin a brotherhood of lepers whom he took into the streets, exposing them to abuse, revulsion, and mockery.

They had permitted Fra Filippo to request from the Bishop letters of protection, which Francesco had forbidden, and to make unnecessary visits to Madonna Chiara's Poor Enclosed Ladies.

"Francesco, these are crosses," Ugo gently agreed. "Resume your authority and forbid the changes."

Francesco shook his head. "I'm incapable. After Messer Cardinal Giovanni di San Paolo died, I had a vision of a small black hen with feathered legs and the feet of a tame dove. She had so many chicks that she was unable to gather them all under her wings." He flapped his arms as if they were wings, trying to coax imaginary chicks into his embrace. "She couldn't fit them all." He stretched his arms wide. Had Francesco not looked so doleful, Ugo would have chuckled at the pantomime. "They wandered around her in circles. Now I understand this vision. I am that hen, short in stature, and dark by nature. I must be simple like a dove, flying up to heaven with the feathered strokes of virtue, if only I could do such a thing." He smiled weakly. "The Lord in his mercy has given, and will give me, many sons whom I will be unable to protect with my own strength. I must, therefore, commend them to the holy Church who will protect and guide them under the shadow of *her* wings." Ugo caught the emphasis on the word *her*.

"It's *your* religio, Francesco." He emphasized the word "your." "The Church may make more changes than your brothers would. I'll help you as much as possible."

"Grazie for understanding, Messer Cardinal. You can protect us."

"I'm only one cardinal among many."

"Aren't you dean of the College of Cardinals?"

"Sì, but I'm still one cardinal."

"I'll ask Lord Pope to make you our father."

What?

"You're asking me to be the head of your religio?"

"Sì."

Ugo sat forward and rested his head in his hands. To save the religio, Francesco was willing to relinquish his authority. Asking a cardinal to be head of the religio was brilliant. Inspired? Did God want it? If so, did God want Ugo?

He lifted his head and looked at the weakened man before him. "Brother, we both need to pray about this. Can we talk more tomorrow? You and your brothers stay here tonight. I'll ask our doctor to see you. You're not well."

By mid-afternoon, having completed his other duties for the day, Ugo went to the palazzo's chapel to pray. As he opened the door, he saw, sitting and kneeling before the altar, five gray-robed men, their hoods up over their heads in prayer.

Quietly he shut the door and knelt in the back of the chapel. Slowly he made the Sign of the Cross and began to pray the Our Father, but the words he heard in his spirit overrode the prayer in his heart.

He must do as Francesco requested.

The next day, Ugo sent for Francesco, who met him in the great hall. His hood was up, pulled over his face.

"What did the doctor say?"

"To bathe each eye three times daily with its own clean water and its own clean cloth and to then discard both water and cloth. What touched one eye must not touch the other. And to keep my eyes shaded."

That explained the hood.

"I need to rest and keep cool until the fever breaks."

"Then rest," Ugo smiled. "If you still want me to be your protector, I will ask Lord Pope."

And ask he did, but, before agreeing, Pope Onorio wanted to speak to Francesco personally and hear him preach.

What could an unlettered deacon say to impress a well-educated theologian? Ugo wrote a short speech to summarize the religio and convince the Lord Pope to link it more closely to the Church. That evening, he gave the speech to Francesco.

"Memorize this. Lord Pope wants to see you at the consistory tomorrow."

When Francesco was called to address the consistory, he looked perplexed.

"Cardinal Ugolino gave me a speech to present, but I've forgotten every word."

The cardinals laughed.

Ugo blushed.

The Lord Pope smiled indulgently. "Perhaps you have your own speech?"

"I'll share whatever our Lord wishes." Francesco reached into a pouch sewn into his tunic and brought out a small book that he opened. Then, without turning a page, he read a passage. "'All day long, my disgrace is before me, my face is covered with shame.'" Ugo recognized the passage from Psalm 44. Francesco closed the book and looked up at the assembly.

"Listen, sons of the Lord," he paused, "and my brothers. Obey the voice of the Son of God." Francesco's voice was a fervent plea. "If the Blessed Virgin is so honored, as is becoming, because she carried him in her most holy womb,"—he walked back and forth before the cardinals and the pope, looking squarely at each in turn—"if the Baptist trembled and did not dare to touch the holy head of God,"—he paused—"if the tomb in which He lay for some time is held in veneration,"—another pause—"how holy, just, and fitting must be he who touches with his hands,"—he held his palms toward them— "receives in his heart and mouth,"—he brought his hands to his breast—"and offers to others to be received the One Who is not about to die but Who is to conquer and be glorified,"—his voice rose—"upon Whom the angels longed to gaze?

"'All day long, my disgrace is before me, my face is covered with shame,' if I do not recognize and honor these mysteries by my life and my example. Therefore, incline the ear of your heart and *obey* the voice of the Son of God." Ugo felt the earnestness of the plea, with its emphasis on the word *obey*. "Observe His commands with your *whole* heart and fulfill His counsels with a *perfect* mind." Again, Francesco emphasized the adjectives. "Give praise to Him because He is good." He raised his hands toward heaven. "Exalt Him by your deeds." He extended his hands toward his listeners. "For this reason He has sent *you*," he emphasized "you," "into the whole world: that *you* may bear witness to His voice in word and deed," Francesco spoke every word slowly, with feeling, "and bring everyone to know that there is no one who is all-powerful except

Him." He looked heavenward, then back at the papal court. "Persevere in discipline and holy obedience and, with a good and firm purpose, fulfill what you have promised Him. The Lord God offers Himself to us as to His children."

Francesco paused, then knelt, and raised his face and arms to heaven. Ugo had the sense that neither walls nor ceiling, neither Pope nor cardinals, stood between Francesco and the Lord. "Almighty, eternal, just and merciful God, give us miserable ones the grace to do for You alone what we know You want us to do, and always to desire what pleases You. Inwardly cleansed, interiorly enlightened, and inflamed by the fire of the Holy Spirit, may we be able to follow in the footprints of Your beloved Son, our Lord Jesus Christ, and, by Your grace alone, may we make our way to You, Most High, Who live and rule in perfect Trinity and simple Unity, and are glorified, God almighty, forever and ever. Amen."

The entire consistory was hushed. In the most charitable way, by setting before them what they should be and do, Francesco had just admonished them all.

Pope Onorio broke the silence. "Your words are well received, my son." He looked pointedly at the cardinals on either side of him. "May we take them to heart." Then, to Francesco, "Did you come to share these important thoughts with us, or might there be another matter also at hand?"

"Lord Pope, there is another matter. As you know, it is not easy for poor and unimportant men to gain access to such majesty. You hold the world in your hands, and the pressure of important business does not allow you time to look after little things."

Francesco paused and looked at Ugo, who nodded. Francesco returned his gaze to Pope Onorio. "For this reason, Messer, I beg your holiness to give us the lord of Ostia as pope. That way, while always saving your preeminent dignity, the brothers can turn to him in their hour of need, to benefit from his protection and direction."

Pope Onorio glanced at Ugo, who nodded his assent.

"Gladly, then, I place Messer Cardinal Ugolino, Bishop of Ostia, over your religio as you request. May God bless your religio through him. If that is all, my son, you may go in peace."

NOTES

Hearing of changes in the brotherhood, Francesco sought Cardinal Ugolino to assist him (1C, second book, chapter V; and L3C, chapter XVI). The histories are inconsistent on how, where, and when this happened. The words of Francesco's request to the pope are found in 2C (first book, chapter XVII).

L3C (chapter XVI) records the vision of the black hen.

Bonaventure (*LMj*, chapter 12) records Francesco preaching to the pope after forgetting the words of a speech which Ugolino had written for him. A later writer, Stephen of Bourbon (*Early Documents II*, pp. 789–790), states that Francesco randomly found Psalm 44:15 in his Psalter and based his spontaneous homily on it. Stephen also states that Francesco admonished the Curia for their poor example. This chapter uses Francesco's words from his *Letter to the Entire Order* to make this admonishment.

98

Fra Riccerio

House, Bologna (Mid-August 1220)

Although Fra Riccerio lay abed in the newly constructed house for the brothers who were studying at the University of Bologna, he couldn't rest. Sweat plastered his thick reddish curls against his skull. His stomach was turning somersaults. He had formerly felt this way after a night of too abundant wine, too loud bantering, too many dice games, and too willing women. He had relinquished that life after hearing Fra Francesco preach on the privileged holiness of the Blessed Mother. Her obedience and faith had merited her to be the Mother of Christ and had brought her sinless to heaven. What beautiful names Francesco had given her!

"Hail, His Palace!

"Hail, His Tabernacle!

"Hail, His Dwelling!

"Hail, His Robe!

"Hail, His Servant!

"Hail, His Mother!"

That address about purity of body and soul had burrowed into Riccerio's heart, making him realize that the path of everything that money could buy was leading straight to hell. He had begged Francesco to accept him as a brother so as to snatch his soul from destruction.

Today's sickness wasn't from indulgence. Something he had eaten must have been tainted. He retched again into a basin, but nothing came out. His stomach must be empty.

Riccerio closed his eyes to await the next bout of nausea. *Get better!* he ordered himself. *Fra Francesco is coming today to speak to us.*

"Brother, can you get up? We must leave this house. I'll help you."

He felt Fra Luciano's strong grip under his arms, helping him to his feet, but Riccerio's long, thick legs were as wobbly as a newborn calf's. As soon as he stood, he almost retched with dizziness. His head was still spinning when Luciano sat him down beside a fountain and then returned to the house to escort out more students until the piazza was full of ill young men, broiling in the sun.

"The Friars Preachers will allow us to stay with them," Luciano announced. He summoned the able brothers. "We'll take you there."

Riccerio was feeling steadier. "Why do we have to leave? Does Fra Francesco know where we'll be?"

"Fra Francesco isn't coming," Luciano said. His voice was sharp, clipped. "He was on his way when someone said he was going to the house of the brothers. He must think we built it, so he refused to come. He sent the command that we all had to leave. We had to figure out where to go."

NOTES

2C (second book, chapter XXVIII) relates that, in an unnamed year, Francesco expelled the friars from the house in Bologna. Several historians believe that Riccerio (Rizzerio, Ruggerio, possibly also called Boncontuzio and Bonizio) was one of the sick friars.

Francesco's titles of the Blessed Mother are found in his *Salutation of the Blessed Virgin Mary*.

99

Fra Giacomo the Simple

San Rufino dell'Arce, Assisi (September 1220)

In the soothing sunlight flooding the leper hospital of San Rufino dell'Arce, Fra Giacomo the Simple had set up his nursing station. While all the brothers tended the lepers and often stayed with them, Francesco had put Giacomo in charge of caring for lepers whose sores were most severe.

"Your touch is tender," Francesco had told him. Right now, he was trying to be very tender as he dipped Messer Rinaldo's left hand into a scratched wooden basin of cool water. Then he swabbed the ulcerating sores with a scrap of soft saffron cloth. Rinaldo's crooked fingers had so many sores. Carefully Giacomo's plump hands swabbed away the pus and blood. It took him a long time.

"Do they hurt?" Giacomo asked.

"Nope."

There. That hand was clean. Giacomo dried the sores with a clean scrap of green cloth. Then he gently guided Rinaldo's other hand into the basin and cleansed the sores that covered that palm and its fingers.

"Do they hurt?"

"Nope."

"Your fingers might fall off because you have leprosy, but mine won't fall off because I don't. Right?"

"Right."

Giacomo smiled, proud that he remembered what Messer Rinaldo had taught him. He dried Rinaldo's hand and helped him to his bandaged feet. He would unwrap the cloths, wash Rinaldo's feet, and wrap them in clean cloths after they returned to the hospital.

"We'll walk to the church today," Giacomo announced as he did daily. His tongue couldn't twist itself around the church's long name.

With Rinaldo leaning on his arm, Giacomo led him through the woods to the little church where the brothers prayed. He waved at Pietro, who waved back. He waved at Rufino, who waved back. Then they walked inside, knelt on the floor, and looked at the altar where God lived in a wooden dove. Giacomo loved God, Who had many names like "Our Father" and "Holy Spirit" and "Our Lord Jesus Christ." Giacomo couldn't remember all the beautiful names that Francesco used. Some of the names Giacomo couldn't pronounce, so he just called Him "God."

God lived in the wooden dove, Francesco said, but He also lived in Giacomo and in Messer Rinaldo and in everyone else. Maybe each person called God by a different name.

Giacomo knelt, thinking of different, beautiful names for God. Was Messer Rinaldo thinking of names, too? Rinaldo had been a brother with a group of other holy lepers whom Fra Giovanni di Cappella had been organizing, but Francesco had said "no" and so had Lord Pope. So, Messer Rinaldo was no longer a brother.

Several brothers came into the church. Giacomo and Rinaldo stood.

The brothers with books stood together on one side of the church. Today Francesco was with them. So were some other men who weren't brothers. Giacomo recognized some because they lived in Assisi.

The brothers without books stood by Giacomo. Giacomo didn't recognize two other men who had no books but who stood far away from him and Rinaldo.

The brothers with books began to read prayers and sing chants.

The ones without books began to pray "Our Father." Sometimes they prayed "Our Father" more times than others. Giacomo followed their lead.

When the brothers were done praying, Francesco tapped Giacomo on the shoulder and motioned for him to come outdoors. Obediently Giacomo followed.

Francesco led him a short distance from the church and spoke quietly. "Brother, you should not take our Christian brothers about in this way since it is not right for you or for them. You know that many people dislike our Christian brothers, especially when they have severe sores like Messer Rinaldo."

At the rebuke, Giacomo's eyes welled with tears. He thought Francesco liked the lepers. That's why he called them "our Christian brothers." That's why he taught the brothers to call them Messer and Madonna. Shouldn't other people like them, too?

Suddenly Francesco threw his arms around Giacomo and hugged him tightly. "I'm sorry," he said. "Forgive me. You do such loving work with our Christian brothers. I shouldn't have said that. I have shamed both you and Messer Rinaldo. I'm sorry."

Before Giacomo could understand, Francesco called to Fra Pietro. As they walked off, Giacomo heard Francesco say, "I tell you to confirm for me the penance I have chosen for this and do not oppose me in any way."

"Brother, do as you please," Pietro said.

"Grazie."

Francesco came back to Giacomo. "I'm sorry," he said again. "Bring Messer Rinaldo to eat with us as you always do. Forget my rebuke."

Giacomo smiled his wide smile that puckered his chubby cheeks and narrowed his narrow eyes to slits. Throwing his arms around Francesco, he laughed and laughed with joy.

The night was beautiful and warm. On such nights, the brothers ate outdoors. Tonight, they sat on the ground around a low log table. Giacomo patted the table. He had helped make it smooth by rubbing it with sand. That had taken a long time.

Giacomo sat down next to Rinaldo and across the table from Rufino. Francesco sat across the table from Rinaldo. Pietro sat across the table from Angelo. All the other brothers sat across the table from each other. Some of the men who had prayed in the church were eating with them, too. A lot of men were at tonight's meal.

Francesco stood and led them all in praying an Our Father. Then the serving brothers brought in food. Between each pair of brothers sitting across from one another, the serving brothers set a bowl of broth swimming with scraps. Each person received a begged trencher.

Giacomo tore off a chunk of his trencher and dipped it into the bowl between him and Rufino. He scooped up some of the scraps and ate them, grunting at the tasty combination of flavors. Then Rufino dipped and ate.

Messer Rinaldo dipped his trencher into the bowl between him and Francesco. Giacomo moaned. Poor Messer Rinaldo. He needed to have his hands washed again. Pus and blood were oozing out of his sores. Some fell into the bowl when he dipped into it.

Then Francesco dipped a piece of his trencher into the same bowl and ate the bread.

Giacomo dipped again into the bowl that he and Rufino shared. But Rufino didn't dip again. He was looking at Francesco.

Giacomo looked around. The only ones eating seemed to be Rinaldo and Francesco, who were dipping and eating and smiling at each other. Why, Pietro hadn't even torn his trencher to dip into the bowl that he shared with Angelo. Pietro looked sad. Was he going to cry?

NOTES

AC (section 64) records an undated account of Francesco scolding James (Giacomo) the Simple for bringing an unnamed, badly ulcerated leper into public. Immediately regretting this, Francesco asked the minister servant Pietro to approve his penance, namely, to eat with the leper out of the same bowl. Francesco's and Pietro's words are taken directly from AC.

Chapter III of *The Early Rule* describes how the brothers prayed the Divine Office.

100

Fra Pietro di Catanio di Guiduccio

Porziuncula, Assisi (September 29, 1220)

Fra Pietro di Catanio di Guiduccio was sitting on the forest floor outside the Porziuncula. He wasn't far from Francesco, who was facing this special gathering of his brothers on the feast of Saint Michael the Archangel. Pietro listened attentively as Francesco encouraged the brothers to follow their way of life as Lord Pope had approved it.

"The rule and life of these brothers is this, namely: 'to live in obedience, in chastity, and without anything of their own,' and to follow the teaching and footprints of our Lord Jesus Christ."

Every time he heard Francesco speak, Pietro felt humbled. Who was he, to be his guardian?

On their way to Rome eleven years ago, the brothers had selected Bernardo as leader. However, they obeyed Francesco since, through him, the Lord had brought them all together. Because Francesco wanted to be obedient to someone, Bernardo had assigned Pietro as his guardian.

"If anyone, wishing by divine inspiration to accept this life, comes to our brothers, let him be received by them with kindness," Francesco continued.

They had a complex relationship. Sometimes Pietro was able to revert the authority to Francesco. This had happened several months ago when Fra Stefano had found them in Acre and told them about the new regulations that Fra Gregorio and Fra Matteo had made when Francesco was in Damietta. Stefano had found them on an abstinence day in the new regulations, but Francesco and Pietro had been given meat for their meal.

"Messer Pietro, what shall we do?" Francesco had jokingly asked in a high-handed voice.

Pietro had fallen in with the charade, bowed, and answered, "Messer Francesco, whatever pleases you, for you have the authority."

"Let us eat, then," Francesco had said, "according to the Gospel, whatever is placed before us." And eat they did.

Now Francesco's sonorous voice instructed, "No one may be received contrary to the rite and practice of the holy Church."

Sometimes Pietro was glad that Francesco had subjected himself to obedience so that he would be forced to care for his health. One winter, during a time of abstinence, Pietro insisted that an ill Francesco eat chicken to bolster his failing strength. Later, however, while preaching to the Assisiani before fully recovering, Francesco asked his listeners to wait a moment. Taking Pietro with him when he ducked out of sight, he disrobed, and had Pietro tie a rope around his neck and lead him, shivering, back to the crowd. There Francesco proclaimed, "You believe me to be a holy man, as do others who, following my example, leave the world and enter the religio and life of the brothers. But I confess to God and to you that, during my illness, I ate meat and broth flavored with meat."

Francesco obeyed when Pietro ordered him to have a fox fur sewn inside his tunic for winter warmth. However, he stipulated, "If you want me to wear that fur under the tunic, allow me to sew a piece of fur on the outside of my tunic as an indication to the people that I have a piece of fur underneath." Pietro acquiesced.

"Let all the brothers," Francesco opened his arms wide as if to encompass everyone in the room, "be careful not to be disturbed or angered at another's sin or evil, because the devil wishes to destroy many because of another's fault."

Francesco readily acknowledged his faults. He had assumed that the brothers had built the house in Bologna against his wishes. After Francesco evicted the brothers, Cardinal Ugolino had mentioned, in a public speech, that he had built that house. Chastised, Francesco permitted the brothers to return, but his hasty mistake greatly troubled him. "I am *un idiota* whom many of the brothers wish had died in Egypt. I'm not fit to manage them."

"Let no one be called '*pater*,' but let everyone in general be called a lesser brother. Let one wash the feet of another." Francesco paused, and then spoke again in a resolute tone. "From now on, I am dead to you."

What? He had not consulted Pietro about this.

"But here is Fra Pietro di Catanio. Let us all, you and I, obey him."

What?

Francesco was walking toward Pietro. He was bowing before him as a knight bows to his lord. "Fra Pietro, I promise you my obedience and reverence."

Pietro was shaking. If he stood, he might topple. The brothers, many of them weeping, began to approach him, bow, and say as did Francesco, "I promise you my obedience and reverence."

What had just happened? The gathering was closing. Francesco, who always dismissed the brothers with a blessing, was sitting. The brothers were gazing at Pietro. He rose unsteadily, blessed them, and led them in Vespers.

After the dinner meal, Francesco drew Pietro aside. They sat cross-legged in the shade of a huge oak.

"Excuse me for thrusting this upon you, but you are best qualified to manage the brotherhood."

"I have no idea how to manage it."

"It's your obedience."

He nodded. "Sì." He never could argue with Francesco.

"I ask you, as minister servant, to give me a new guardian, for you will no longer be able to be with me always."

No! To lose Francesco!

"I'm willing to obey a novice of one day as well as anyone seasoned in obedience."

Pietro's voice shook. "Whom do you wish?"

"The newest novice. Fra Riccerio di Muccia."

Riccerio di Muccia was a former libertine, now studying to become a priest. Young. Sturdy. Eager. Somewhat insecure. Francesco admired his humility and his knowledge of Scripture. Riccerio was strong and capable of caring for a physically weak man.

NOTES

In section 12 of his *Chronicle* (13CC), Fra Jordan of Giano told of Fra Stefano finding Francesco, and his conversation with Pietro regarding eating meat on an abstinence day. AC records Francesco's confession about eating meat during the fast (section 80) and the fox fur incident (section 81).

Most historians agree that Francesco resigned his position as head of the brothers (AC, chapter 11) at a September 29 gathering, although some assign this to a Pentecost gathering. When Francesco assigned Pietro as minister servant to the brothers, Riccerio seems to have replaced Pietro as Francesco's guardian (*La Civiltà Cattolica*, Issues nos. 3145–3150).

Francesco's words to the gathering are stipulations in the *Earlier Rule*.

101

Madonna Abriana

Main Piazza, Perugia (March 1, 1221)

Madonna Abriana lingered in the main piazza of Perugia, chatting with other women. Their husbands, lovers, and sons galloped around the piazza in their endless games to celebrate the feast of Saint Herculanus. He was the city's bishop-martyr and patron, but would he have approved of this yearly boisterous revelry?

Unexpectedly Abriana heard a loud, clear voice ring out across the piazza. "Listen, good people, and remember this which was at the heart of Saint Herculanus and every saint!"

Who said that? Standing on tiptoe, Abriana scanned the crowd. There, on the topmost rim of the fountain, stood a short, raggedy penitent whose face was shaded by a huge hood. The man's voice rang out deep and clear across the piazza, as musical as the trickling fountain water but more forceful.

"The Most High Father made known from heaven through His holy angel Gabriel this Word of the Father—so worthy, so holy and glorious—"

Abriana drew near, joining the gathering crowd.

"—In the womb of the holy and glorious Virgin Mary, from *whose* womb *He* received the flesh of our humanity and frailty." The emphasis on *whose* and *He* made Abriana think.

Yes, that was true! Women gave flesh to men. The Virgin Mother gave flesh to the Son of God. Children grew in women's wombs. Men's seed sparked the growth, but who kept it growing? Women. With self-conscious awe, she touched her belly from which three children had sprung. Three children, now grown, jousting with the other knights and with her husband on this feast. Their flesh was hers.

"Though He was rich, He wished, together with the most Blessed Virgin, His mother, to *choose* poverty in the world beyond all else."

Our Lord chose to be poor? Chose?

Abriana turned to the woman standing beside her. "Who's that?" she asked, pointing to the speaker.

"Fra Francesco di Assisi," the woman said.

Without warning, a group of mounted knights galloped into the piazza, raced around it, and began jousting.

"Go away! Do that somewhere else!" a man called from the crowd.

"We're listening to a preacher!" called another man.

"Go away!"

"Be quiet!"

"Let us listen!"

The crowd was shouting at the knights. Oh, goodness! There was Abriana's husband. There, her three sons.

The large group of knights circled the crowd, their destriers prancing, the knights laughing. Brandishing their weapons, they again challenged one another.

"Go away!"

"Show a little respect!"

"Do that somewhere else!"

One of the knights called back. "You go somewhere else and take that Assisiano with you!"

"Listen!" the preacher called out in a startlingly strong voice. "And understand what the Lord is telling you through me, His servant, and don't say, 'This one is from Assisi!'"

The knights reined in their mounts. The voice of the preacher rose over the subdued crowd.

"The Lord has exalted and elevated you above *all* your neighbors," Francesco called out. "Because of this, you must acknowledge your Creator all the more, and humble yourselves not only before almighty God but also before your neighbors." His arms swept across the crowd. "But your heart is puffed up by arrogance in your pride and might. You attack your neighbors and kill many of them. Because of this I tell you, unless you quickly turn to Him and compensate those whom you have injured, the Lord, who leaves *nothing* unavenged,"—he emphasized the word "nothing"—"to your greater punishment and disgrace, will cause you to rise up against each other. You will be torn apart by sedition and civil war, suffering a far greater calamity than your neighbor could ever inflict upon you."

"This is our feast, and this is our piazza!" one of the knights shouted. "If you want to talk, go into the church." The knights spurred their steeds and began again to race one another along the piazza, shouting jubilant challenges.

The preacher climbed down from the fountain and led the way across the piazza toward the Cathedral of San Lorenzo. Abriana's heart was pounding. There was her husband. She would walk right past him. She should ask him to stop jousting and listen to the preacher. But he mocked religion. If she said anything, he would mock her. She hated to be mocked. She needed to be quiet. She needed him not to see her. But she should say something. No, she should be quiet. She was coming right up to him.

Lord, what should I do?

LOOK AT HIM. NOD AT HIM. SAY NOTHING. KEEP WALKING. AND MAKE EVERY STEP A PRAYER FOR HIM.

Abriana kept walking. She looked at her husband, nodded to him, and prayed with every step. He looked at her, tossed his head, and wheeled his steed away.

HE IS YOUR CROSS. HE AND YOUR SONS. LET YOUR EXAMPLE BE YOUR WORDS TO THEM. LET YOUR PRAYERS FOR THEM BE YOUR WORDS TO ME.

NOTES

AC (section 75) records Francesco's words (reproduced in this chapter) to the boisterous Perugian knights on the feast of Saint Herculanus (San Ercolano), which is

March 1. Historian Augustine Thompson, OP, suggests the year 1221 (p. 41) 1, while Fortini suggests sometime immediately prior to 1214 (p. 569) when factions between Perugian nobles and commoners first erupted. Other than his admonition to the knights, Francesco's homily is from his *Later Admonition to the Brothers and Sisters of Penance*.

Madonna Abriana is a fictional representative of a huge number of faithful wives.

102

Fra Pietro di Catanio di Guiduccio

Porziuncula, Assisi (March 6, 1221)

As the early morning light filtered into his chilly cell at the Porziuncula, Fra Pietro di Catanio was shivering. Some illness had struck him, something that was sapping his strength so that, each day for the past two months, he was weaker than the day before. His life was ebbing away. He could no longer stand or care for his bodily needs. He had done the best he could with his life. Now he too, like Francesco, must be an example to the brothers—Francesco, an example of how to live and Pietro, an example of how to die.

"Pietro?"

He recognized the voice. "Come in," Pietro said weakly.

Francesco opened the door to the wood-and-mud cell and sat down on the log stool, next to Pietro.

"I've brought soup."

"Does it have meat in it?" Pietro smiled.

Francesco laughed. "Sì. Chicken. You need meat to regain your strength. And here is a rope," he said, pointing to his cord, "to lead *you* around Assisi if *you* get well, and then I will proclaim how *you* broke the fast."

Pietro smiled weakly. "I am afraid that I will never again walk around Assisi. Soon you will bury me. I am ready to stand before Him and beg His mercy."

"For all that you've done for me, He'll show you abundant mercy. When you come before Him, remember me to Him."

"Francesco, how could I forget?"

NOTES

Pietro died on March 10, 1221, from unspecified causes (*Early Documents I*, p. 204, footnote a). The banter about the chicken and the rope refers to an incident in which Francesco, being ill, had eaten some chicken during a period of abstinence and then had Pietro, his guardian, lead him, naked except for his breeches, around Assisi in the bitter cold, proclaiming that Francesco was a hypocrite for eating meat during a time of abstinence (AC, section 80).

103

Lacole

Todi (Spring 1221)

With her firstborn, three-month-old Justina, suckling contentedly at her breast, Lacole sat on a wooden bench under the holm oak next to her family's small house on the outskirts of Todi. A breeze was blowing up from the Tiber, caressing her youthful face as tenderly as did her husband, Rocco. He was tilling the fields for Messer Fabrice and would be home late, sweaty and ravenous. She would have bread and bean pottage ready, now slowly simmering on the hearth, adding warmth to this warm day.

A penitent cradling a bundle trudged up the road from the direction of the Tiber.

"Fra Francesco!" Lacole's thin face was beaming.

As he bowed to her, Lacole blurted out what was uppermost in her mind. "Did you bring the Rule?" Francesco had promised his followers in Todi a Rule of Life that could be lived at home in order to follow our Lord more closely.

"Lord Pope has the Rule and must approve it first. But I have brought you something else."

Tenderly Francesco parted the folds of the grayish cloth bundle. Inside lay a curled up, blood-and-grime encrusted, snoozing, naked newborn boy. Lacole's dark eyes widened. "Where did you get him?"

Francesco wrapped the cloth around the slumbering infant.

"I met a woman carrying a basket and asked if I might help. 'I'm going to wash my laundry in the river,' she said. But I saw blood on the laundry and saw it move."

Lacole gasped. "She was going to drown him?"

"Sì. To hide her sin. I promised to look after the child if she would give it to me." Francesco paused. "Madonna Lacole, can you nurse him and care for him?"

Lacole's heart melted. "Certainly. Rocco will not say no."

NOTES

In their pictorial biography, *Saint Francis of Assisi* (p. 57), Leonard von Matt and Walter Hauser mention this incident, without giving any names. The incident appears to be a local story about the beginning of the Third Order in Todi.

Part Fifteen

"Let Us Produce Worthy Fruits of Penance"

104

Pope Onorio III

Garden, Lateran Palace, Rome (Late Spring 1221)

Sitting on a bench in the Lateran Garden with two sheaves of parchment beside him, Pope Onorio III was enjoying these moments of peaceful waiting while the sun warmed his sagging, silver-bearded face. Having sent his gilded mantle indoors with a servant, Onorio smoothed his billowing white tunic around his legs. He'd seen over seventy springs, but each thrilled him.

"Cardinal Ugolino!" announced a servant.

Onorio stood and faced the gray-bearded cardinal perhaps twenty years his junior. As he strode into the garden, Ugo was removing his scarlet mantle and broad rimmed cap, which he handed to the servant. Kneeling, he kissed Onorio's hand. Onorio raised him to his feet, embraced him, and heartily slapped his back.

"Sit, Ugo."

Ugo sat and stretched out his legs.

"So, you have met with your Dominic de Guzman and your Francesco di Assisi?"

Ugo nodded.

"How did that go?"

"They'd met before. Apparently, Dominic attended one or two of Francesco's gatherings with his brothers, to see what his religio was about. When they came to me, they were like old friends and were talking about joining their groups. Something about a dream Dominic had."

Joining groups? That would change things. "Are they going to join together?"

"No. Their lifestyles are different. Francesco refused."

"Good. Then what I have to say will apply."

"They both also refused to have their brothers become bishops and prelates."

Onorio and Ugo had discussed this possibility several times.

"You couldn't convince them?"

"They're both stubborn. That's why they're leaders."

Onorio shrugged. "Too bad. They have some men who would be good examples and teachers." *Maybe,* Onorio thought, *if their following continues to grow, future leaders will see things differently. God's patient. The Church has to be patient, too.*

Onorio picked up one of the parchment sheaves beside him. "What did they say about this?" He scanned the text. "This Rule you wrote for their laity. The Brothers and Sisters of Penance?"

Ugo leaned forward. "Dominic likes it very much. Says it's very precise. The way he thinks."

"Precise, sì. You're always precise, Ugo."

Ugo smiled. "Grazie."

"What about your Francesco?"

"He accepts it."

"What does he dislike?"

"He doesn't write this way. The Rule is very juridical."

"As it should be. The Curia accepted it, and I approve." Onorio handed Ugo the sheaf of parchment to which was affixed his own handwritten approval, his papal wax seal dangling from it.

"The Curia thought it a bit strict," Onorio added.

"Strict only if you're not a penitent, Lord Pope. I've visited penitents in Rome and Umbria. This Rule describes how they're already living. I've simply recorded their way of life into a juridical form."

"So, I told the Curia." Onorio chuckled and leaned close to Ugo, lowering his voice as if in a conspiracy. "Perhaps living that way should become a requirement for those in the Curia." He thought of the provisions about being at peace with all and living a simple, unostentatious life. "Might solve a lot of problems," he whispered, his silvery eyebrows arching.

Ugo laughed. "It might. Are you going to suggest it?"

Onorio sighed and sat back on the bench. "That way of life isn't imposed. It's chosen. I doubt that anyone in the Curia would choose it. But, for your lay people who wish it, here it is. Perhaps it will keep some from running off to join the friars and nuns. Someone must bear children for the sake of the world, the Church, and the faith." Onorio paused. "Now the other Rule—the one you wrote for Francesco's friars."

"Excuse me, Lord Pope, but you recall that I didn't write that one. Fra Francesco wrote it."

"The Latin is excellent. The many Scripture references, exact. Isn't your Francesco an uneducated merchant? This Rule doesn't show lack of education."

"Because, Lord Pope, educated friars wrote what Francesco and some of the others dictated."

"The Curia noted that this style differed from that of the Rule for the Brothers and Sisters of Penance."

Ugo nodded.

"We cannot accept it."

"I told Francesco that it was unacceptable, but he wanted me to present it nevertheless."

"It needs to be more juridical."

"Precisely," Ugo said.

"Will he rewrite it?"

"He'll have to."

NOTES

The opening quotation for Part Fifteen is from Francis' *Later Admonition and Exhortation to the Brothers and Sisters of Penance (Second Version of the Letter to the Faithful)*, 25.

AC (section 49) records the meeting of Francesco, Dominic, and Ugolino. Gerard de Frachet (*Early Documents II*, pp. 786–787) recounts Dominic's dream. While Frachet places this meeting with Ugolino in 1215 during the First Lateran Council, historian William Hinnebusch (p. 451) states that, chronologically, this meeting could have taken place only in 1221, sometime before Saint Dominic's death on August 6. *Fioretti* (chapter 18) relates Dominic's attendance at a large general chapter meeting of Francesco's brothers at the Porziuncula. Fortini (p. 388, footnote) provides additional proof for Dominic's attendance at one, and possibly more, of Francesco's chapters.

At the request of the followers of Francesco and Dominic for a rule of life for lay people, Cardinal Ugolino visited penitents throughout Italy and recorded how they lived. He reviewed the Rule of Life approved by the papacy for the lay order of the Humiliati. He spoke with Francesco on how he and his friars were advising their lay followers. Then Ugolino organized the information into a Rule of life for the laity, which both Francesco and Dominic accepted. Pope Onorio III and the Curia approved it in 1221. (See Stewart, pp. 183–201 and Habig, pp. 166–67).

Francesco's Rule for the friars was not approved (*Early Documents I*, p. 63), possibly for the reasons stated in this chapter.

105

Fra Giordano di Giano

Porziuncula, Assisi (First Week of June 1221)

So swarthy that sunlight hardly ever burnt his skin, and so short that he hardly ever saw over others' heads, twenty-five-year-old Deacon Fra Giordano di Giano possessed one other distinguishing trait. He longed to meet a martyr.

Although Francesco refused to discuss or have read an account of last year's martyrdom of five brothers in Morocco, Giordano could name the martyrs—Bernardo, Pietro, Oto, Accuro, Adjuto. Two years ago, at the brothers' gathering, they had been assigned to their mission. Despite attending that gathering, Giordano hadn't conversed with those brothers. Too late now.

"Everyone should glory in his own suffering and not in that of another," Francesco declared. Giordano wasn't sure he agreed.

Today was the last day of this Pentecost gathering, conducted by Fra Elia, who had become Pietro di Catanio's replacement after his death in March. Thousands of brothers were sleeping in hastily constructed mat huts and feasting on twenty-three tables of food, which the Assisiani daily carted in.

On the platform on which Elia, Francesco, Cardinal Rainiero Capocci, and other cardinals and bishops had spoken, Francesco was seated at Elia's feet. Today he looked frail and spent from an intermittent illness.

Several days ago, a stronger Francesco had addressed the gathering. "The Psalmist wrote, 'Blessed be the Lord my God, who trains my hands for battle,' but 'our battle is not against flesh and blood.'" Francesco had mimed a brief encounter with an imaginary swordsman. "We battle against our pride." He strutted about, head high, as arrogant lords sometimes did. "We are reprimanded, accused, disciplined. We have been attacked!" Francesco whipped an imaginary sword from an imaginary scabbard at his side and wheeled about. Then he sheathed the weapon. "Is pride our lord so that we fight to defend it? Or are we servants of our Lord Jesus Christ?" He paused, looking from face to face. "Blessed is the servant who endures discipline, accusation, and reprimand from another as patiently as he would from himself." Pause. "Blessed is the servant who, after being reprimanded, agrees courteously, submits respectfully, admits humbly, and makes amends willingly." Pause. "Blessed is the servant who is not quick to excuse himself, and humbly endures shame and reprimand for a sin," Francesco had lowered his voice, emphasizing each word, "when he did not commit the fault."

Giordano could still visualize that battle over oneself. He had joined the brotherhood to bolster his faith, so he had promised himself to avoid heretics in Lombardy, Germany, and everywhere else so as to not weaken his belief. However, Francesco's homily made him wonder. Was faith's greatest enemy neither heretics nor unbelievers but pride?

Today on the platform, Francesco tugged at Elia's tunic. Elia bent down to him, listened, then straightened and addressed the brothers. "Brothers, thus says the Brother: There is a certain region called Germany, where there are devout Christians who, as you know, often pass through our country, perspiring under the heat of the sun, bearing large staves and wearing large boots, singing praises to God and the Saints and who visit the shrines of the Saints. And because once the brothers who were sent to them were treated badly and returned—"

Treated badly! Giordano thought. *They were almost killed!*

"—the Brother does not compel anyone to go to them; but to those who, inspired by zeal for God and for souls, may wish to go, he desires to give the same obedience that he gives to those who go beyond the sea, and even a broader one. If there are any who wish to go, let them rise and gather in a group aside." Elia pointed to the left of the platform.

Scattered brothers stood and hurried to the spot.

Germany! Some brothers might be martyred there!

Jumping to his feet, Giordano hurried to speak to the volunteers. There had to be nearly a hundred! He made his way from one brother to the next, asking, "Who are you and where do you come from?"

If that brother were martyred, Giordano could say, "I knew him!"

"I am called Deacon Palmerio di Monte Gargano in Apulia," answered an angular-faced friar with a thick, black beard, "and you, too, are one of us and shall go with us," he laughed.

Fear spurted in Giordano's soul. "I am not one of you. I came to you wanting to know you, but not with the desire of going with you."

"Nonsense!" Palmerio teased, his deep-set eyes sparkling. "You know you want to come with us. Now don't try to get away," he said, grabbing Giordano's hands and pulling him into a sitting position with the other waiting brothers. The more Giordano struggled, the tighter Palmerio, laughing, held onto him.

Elia was calling out where each brother was assigned. The list was endless. Giordano heard his name. *Grazie, my Lord!* His assignment was not to Germany.

"Fra Cäsar von Speyer will be your minister," Elia announced, looking at those who had volunteered for Germany. "He will select those he wishes to take, and the rest of you will keep the assignments which I have just read."

Giordano's heart beat faster as Cäsar walked among the brothers, speaking to each and selecting some. Cäsar's fair skin and red beard distinguished him from most of the other brothers, and he spoke with the sharp, clipping accent of a native German. He'd teach the brothers the language so that people would understand them to be Christians, not heretics. Why, not one of the brothers might be martyred!

"Take him," Palmerio was saying to Cäsar.

"Sì. Take him," another brother declared.

Giordano was the "him."

"Pardon me," he said to the brothers, "but I am not one of you, because I did not rise with the desire of going with these others."

"But I would like to have you," Cäsar declared.

"I have been assigned elsewhere."

Another brother spoke. "He was assigned to our province, which is warmer than Germany. Fra Giordano is weak and can't tolerate cold."

Cäsar looked confused. "Fra Elia will decide."

Dutifully Giordano accompanied Cäsar to Elia. While Cäsar explained the situation, Giordano felt confused. He remembered Francesco's sermon about agreeing courteously and submitting respectfully. He didn't want to go to Germany! But did God have other plans?

Elia grunted. "I command you, Brother, in holy obedience, to decide finally whether you wish to go or to be released. Come back to me with your decision."

Giordano felt like a bird freed from a snare only to be caught in a trap. What to do? Stay as he wished? Go to Germany where cruelty and suffering might endanger his faith?

He needed to speak with someone. Ah! Over there. That brother who had been sent to Hungary and who had been forced six times to give up his clothing, including his breeches. He'd been beaten and humiliated and had achieved only derision. He'd have good advice.

Giordano explained his dilemma. The brother listened thoughtfully. "Go to Fra Elia and say to him, 'Brother, I neither wish to go nor to stay behind, but whatever you command me, I will do.'"

Giordano nodded. Of course. Be obedient to a superior's decision. Agree courteously. Submit respectfully.

Elia had no difficulty deciding. "I command you by the virtue of holy obedience to go with Fra Cäsar to Germany."

NOTES

In sections 16–18 of his *Chronicle* (13CC), Fra Giordano di Giano describes this Pentecost gathering and how he was sent to Germany. This chapter follows his account, using the words he records Elia and other friars as saying. The author has used Francesco's *Admonitions*, section XXII, to expand the Psalm text recorded by Giordano as the theme of one of his sermons. Giordano's physical description is given by a sixteenth-century compiler named Nicholas Glassberger (13CC, p. 3). Since Giordano died in 1262 and was a deacon when Francesco accepted him in 1219, it seems likely that he was born around 1195.

106

Madonna Buonadonna de Segni

House, Poggibonsi (Late Summer 1221)

Madonna Buonadonna was sitting on a stump in the shade of a large elm in her yard. She spread her arms and legs as much as would be proper and hoped for a breeze. Mid-morning and already sweltering! Heat on top of heat! She groaned as another heat wave bubbled up inside her, engulfed her, and made her perspire more. Ugh! Hot flashes.

"Good morning!"

Who was coming? Quickly she brought her arms down and pulled her legs together.

Fra Danilo and Fra Placido. They'd be looking for her husband, Luchesio.

"Good morning!" she called out. "He's not here. I think he went to the hospital."

"Tell him that Fra Francesco is coming to clothe him."

Buonadonna's heart sank. "When?"

"Maybe tomorrow. Maybe a few days. Soon."

"I'll tell him." Her voice was flat.

"Grazie!"

The brothers continued walking down the road. Buonadonna felt hotter than ever. So, he was going to do it. Her husband, the respected merchant

Messer Luchesio Modestini, was going to become a Brother of Penance. Did that mean he was going to give away all their bread like he did once before? Or so it seemed he had given it away. She had screamed at him, and he calmly told her to check the cabinets again. Scowling, she had done so, and the bread was still there. Yet she had seen with her own eyes that poor, begging father carrying away a mantle full of loaves. She couldn't explain it.

She almost wished that Francesco had never come to Poggibonsi. When had he first come, and which friar had been with him? She couldn't remember. All she remembered was what his preaching in the town piazza had done to Luchesio.

How she loved that man! Average height, just like her, with a curly, deep-brown beard to match his curly, deep-brown hair, the same color and texture as hers. His eyes! Unlike her languid gray eyes, Luchesio's were a piercing chestnut. She swore they twinkled when he looked at her. Before her parents had arranged the marriage with the confident young captain who was defending the papal cause, he had already mesmerized their daughter.

Their marriage had been good. Luchesio had left soldiering to move to Poggibonsi, where he and Buonadonna had opened a money exchange. They'd loaned money to local aristocrats and exchanged money for merchants. The couple had made plenty of money to support themselves and the two infant sons God sent them.

But then! Life with Luchesio became one totally unexpected occurrence after another. Her confident, almost cocky, young husband began to grow reflective! She couldn't understand him. For years, he seemed troubled until he finally decided that the interest on his loans was exorbitant. So, he sold his business to become a grain merchant. Buonadonna had railed at this rash decision, but Luchesio calmly proceeded with it. Admittedly, he had been astute. Money rolled in.

Buonadonna calmed down, and they lived comfortably until the Lesser Brothers came through Poggibonsi on a preaching mission. Luchesio couldn't stop talking about their spontaneous, roadside harangues and how little they possessed. He became convinced that he was still making too much money and not doing enough for the poor. He started talking more about God and less about gold. In addition to selling grain, he started to care for hospital patients.

His political interests waned. Maybe he'd stopped liking money, but she hadn't. Ineffectively, she sharpened her tongue on his conscience.

When the converted merchant Francesco preached in Poggibonsi, Luchesio was enthralled. He invited Francesco and the other whoever-he-was friar to dinner, and they preached at him even more. Two of Francesco's teachings especially touched Luchesio. "We must never desire to be above others, but, instead, we must be servants and subject to every human creature for God's sake." And "the Spirit of the Lord will rest upon all those men and women who have done and persevered in these things, and It will make a home and dwelling place in them. And they will be children of the heavenly Father, Whose works they do."

After the friars had left, Luchesio discussed these teachings so much that Buonadonna had asked, "Are you going to join him?"

"How could I leave you, my Buonadonna?" he had asked, taking her hand and kissing it tenderly.

He didn't leave her. Instead, he sold the grain business and bought enough land to support a family, working the fields himself. Oh, the gossip that Buonadonna endured! The scathing words she spewed at Luchesio! Remaining silent, he tended the farm, continued his hospital work, and earned enough to get along.

Then contagion claimed their sons' lives. When Francesco returned from Egypt, she and Luchesio had just been emerging from the darkness of their loss. With the guild merchants, Francesco shared ways to grow closer to God. Several men, including Luchesio, began to follow his advice.

Then, three months ago, Fra Danilo and Fra Placido had brought a copy of a written Rule to Poggibonsi. Francesco had accepted this from a cardinal as a religious way of life for people not living in religious houses. Some of the guild had been meeting to discuss and live this Rule, which was similar to what Francesco had originally proposed.

Luchesio was going to promise to live this Rule. A promise was binding. No retraction. Buonadonna needed to clear her head about this.

VERDIANA.

Verdiana! Of course! Buonadonna occasionally visited the holy anchorite when she needed advice. Verdiana had a level head. She would listen.

Luchesio had stopped using one of their two rounceys. Why? The Rule didn't mention horses. Nevertheless, Luchesio was determined to do more penance by walking to the hospital. If he wanted to cart some poor soul from the malarial contagion of the valley to the healthier hilltop air, he would use their donkey. Well, good, because she would take the rounceys and reach Verdiana in a few hours. When she asked their young farm servant Maurizio to ready the animals, she had him drape two sacks of beans over his rouncey's back.

The sun was high when Buonadonna and Maurizio arrived at Verdiana's anchorage and tethered their horses near the well. Maurizio drew water and gave the thirsty beasts a hearty drink, while he and Buonadonna drank themselves from their cupped hands. Maurizio sat down, his back against the trunk of an oak, and closed his eyes. That was Maurizio. Take any chance to nap.

Buonadonna noticed a clay pot sitting near the well. Maybe Verdiana needed water. She filled the pot and carried it toward a narrow stone cell that had been built against a wall of the Church of Sant'Antonio. At a small, grated window opening into the cell, Buonadonna knocked, then sat on the bench below the opening.

"Sì?"

"It's Buonadonna. Can I talk to you?"

"Sì!" The joy in the voice thrilled her.

"Am I disturbing your prayers?"

The laugh from within made Buonadonna laugh, too.

"I know. You're always praying. I brought you some water."

"Grazie." Verdiana's pasty-colored face appeared at the window. A white hand passed Buonadonna a clay cup. *You turn white if you're never in the sun*, Buonadonna thought. She gazed at her own bronze hands as she dipped Verdiana's cup into the pot of water. She gave the cup to Verdiana, who drank and handed it back. Buonadonna filled the cup again, and Verdiana took it inside her cell, then reappeared at the window.

"I brought you some beans," Buonadonna said, walking toward Maurizio's rouncey to retrieve the sacks.

Verdiana took them gratefully. "What can I do for you, my friend?" she asked.

Buonadonna felt the heat wave coming again. "Do you get heat waves?"

"It does get hot in here."

"No. No. Hot flashes."

"Hot flashes? Not yet!" Verdiana smiled.

"No? Oh well."

"You came to ask me about hot flashes?"

Buonadonna flapped her arms, trying to cool the heat. "No. No. Messer Luchesio is going to become a Brother of Penance."

"Sì. You told me."

"Soon. Like maybe tomorrow."

"So?"

"So, what am I going to do?"

"What you're doing now. He's already living their way of life, isn't he?"

"Sì. But this makes it official."

"What is he going to be doing after he makes his promises that he's not already doing?"

"I don't know. Nothing, I guess."

"Why are you afraid?"

"It's so, so . . ." Buonadonna stumbled, "official."

"No changing his mind."

"Sì."

"You're still not comfortable with this, are you? If you say no, he won't be able to profess. You need to give permission, don't you?"

"A husband has to give permission for his wife to become a Sister of Penance. The Rule says nothing about a wife giving a husband permission."

"Messer Luchesio won't profess without your permission."

"I know, and I'm not going to tell him no. He wants to do this. It's his faith."

"Isn't it your faith, too?"

Buonadonna felt flustered. "Sì. But all those prayers. And those days of fasting. You have to give up colors." She ran her hand along the skirt of her green tunic.

Verdiana was quiet.

"All right. I know you pray and fast and you only wear black. But that's you. This is me."

"I thought we were talking about Messer Luchesio, not you or me."

Buonadonna was flustered again. "Sì. No. Just because you pray, and fast, and wear black doesn't mean I should."

"Of course not. But are you thinking of doing this?"

"No!" Goodness, she wasn't thinking of that, was she? She, a Sister of Penance? How ridiculous! How unthinkable! How—

"I could never do it!"

"Why not?"

"All those prayers. I don't have the time."

"What's more important than praying?"

"Uh. Uh. I have to take care of the house."

"Praying will help you care for it better."

"How is that going to happen?"

"When you pray first, God shows you how better to manage everything else."

Was that true? She had never considered such a thing.

"All that fasting. And no meat. Four days, no meat."

"Aren't you already cooking like that for Messer Luchesio?"

"Sì."

"Do you eat with him?"

"Sì."

"Are you missing the meat?"

"Well, no. But then there are only two meals a day."

"How many are you eating?"

"Just two. We eat together."

"So?"

"Verdiana, I would have to give up my clothes. I like colors! Undyed cloth of humble quality. Ugh!" She looked at Verdiana's black tunic and white veil. "Uh, I'm sorry. I didn't mean to criticize your clothing."

Verdiana laughed. "I'm not trying to impress anyone!"

"Neither am I."

"So?"

"I like colors."

"So do I. I like them very much on others."

"I like them on myself!"

"And when you die, what will you wear before the Judgment Seat?"

Buonadonna was miffed. "It's unfair to ask that."

"Don't you think you should be thinking about the Judgment? We're not getting younger."

Buonadonna groaned. But she understood. The Rule was a way to prepare oneself to meet the Lord by giving up in this world what she'd have to give up in the next—all her attachments to her time, her food, her clothes, her possessions. What had Francesco told them when he had visited Poggibonsi the first time? Something like "When you die, all you can take with you is your sins. Everything else isn't yours. It's God's grace."

"What should I do?"

"I think you need to pray about what to do. And then follow the advice that Our Lady gave to the servants at the wedding feast of Cana. 'Do whatever He tells you.'"

"What if He tells me to become a Sister of Penance?"

"What if He does?"

Buonadonna groaned.

And that is precisely what He did tell her. Perhaps He had told Francesco, too, because when he arrived three days later, he carried with him an extra tunic of undyed, gray wool. Buonadonna asked to be clothed in it.

NOTES

Luchesio, a wealthy merchant from Poggibonsi, is traditionally considered to be the first to live the Rule of Life for the Brothers and Sisters of Penance. His wife Buonadonna (which means "good woman"), who had originally opposed his conversion, joined him as a penitent. His story is told in the *Lives of the Saints of the Three Orders of Saint Francis* (Vol II, pp. 131–137) and on several Internet sites.

Verdiana was an anchorite to whom many people of the surrounding area came for counsel. We don't know if Buonadonna knew her. They both would have probably been in their late thirties to mid-forties at this time.

Francesco's words are recorded in the *Later Admonition to the Brothers and Sisters of Penance (Second Version of the Letter to the Faithful).*

107

Verdiana

Anchorite Cell, Church of Sant'Antonio, Castelfiorentino
(Late Summer 1221)

Verdiana sat on the two-arms-length bench mortared into the wall of her anchorage. She gazed through an iron filigree-covered window at the finely wrought silver dove suspended by slender chains over the altar. Dawn was just beginning to filter into the Church of Sant'Antonio, and soon Matins would begin.

This window was her way to communicate with Jesus. Through it, she confessed her sins to a priest. Through it, she prayed the Office with him and with other pious souls in the church. Through the window, she assisted at Mass and, occasionally, received the Body and Blood of Christ. She spent her days in sorrow for her own sins and those of others, in prayer for her soul and the souls of others, and in adoration of God.

She was speaking now with her Lover. After every Mass, the priest would take any remaining consecrated Bread, open a latched door on the dove's back, and deposit the Sacred Bread into the small hollow. That Sacred Bread was our Lord Jesus Christ, her Spouse, her Beloved Who had given His life for her, for everyone. The dove reminded her of the Holy Spirit, come to earth at Pentecost so long ago. The Holy Spirit was with her now as surely as were the two huge, speckled whip snakes that were stirring awake in a nearby corner of her anchorage.

Years ago, the Holy Spirit had sent those snakes to test her patience, foster her humility, and be her companions. The first evening they'd come, she had been meditating on the temptation of Christ in the desert. She hadn't seen the snakes until her meditation was complete, and then she'd spotted them devouring the plate of beans she had placed on the floor. For the briefest moment, she'd shuddered, knowing that she had no escape for, years before, she had been walled into this short, narrow cell as a recluse. Even the two windows were too narrow for her to exit.

With wonder and disgust, she had watched the snakes snap up the last bean and then curl on top of one another near the empty plate and slumber. She had lain down against the opposite wall, not four arm's length from the reptiles, and slept fitfully.

By dawn, the snakes were gone.

She thought she'd never see them again.

The next evening, she had just placed her plate of beans on the floor and was preparing for her meditation on the calling of the apostles when, startled, she saw the two snakes sliding through the open window through which she spoke to visitors. As they dropped to the floor, she darted to grab her plate of beans lest they devour today's meal. Terrified by her quick move, the snakes had slithered madly around the interior perimeter, their arm-and-a-half lengths quickly completing the circuit. No escape! Terrified, they whipped her with their tails. She jumped onto the bench to get away from them.

Frantic, they slithered up and around the walls, finding the entry window and dropping outside. Instead of being gone for good, they returned that evening. This time, she had placed her plate on the ledge. She began to eat warily, then, feeling pity for the reptiles, tossed them some beans. Tongues flickering, they snapped up the morsels, then curled together and fell asleep. She slept as far away from them as she could. By morning, they were gone again.

Coming and going became the snakes' daily pattern until they disappeared for winter when the weather turned cold. But each spring they reappeared to reside with her until the temperature grew frosty.

The snakes were gone and Matins long ago concluded when a gentle tapping at her outer window disturbed her meditation on Jesus' transfiguration. She blessed herself, rose from her bench, and went to speak to whoever had come.

Two clerics dressed in dusty, gray habits were outside. "Messer Luchesio from Poggibonsi sent us," explained the shorter one with the tearing eyes, "to meet you and to bring you these." The taller cleric handed her two loaves of bread.

"Grazie."

"Madonna Buonadonna thought you might also wish to become a Sister of Penance."

"Also?"

"We clothed them both today."

A laugh bubbled up from her soul. "Sì. I will join her."

NOTES

The history of Saint Verdiana and the location of her anchorage are told in the *Lives of the Saints of the Three Orders of Saint Francis* (vol. I, pp. 239–249) and on several Internet sites. The description of the snakes and their behavior matches that of the Western Whip Snake, one of Italy's most common, nonvenomous species. Francesco clothed Verdiana as a Sister of Penance, probably in 1221.

108

Sultan Malik al-Kamil

Cathedral of the Holy Virgin, Damietta, Egypt (September 8, 1221)

Sultan Malik al-Kamil sat cross-legged on the beautifully patterned floor of the mosque of Damietta, now changed by the Crusaders into their place of worship. The Cathedral of the Holy Virgin, they called it. Now that Damietta was again in his hands, al-Kamil would return this place to worship of Allah.

Al-Kamil had sent everyone out and stationed soldiers around the perimeter of the mosque because he wanted to be alone with Allah. His mind was running back over the years and running ahead into them. He needed to quiet it.

That Christian Sufi Francesco had shown him how some Christians stilled their minds. Al-Kamil tried it when he was completely alone.

Turning toward the east, Al-Kamil lay face down, his arms spread straight out from his side like wings, the left cheek of his stubbly bearded face pressed to the pavement, his legs straight out behind him. The shape of the cross, Francesco had told him. A cross had been the weapon that had killed their prophet. To Christians, that weapon seemed a holy thing.

Lying facedown, stretched out like this, made al-Kamil feel vulnerable, helpless. Should an enemy rush him, he'd have no time to leap to his feet, much less fumble for his dagger. The warrior in him pressured him to stand but he remained prostrate, his bulky turban cushioning his head against the pavement, his red robes cushioning his body. Maybe vulnerability was the intention of this prayer position. To be completely vulnerable to Allah. He had memorized Francesco's words to him and his leading men. "Humble yourselves that you may be exalted by Him. Hold back nothing of yourselves for yourselves, that He Who gives Himself totally to you may receive you totally!"

Allah, I give myself totally to you, he prayed. *Let these images from the past fade so that I may think wisely into the future, for the sake of your people.*

He was sick of warfare. Battles with family. Battles with Christians. Battles with Mongols. Why these wars? Francesco had been right. Let us make peace.

Peace had to come from both sides. After taking Damietta two years ago, the Christians had continued to fight. Al-Kamil had despaired of ever seeing or occupying his beloved city again, so he had built the massive city of El-Mansoura farther south. He had prayed that Allah would make the new city's name—the Victorious—prophetic, for al-Kamil had never surrendered in his heart. Now, through a series of stratagems, he had finally battered the Christian army into surrender. He had fed what remained of their tattered troops, released their hostages, sold them some of his own ships at a fair price, and returned the masts of their conquered vessels. He had exchanged a relic of their beloved True Cross for his beloved Damietta.

The True Cross didn't seem to matter much to some of those brutal, wanton beasts who purported to follow a prophet who preached and practiced holiness. Why were some Christians so unlike one of their warrior leaders, Jean de Brienne, the king of Jerusalem? Al-Kamil had eaten with Jean as he had with Francesco. He could speak to Jean as he had spoken to Francesco. He considered both men of honor as his friends.

Allah, why aren't all men honorable? Why so much evil?

YOU CAN BRING GOOD. The response came in his calmed mind.

I've tried.

I'LL HELP YOU DO MORE.

He lay still, never wanting to rise and fight again. He remembered the day those two Christian Sufis had come to him. They said it was the day on which their religion celebrated the birth of their prophet's mother. Wasn't this the same day, three years later? The Christians had renamed this mosque in honor of that mother.

Al-Kamil pushed himself to a sitting position. Was that statue of a sitting woman holding on her lap a sitting, naked infant, a statue of that mother and the infant prophet? Both Jean and Francesco had spoken tenderly of this mother and son. Indeed, isn't the love of any mother and son a tender love?

A thought flew like an arrow into his mind.

YOU, TOO, ARE MY SON. YOU, TOO, HAVE MY TENDER LOVE.

His gaze, like loving hands, traced the face of the statue.

"The Christians may remain in Damietta," he said softly as if to the woman. "And their Sufis." He had seen Sufis here, dressed like Francesco and his friend. He had learned that they lived together in a small house in the city and went about helping everyone in need.

Perhaps Damietta could again become a city where people lived in peace no matter which God they served.

NOTES

Sultan Malik al-Kamil entered Damietta on September 8, 1221, after concluding peace negotiations as stated in this chapter (see *Moses*, pp. 166–176). We have no proof of him praying in the mosque-turned-cathedral. However, he did allow Christians, including the brothers whom Francesco had left in Damietta, to remain peacefully in the city. The words al-Kamil remembers are from Francesco's *Letter to the Entire Order*.

Part Sixteen

"A Servant of God Can Be Known to Have the Spirit of the Lord in This Way"

109

Magpie

Field outside Bevagna (Summer 1222)

The magpie strutted around the field, just one of a flock of other magpies, crows, and doves, who were feasting on a swarm of locusts. It thought nothing of its shimmering black head, wings, and tail, or their striking contrast against its white breast. It thought nothing, too, of a herd of gray-clad men who came walking down the road, nor of one man who struck off from the herd and started to slowly approach. Like the other birds, the magpie glanced curiously at the man, but he seemed no threat and the locusts were abundant and tasty. Like the other birds, the magpie kept snatching and eating.

Here was the man, standing right among them. The birds milled about him, pecking and eating. The man was making sounds. Humans could make many more sounds than birds.

"My brother birds, you should greatly praise your Creator, and love Him always. He gave you feathers to wear, wings to fly, and whatever you need. God made you noble among His creatures and gave you a home in the purity of the air, so that, though you neither sow nor reap, He nevertheless protects and governs you without your least care."

So many sounds! The man continued to walk among the birds. He was so near! The magpie felt mildly threatened. But it was not about to leave this locust banquet, so it assumed a threatening posture, stretching its neck, spreading and flapping its wings, and opening its beak, staring at the man who paused and looked at it, his mouth curling up. Was he about to growl? Other birds flew at him, trying to chase him off. His mouth opened in a quiet, odd gurgling sound like quick, deep chirps.

The magpie was filling up. It grabbed one more locust and swallowed it.

The man was making more sounds. "Grazie for listening to me. You obey the Lord better than we. Grazie for showing me that the Lord wishes me to exhort all creatures to praise Him!"

The man raised his hands and made some odd motions. "God bless you, brother birds, in the name of the Father and of the Son and of the Holy Spirit."

The magpie cocked its head, looked again at the man, realized that it could eat no more, and, lifting its wings, flew off to roost and rest.

NOTES

The opening quotation for Part Sixteen is from Francis' *Admonition XII*.

1C (first book, chapter XXI) records this undated incident as well as Francesco's homily.

110

Dorotea

Square in Front of the Town Hall, Bologna (August 15, 1222)

Was that the saint? Impossible! Saints glowed with holiness. This short fellow in a filthy, patched tunic hadn't even bathed. Through the blazing heat, Dorotea had hobbled here from the palazzo where she served Madonna Eligia. Through the huge crowd of students, merchants, lords and ladies, and just about everyone else from Bologna, Dorotea had elbowed her way close to the steps. There her dull ears would be able to hear the saint and her dim eyes take in his every elegant feature. She had stood, waiting and waiting while her bad hip complained with pain. Never in her long life had she seen or heard a saint. And that was the saint?

Everyone talked about Fra Francesco. He had turned water into wine at some hermitage. He had saved a child from being eaten by a wolf. He had even tamed a wolf! Swallows obeyed him when he told them to be quiet and let him speak. He healed a blind woman, a paralyzed man, a crippled boy. He was a miracle worker. And that was the man?

Standing at the top of the town hall steps, the dingy brother flung his arms out and called in a firm, strong voice, "To all here, welcome. God's blessings to you good people." Then he made the Sign of the Cross over them.

"God's honor to you angels!" The saint scanned the crowd as if seeing angelic beings among them.

"God's punishment to you demons!" Demons? Dorotea looked left and right. She saw no demons. She saw no angels.

"Consider, O human being, in what great excellence the Lord God has placed *you*," he emphasized "you."

". . . for He created and formed *you*," again, the emphasis on "you."

". . . to the *image*," emphasis on "image."

". . . of His beloved Son according to the body." He poked his arms and chest.

". . . and to His likeness according to His Spirit." He raised his arms upward and twirled.

In the pause that followed, Dorotea considered this. It seemed incredible. God had made *her*. He could have made someone else. But He made *her*. And she was not merely a creation. She was God's *image*. Remarkable!

"And all creatures under heaven,"—he swept his arms outward, upward, downward—"serve, know, and obey their Creator, each according to its own nature, better than you,"—he swept his arms over the crowd—"and even the *demons*"—emphasis on demons—"did not crucify Him, but you,"—his dark eyes seemed to penetrate Dorotea—"together with them, have crucified Him and are still crucifying Him by delighting in vices and sins." Pause again.

Vices? Sins? He must mean people like Messer Aldo, the usurer. Or Mila, the dishonest fruit vendor. She'd cheat you if she could.

But Dorotea? She was too old to have vices or sins.

"There are many who, while insisting on prayers and obligations, inflict many abstinences and punishments upon their bodies."

Sì. She did that. She took less to eat and wore a hair shirt. She tried to be holy. But she never told anyone. Jesus said to perform penance in secret.

"But they are immediately offended and disturbed about a single word which seems to be harmful to their bodies or about something which might be taken away from them."

Oh, dear. It was true she disliked being corrected by others. And, well, yes, she had been very upset when she couldn't find the comb that Madonna Eligia had given her. Surely one of the other servants had stolen it. But no one admitted it.

"These people are not poor in spirit, for someone who is poor in spirit hates himself and loves those who strike him on the cheek."

The raggedy saint was still speaking, acting out what he said, going on to serving Christ and explaining how angels did and demons didn't serve Him.

Dorotea, however, was thinking about how she served Him. *Why, I don't*, she thought with a start. *I serve myself. Even in serving my lady, I'm serving myself. I care for her, and she cares for me. If I didn't care for her, I'd be a beggar.*

Was "God" anything more than just a word that she said?

The saint was done speaking. A brief hush fell over the crowd. Then Dorotea felt the crowd pressing past her, thronging the saint. This was why she had come. She pushed forward with them, wriggling to get closer to the holy man. Other tattered penitent men were unsuccessfully trying to hold back the crowd, which shoved past them. Dorotea was near the saint now. She wrestled a sack from her shoulder and drew out a pair of shears. Elbowing her way closer to the holy man, she eyed the hem of his tunic for the least muddy spot. There was no such thing. Therefore, quickly, she grabbed the hem and snipped off a small section which she clutched in her hand as she straightened up. She saw another, younger woman also attempting to cut a relic, but one of the penitent men caught her by the arm and pulled her away. Now the saint was surrounded by the penitent men. No one could get near him.

But Dorotea had her relic.

Over there was the woman who had been foiled in her attempt. Dorotea elbowed her way through the crowd to that woman.

"Come with me," she said to her.

The woman followed Dorotea as they wove through the thinning mob and down an alley away from the crowd. In the shadows, Dorotea opened her hand. The other woman stared at the mud-caked slice of gray wool.

"You can have half," Dorotea said. She took out her shears, cut the cloth in two, and gave half to the woman, who reverently pressed it to her lips.

"Grazie," the woman breathed. She flung her arms around Dorotea in a strong hug.

Grazie, Dorotea thought. Had she not heard the saint speak, she never would have thought to share her relic.

NOTES

Thomas of Split [Spalato] (*Early Documents II*, p. 808) shares his eyewitness account of Francesco preaching in Bologna on this date, how he appeared, his sermon topic, and the mob that thronged him afterward, seeking relics. The miracles which the fictional Dorotea recalls are recorded in the following sources:

— Changes water into wine at Sant'Urbano (1C, first book, chapter XXI).

— Saves child about to be eaten by wolf (related by Luke Wadding in *Annals Minorum* and a tale remembered in the town of Lugnano in Teverina, Italy, where a church and convent of Saint Francis have been erected on the site of the miracle (see http://www.sanfrancesco.com/san-francesco-assisi.asp?group=20&post=107).

— Tames wolf (*Fioretti*, chapter 21).

— Quiets swallows at Alviano (1C, first book, chapter XXI).

— Heals blind woman at Narni (1C, first book, chapter XXIV).

— Heals paralyzed man at Narni (1C, first book, chapter XXIII).

— Heals lame boy at Toscanella (1C, first book, chapter XXIII).

Francesco's words are taken from his *Admonitions*, sections V and XIV.

111

Fra Agnollo (Angelo) Tarlati

Hermitage of Monte Casale (Late Summer 1222)

At the bell's tolling, Fra Agnollo woke sleepy-eyed for the Office. This was the last day of his Maria week when he could give all his time to prayer. Tomorrow, all four brothers switched duties, and the Marias who prayed in solitude this week became next week's Marthas. They did the physical work in between their prayers with the other brothers. Tomorrow, Agnollo would be hoeing the vegetable gardens, mending the hermitages, and begging. Maybe it would rain tomorrow and impede outdoor work.

Ugh! Here he was, daydreaming about avoiding work just the way he used to daydream about avoiding hunting with his noble friends. Hunting had exhausted his delicate body more than gardening. He could always put his hoe aside and rest, but, on the hunt, rest came only when the quarry fell. Odd, though. With simple food and less sleep, his body was tougher and hardier than it had ever been in his father's castle. His mother never would believe it true.

The four brothers lifted their voices in Prime and Lauds, their singing and chanting mingled with birdsong. When Agnollo left the chapel, rays from the just risen sun were lifting the cabbages out of darkness. Agnollo smiled at the years-old memory of Francesco telling him and another inquiring noble brother to plant cabbages with the leaves under the soil and their roots upward. Odd, but Agnollo had never planted cabbages nor dug soil so he followed instructions. The other fellow proceeded to instruct Francesco about the proper way to plant with the roots underground. Francesco dismissed him but accepted Agnollo. The cabbage-planting had been a test of obedience, not of horticulture.

In his hermitage, Agnollo took a partly finished basket from a corner and began to weave a willow shoot through the side. Although the large basket would carry vegetables or alms, Agnollo was weaving it to help focus his attention while praying. When God gave him an insight, he'd put the basket aside and meditate on the thought.

The day proceeded quietly and peacefully. Agnollo prayed the remaining six Hours with the other brothers and rejoiced that Francesco was there for the hour of None. Francesco greeted all the brothers with a welcoming embrace but spoke little. Why speak if nothing need be said?

Today's daily meal, delivered with a knock to his cell after the hour of Vespers, was especially flavorful. The begged trenchers were saturated with succulent venison drippings. Compline. Silence and sleep. And then Agnollo was checking the height of the moon to know when to wake the brothers for Matins. His Martha day had begun.

As he walked to the chapel to toll the bell, he felt connected to all the other hermitages Francesco had established. Monte Lacerone in Greccio. Sant'Urbano near Narni. The Romita near Cesi. San Gemini. Stroncone. Sant'Apollinare in Spoleto. Le Celle in Cortona. Santa Maria della Vittoria in Gubbio. Hermitages, too, in France, Spain, Germany, Syria, Hungary. In each of them, a brother would be tolling the bell and then he and his sleepy-eyed, yawning brothers would pray together in the chapel, lifting their songs of praise to God.

Shortly after the hour of Terce, Agnollo answered a knock at the door.

Oh, no! Three young thieves who lived in the forest. They'd brazenly named themselves—Vagabondo, Vipera, and Verro.

"Please," Vagabondo said, removing his cap, "have you anything to eat? We have no food."

Agnollo was guardian, the one whom Francesco had placed in authority over the other brothers. Some brothers would feed these no-goods out of pity or fear, always exhorting them to do penance. To what effect? The robbers politely took the food, promised amendment, and then continued to accost travelers. What duplicity!

"It is not right to give you alms because you are robbers and do many very evil things to people." Agnollo closed the door in their face.

Shortly thereafter, another knock came.

It had better not be the robbers.

It was Francesco, shading his eyes with one hand, and his guardian Fra Riccerio. After embracing one another, Francesco asked, "Do you know those angry men we passed?"

"Sì. Three robbers who came begging."

"Were they upset with what you gave them?"

"I gave them nothing," Agnollo said. "They do many evil things and will not repent."

Francesco groaned. "Fra Agnollo, when you first came to us at Monte Casale, you were very young, very delicate, and very courteous. Do you remember?"

"Certainly. You said I couldn't endure your harsh life."

"Sì. Then you said, 'Are you not men like me? Therefore, if you can endure it, so shall I be able to, by the grace of Jesus Christ.'"

"Sì." He had endured. And flourished.

"Your name Agnollo certainly suited you as you appeared to be angelic. Has the gentle angel now become an aggressor?"

Agnollo felt suddenly ashamed for turning away the robbers. However, should he enable vice?

"Turning them away is no way to convert someone," Francesco said. "I'll tell you what to do." And he did.

So, within a few minutes, Agnollo, carrying a jug of wine, and Riccerio, carrying two huge trenchers, were walking deep into the thick forest, calling out, "Come, Brother Robbers, come to us, because we are brothers, and we are bringing you some good bread and good wine." They had not been walking long when the thieves appeared among the trees and surrounded them.

"Forgive me for turning you away," Agnollo said, following Francesco's instructions. He set the jug at his feet, reached into his tunic's hood, and pulled out a clean, grayish square of cloth which he smoothed on the forest floor.

"Sit. Bring forth your cups and knives, and I will serve you," he offered.

Wordlessly, the robbers untied their cups from their belts and pulled their knives from their sheaths. Then they sat, looking incredulously at Agnollo, and held their cups toward him.

Agnollo offered a brief prayer. "My Lord, bless these good men and this good food, to Your great glory. Amen."

Then he filled each cup with wine while Riccerio tore in half the two huge trenchers. They passed a half to each robber.

The Eucharist.

The Last Supper.

Christ's breaking of bread at table on the way to Emmaus.

Christ died for sinners. Sinners like these men. Sinners like me.

These youths aren't evil. They're tarnished good.

Oh, God, save them!

He remembered Francesco's advice. *When they are done eating, offer them some brief words about the Lord.*

They ate ravenously until nothing was left but an empty jug and crumbs on the gray cloth.

My Lord, give me the words.

Agnollo swallowed his nervousness and began to pray in a steady voice. "Grazie, my Lord, for this meal. May it sustain us to serve You. Amen."

Then to the robbers. "My brothers, our Lord shared bread and wine with His apostles and disciples whom He loved. At His Last Supper with them, He changed bread and wine into His Body and Blood. He offers Himself to us in every Holy Mass. Perhaps you have not been to Mass in some time?"

The robbers looked at each other and then looked away. "Our Lord waits for you there because He loves you as He loved His disciples. He weeps for your love, my brothers. Now, for the love of Him Who loves you, I ask you, my brothers, to promise me that you will not strike anyone or injure another person, for they are children of God just as you are. Can you promise that?" Riccerio, sitting quietly next to the robbers, was nodding. Agnollo had phrased rightly what Francesco had told him to say.

"I promise!" Vagabondo's agreement fairly burst from his lips.

"I also." Vipera nodded.

Verro shrugged. "I guess so."

"Wonderful!" Agnollo hoped they could hear his glee.

They chatted about how welcome the balmy weather was after the winter chill. Then Agnollo realized he should return to work. He gathered up the gray cloth, shook out the crumbs, and folded it back into his tunic's hood. Taking the empty jug, he bid the robbers farewell and returned with Riccerio to the hermitage.

The next day, after advising Agnollo about his next encounter with the robbers, Francesco left with Riccerio. Thus, after None, Agnollo, accompanied by youthful and spry Fra Florencio, pushed into the thick forest, calling, "Come, Brother Robbers, we have brought you eggs and cheese, bread and wine. Come, eat, and praise God!" When they were deep into the woods, the robbers appeared.

Agnollo spread the gray cloth on the ground. "Come, sit, and we'll serve you."

The robbers sat around the cloth and pulled out their cups and knives.

"My Lord, bless this food and these men so that, through this meal, You may be praised for Your goodness. Amen," Agnollo prayed.

Florencio filled each man's cup with wine while Agnollo broke the trenchers in halves, which he handed to each. Florencio gave two hard-boiled eggs to each robber while Agnollo sliced into thirds a small cheese which he had begged that morning. The men devoured the meal and washed it down with wine. Soon the jug was empty, and crumbs and eggshells littered the gray cloth. Now to do as Francesco had instructed. Agnollo breathed a short, mental prayer. *My Lord, help me.*

His smile was genuine as he began to pray aloud. "Grazie, my Lord, for this good food and these good men. May we all serve You well. Amen." Then he looked, gently he hoped, at the robbers who were expectantly looking at him. "My brothers," he began, "why do you stay here all day long, dying of hunger, suffering many evil things and in your actions doing many evil things for which you will lose your souls unless you are converted? It is better to serve the Lord, who will supply your bodily needs in this world and save your souls in the end."

"How?" Vagabondo asked.

"Do as we do," Agnollo said. "Offer to work for your food."

"Can we work for you?" Vipera asked.

"Sì. We will gladly feed you."

"Can we try?" Verro asked, looking at Vagabondo.

Thus, the thieves appeared daily at the hermitage to carry wood, tend the gardens, and help with construction. After Vespers, they ate with the brothers, then disappeared into the woods.

In early October, Vipera asked, "How may I become a brother?" Agnollo clothed him in a gray tunic and changed his name to Innocente.

By then, Verro, who had his eye on a young maid whom he hoped to marry, was farming in Sansepolcro for a lord who had given him a small cottage.

Vagabondo grew restless. In November, he told Agnollo, "I need to see the world, but I want to save my soul."

"See the world as a Brother of Penance," Agnollo advised.

Vagabondo found the tunic of undyed cloth intriguing. Agnollo explained the Rule of Life to him, clothed him, and sent him off. "I'll pray for you in Rome," Vagabondo promised.

Shortly thereafter, on his way to Fonte Colombo to rewrite the Rule, Francesco visited Monte Casale. When told of the three robbers, he said to Agnollo, "You've been God's instrument. Because of you, they'll save their souls."

NOTES

The tale of the three unnamed converted robbers is told in the *Assisi Compilation* (Section 115) which this chapter follows closely. The author has named the robbers Vagabond, Viper, and Boar. Angelo Tarlati's noble background, his being guardian of Monte Casale, and his involvement with the robbers are retold in the *Fioretti* (Chapter 26) although the year is not specified.

The cabbage test is a popular story told in that vicinity. In an article ("Angelo Tancredi: il frate discreto e cortese,") on Angelo Tancredi, Ludovico Perroni states that Angelo's nickname was Agnollo (in modern Italian shortened to Agnolo, which means angel), although Perroni seems to have confused the two Angelos. Tancredi was a tall, robust man as made evident by his skeleton, while Tarlati was delicate and would more likely fit the "angelic" description.

Francesco wrote about the Martha/Mary cycle of living in hermitages in his *A Rule for Hermitages*. This chapter lists a few of the many hermitages in existence in 1222.

112

Cardinal Ugolino dei Conti di Segni

Palazzo, Rome (November 1223)

Near a playful fire in the hearth of the fire room in his palazzo, Cardinal Ugolino dei Conti di Segni sat hunched over a table with carefully penned parchments spread before him. Neatly written in impeccable Latin, the pages belied, he knew, the anguish behind them.

Three days ago, when he had returned home after a series of meetings, he had found Fra Francesco and Fra Riccerio squatting near his doorstep. The brothers had reworded their Rule, they said, at Pope Onorio's request. Riccerio, a notary learned in Latin, had transcribed the wording they had finally agreed upon. Could Ugo review this and suggest any changes before presenting it to Onorio?

He had housed the brothers in another part of his palazzo because he didn't want Francesco, who was obviously ill, staying with lepers. He couldn't send him to Cardinal Brancaleone's secluded tower where Francesco had once endured some sort of violent physical and spiritual attack. Demons, Francesco had said.

Ugo began to read over the Rule.

Hmm. More juridically written than the one Onorio rejected.

That Rule had been longer, flowing from one Scripture verse to another. Francesco had followed his instructions about removing those verses.

Good.

What needed to be reworded, reworked, removed, and reorganized to make this radical life-style palatable to the pope and the other cardinals? Here and there he made changes, finishing by Sext. He called Francesco and Riccerio, gave them new parchment, and asked Riccerio to copy the revision for Ugo to present to Onorio.

Francesco and Riccerio were still lodged in Ugo's palazzo on November 29 when Ugo presented them with the copy of their Rule. It began officially in Latin: "Honorius, Bishop, Servant of the servants of God, to His Beloved Sons, Brother Francis and the other brothers of the Order of the Lesser Brothers, Health and Apostolic Benediction."

Pope Onorio had recognized the religio as an ordine. No more rules would be written. The brothers would live by this one.

NOTES

As cardinal protector of the brothers, Ugolino surely had input into the Rule, which Pope Honorious approved on November 29, 1223 (*Early Documents I,* p. 99). This chapter postulates that Francesco and his guardian Riccerio brought the Rule to Ugolino. AC (section 117) records the demonic attack on Francesco in Cardinal Brancaleone's tower.

113

Fra Leone

Porziuncula, Assisi (Mid-December 1223)

"Leone, we're going to Greccio!" Francesco had announced after Lauds. Now, in the pale morning light, they were on their way, the Porziuncula receding behind them.

Good that today was chill and drizzly. Shivering would distract Leone from brooding about how the Rule had been gutted until only a carcass remained.

Two years ago, at Lord Pope's request, Francesco had written down the brothers' Rule of Life, capturing the joy, simplicity, and faith with which they'd begun. Then Fra Cäsar von Speyer had embellished the Rule with Gospel passages. How could Pope Onorio have rejected it? Then Francesco rewrote the Rule, but Fra Elia lost it. So, during months of prayer and fasting at Fonte Colombo, Francesco again rewrote the Rule. This time, Cardinal Ugolino made changes. To Leone, the approved Rule was flat. Concise. Excised of the fire it once had. Nevertheless, Lord Pope had declared the religio to be an ordine and prescribed its name: the Lesser Brothers.

Ever since the Rule's acceptance, Leone had been seeking a chance to speak alone with Francesco. Now he had the opportunity, as he was temporarily replacing Riccerio as Francesco's guardian, while Riccerio was in Rieti to arrange for his final studies for the priesthood.

"Francesco, what if obedience to the Church conflicts with obedience to God?"

"Leone, that isn't possible. God ordained the Church. Obedience to the Church is obedience to God."

"What if it's not?"

"That cannot be."

"Why not?"

"Because our Lord Jesus Christ gave authority to the Church to speak in His name."

"What if they don't?"

"Leone, if we think that, we are in error. Not the Church."

"The Church has had some bad popes."

"Sì. But they have not taught error."

"What if they do?"

"They cannot. What are you thinking of, Leone?"

"Our Rule. So much has changed from how we began. Why don't we just start over? Live like we did at the beginning? You've told me that this idea tempts you."

Francesco was quiet. Thoughtfully they walked on, their bare feet slurping in the mud.

"Leone, do you remember a few weeks ago when we were walking from Perugia to the Porziuncula and we were talking about joy?"

Leone remembered. "Sì. It was right after you granted Fra Antonio permission to teach the brothers theology."

"Sì. You were admiring his faith and knowledge. He's been well-taught."

Leone remembered. Compared with that Portuguese brother, Leone felt inferior. Both men were priests, but Antonio knew so much more than Leone, and he expressed it much more eloquently. He was even converting heretics. Leone had never converted a heretic.

"What wasn't joy, Leone?"

Leone remembered. When they had arrived at the Porziuncula, he had written down the dialogue. "You said joy was not in the brothers giving good example nor in working miracles."

"Nor in their intelligence or knowledge or ability to prophesy. Nor was perfect joy in how many people they converted," Francesco added.

"Everything I thought was perfect joy, you said wasn't."

They walked on silently. The sun was rising, the drizzle ending. Leone pulled back his hood and lifted his face to the sun. The warmth soothed him.

"What did I think perfect joy was?"

"Being at the end of one's patience and being rejected and ridiculed, but still keeping faith and rejoicing in sufferings because of love for the cross of Christ."

"Sì, Leone." Francesco drew his hood over his face. The sunlight must be irritating his eyes. "So, doesn't it seem that we should remain with the brotherhood and practice perfect joy?"

Francesco paused while Leone tried to imagine living a life under the rewrite of the Rule. Some brothers were already starting to live more like monks than like the vagabond penitents of the beginning.

"Leone, I was at prayer today and in spirit I heard the words of the Gospel. 'If your faith were the size of a mustard seed you could say to this mountain, "Move from here to there," and it would move.' Leone, my faith was smaller than a mustard seed!"

"How can your faith be small after all you've done in faith?"

"Leone, I've told you everything. But you can't know me the way I know myself. And I can't know myself the way God knows me."

Certainly. Who could really know a soul but God?

"I asked my Lord, 'What is this mountain?' What do you suppose He said?"

"I don't know."

"He said, 'The mountain is your temptation.'"

"Your temptation to leave the brothers and start over?"

"Sì. I knew at once that I was tempted because my faith is pitiable. So, I prayed, 'Then, my Lord, may it be done to me according to Your Word.' And He has moved the mountain of my temptation. It's gone. Totally gone. So simple, Leone, to give it all to God."

Francesco turned to Leone with a grin. "Do you know what I must do now?"

Leone had no idea. He was still assimilating the idea of a temptation leaving when one lets God have it.

"I must live the Rule as I always have and be an example to the brothers. That's all. My Lord has used me to bring the brotherhood, His ordine, to the

Church. The Church has approved the Rule. This is what we prayed for! And I must rejoice. This is God's Will."

Leone couldn't escape the inevitable. If Francesco thought that the shift in the ordine's direction was God's Will, then what more could he argue?

"God has the right to change things in ways we don't expect, doesn't He?" Francesco asked. "He doesn't have to ask our permission, eh? We need to keep doing His Will, like little children following where their good Father leads."

Leone caught glee in Francesco's voice. "Do you realize what our Lord did, Leone? He emptied Himself and came to us as a helpless babe. He impressed this on me in prayer. I must give my whole will to others, just as a babe must do. He's making me littler and littler, Leone. What joy!"

The sun was beaming down on them, driving off the morning chill. Francesco pulled his hood farther down over his eyes.

"Leone, it's almost Christmas. Let's show and experience the humble helplessness of our Lord Who made Himself vulnerable for our sake. I've prayed about who will help us. Messer Giovanni di Velita will. In Greccio."

NOTES

AC (section 63) mentions Francesco's great temptation and its resolution. The author speculates that the temptation was to leave the Order, which had grown distant from Francesco's vision. The author also speculates that Francesco's conversation with Leone on perfect joy (See *Early Documents I*, pp. 166–167) was prompted by emulation of the gifted Fra Antonio. Humbled by Antonio's devotion and knowledge, the brothers asked Francesco to allow this highly educated Portuguese priest and brother to teach them (24Gen, section 132).

Sometime after November 29, 1223, when Pope Onorio approved the Rule for the brothers, Francesco sent a brief note to Antonio, stating, "I am pleased that you teach sacred theology to the brothers provided that, as is contained in the Rule, you 'do not extinguish the Spirit of prayer and devotion' during study of this kind" (*Early Documents I*, p. 107). Antonio began to teach after receiving this permission.

Part Seventeen

"Brother Francis, a Worthless and Weak Man, Your Very Little Servant"

114

Messer Giovanni di Velita

Cave, Greccio (December 25, 1223)

With his gray, woolen cap brushing the ceiling of this cave, Messer Giovanni di Velita pressed his tall, lanky body against the cave's wall. Standing here in his simple, undyed woolen mantle and tunic, Giovanni was a marked contrast to his richly dressed, plump wife Madonna Alticama. She was cradling their well-bundled infant son, Arturo. Three beings in a mass of reverent neighbors, vassals, servants, and Lesser Brothers, enjoying the warmth of this torchlit cavern.

Fifteen days before, just after Giovanni had granted permission to two of his servants to marry, Fra Francesco had been ushered into the lord's chamber at the Velita house. "Messer Giovanni," he had said, "the birthday of our Lord approaches. Would you want to celebrate together in Greccio?"

Celebrate with Fra Francesco? Giovanni barely restrained his eagerness. "Sì!"

"Sì!" Francesco's voice was exuberant. Giovanni imagined him grinning under that outlandish hood.

"You own Monte Lacerone, Messer?"

"Sì." That mountain of sheer rock walls, cliffs, and caves towered behind and above Greccio. He hunted there. He kept in check the robbers who hid there.

Years ago, his servants had carved out of the rocks a locus for the Lesser Brothers. Giovanni knew Monte Lacerone well.

"Some believe that the stable in which our Lord was born was a cave," Francesco declared.

Giovanni hadn't known that. But where was this conversation headed?

"I wish to enact the memory of that Babe Who was born in Bethlehem: to see as much as possible with my own bodily eyes the discomfort of His infant needs, how He lay in a manger, and how, with an ox and an ass standing by, He rested on hay."

Before Giovanni could express his confusion, Francesco began to explain.

"I need a cave, an ox and ass, a manger, straw. Big enough for Fra Leone to offer Christmas Mass. Will you help me, Messer?"

"You want me to find a large cave on Monte Lacerone, bring an ox and ass to it, and make it look like the stable where our Savior was born?"

"Sì!" The hood bobbed up and down. "But not a cave of the brothers. Another one. A wild one."

"Not a cave my servants made? One made by God?"

"Sì!"

Giovanni felt tingly with joy. "Might you permit our little Arturo to represent the Holy Child?"

"Ah, Messer. I don't wish to disappoint you. The manger must be empty. Everyone must see the Babe as their own. The Holy Spirit will show the Child to those whom He chooses."

Thus, the next day, Giovanni and a servant were exploring the natural caves on Monte Lacerone. Goodness, there were many. All unsuitable. Too small. Too inaccessible. Too narrow.

Lord, help us! Giovanni had prayed.

And sure enough, He did. About a half-hour's walk northeast from the Lesser Brothers' locus, Giovanni and his servant found a natural cavern in the side of a cliff. It was accessible. Big enough. Tall enough. In it stood a boulder with an impression in its center. The manger!

Grazie, my Lord!

Grazie, indeed, for now all was as Francesco had requested.

With torchlight illuminating their exultant faces, the Lesser Brothers, pressed against the cave wall directly across from Giovanni and Alticama, began to sing. The crowd, most of whom Giovanni knew, joined them. Music swelled the night.

In his thirty years of life, Giovanni had never recognized the hand of God at work so much as he did now. His gaze went to Fra Francesco, standing to the side of Fra Leone. *Through Francesco*, he realized, *God has changed my life.*

The singing ceased. In silence, Leone, followed by Francesco, incensed the altar, then led the crowd in the Sign of the Cross and began the prayers of the Mass.

Giovanni blessed himself and tried to fix his attention on the mysteries happening before him, but his mind wandered to the mysteries of his own life. How he had been a blustery, stylish knight, thinking no more about his soul than about his dinner, until Francesco had come to Greccio—was it ten years ago? Giovanni couldn't remember exactly when he decided to relinquish his sword and lavish wardrobe and become a Brother of Penance. Alticama had accepted his decision but felt no call to join him. God was leading her by a different path.

Leone was quietly offering the prayers of the Mass. Francesco was softly responding.

Peace.

The instant he had come to Greccio, Francesco had brought peace. At that time, wolves and hailstorms, both rumored to originate on distant Monte Terminillo, had plagued the city. Francesco had addressed these in a sermon. "To the praise and honor of God," he had said, "I tell you that, if each one of you turns away from sin and turns to God with the whole heart, firm resolve, and will to persevere, I trust our Lord Jesus Christ that, in His mercy, He will soon deliver you from the scourge of the wolves and of the hail from which, for a long time, you have been suffering. He will make you grow and increase in both spiritual and temporal things. I also tell you if you return to your vomit, this scourge and pestilence will return, and more and worse disasters will afflict you."

Taking his words to heart, Greccio had ceased quarreling and backbiting. Then the hailstorms had ceased; the wolves disappeared.

Francesco was singing the Gospel about Christ's birth. From this weak, diminutive man swelled such a powerful, melodious, clear voice that even those outside the cave could surely understand every word.

Then Francesco began to preach, the gold of his deacon's vestments shimmering in the torchlight. His voice was strong and clear. "Il Bambino di Betlemme," he called the Christ Child. The way Francesco drew out the words was nudging some deep memory. The third time Francesco sweetly called out "Betlemme," Giovanni remembered the lambs at birthing time, bleating for their mothers. Betlemme, on Francesco's lips, sounded like that bleating. The Lamb of God was born in Betlemme.

Francesco's preaching swelled into a powerful, resonant *lauda* throbbing with love.

"Exult in God our help!
Shout to the Lord God living and true with cries of gladness!
Because the Lord, the Most High,
the Awesome, is the Great King over all the earth."

Giovanni felt as if he were surrounded by praising angels as Francesco sang near the manger. When he spoke of Jesus, it was as if he were tasting the words, savoring their sweetness.

"Because the Most Holy Father of heaven, our King before all ages,
sent His Beloved Son from on high
and He was born of the Blessed Virgin Holy Mary.
He called me: You are my Father
and I will place Him, my firstborn, as the Highest,
above all the kings of the earth.
On that day the Lord sent His mercy
and at night His song."

Francesco's voice rose as he stooped over the manger. Suddenly Giovanni saw, resting in the manger, a tiny child sleeping so soundly that he appeared dead.

"This is the day the Lord has made
let us rejoice and be glad in it.
For the Most Holy Child has been given to us
and has been born for us on the way
and placed in a manger
because he did not have a place in the inn."

Giovanni seemed to see Francesco wake the Child, pick Him up, and kiss Him tenderly. Arturo! No. Not Arturo. Jesus.

Giovanni's eyes welled with tears. Francesco had not wanted anyone to represent a human being in this holy tableau. He had wanted each person to find himself or herself in the scene. What was the phrase that Francesco had written several years ago in a letter to the penitents? It was often read at the monthly gathering of the Brothers and Sisters of Penance: "We are mothers when we carry Him in our heart and body through a divine love and a pure and sincere conscience and give birth to Him through a holy activity, which must shine as an example before others."

The impression of the Holy Child was gone. Francesco was singing again.

"And peace on earth to those of good will.
Let the heavens rejoice and the earth exult,
let the fields and all that is in them be joyful.
Sing a new song to the Lord,
sing to the Lord all the earth.
Because the Lord is great and worthy of praise
He is awesome beyond all gods.
Give to the Lord, you families of nations,
give to the Lord glory and praise,
give to the Lord the glory due His name."

The song faded into silence. Giovanni could hear the ox chewing its cud. Francesco spoke, his voice powerful in its plea.

"Take up your bodies and carry His holy cross
And follow His most holy commands even to the end."

Then he took his place at the altar, Leone rose, and the Holy Mass continued. As befitted a penitent brother, and according to his Rule of Life, Giovanni received the Body of the Lord from Leone's hands and the Blood of the Lord from the chalice offered by Francesco. *Il Bambino di Betlemme*, the Man of miracles and preaching, the Lord of the Cross and the Resurrection, had come to him, was dwelling in him. One Lord. The Prince of Peace. Born in a stable like the one Giovanni had re-created.

To that Lord, he prayed. *You have given me life. You have given me everything. I give all back to You. Grazie, my God.*

NOTES

The opening quotation for Part Seventeen is from Francis' *A Letter to the Entire Order*, 3.

1C (first book, chapter X) records how Francesco, with the help of Greccio's lord (Giovanni di Velita), devised a live Nativity scene in a cave on Monte Lacerone, and how a bystander (named Giovanni in later histories) saw Francesco awaken the Christ Child.

Leonard von Matt and Walter Hauser (*Saint Francis of Assisi*, p. 65) state that Giovanni was "a tertiary who knew the Saint's love of solitude."

A local tradition around Greccio names Alticama as Giovanni's wife.

Francesco's words about wolves and hail are found in AC (chapter VII). His song at the Nativity Mass is found in his *Office of the Passion* (Vespers of the Lord's Birth). As he often did, Francesco pieced together phrases from the Psalms to create his own praises and prayers. His words in the letter Giovanni remembers are found in his *Earlier Exhortation to the Brothers and Sisters of Penance.*

We do not know the name of the priest who offered the Christmas Mass at Greccio.

Giovanni's remains are kept in an ossuary in the chapel next to the cave where the Christmas Mass took place.

115

Fra Leone

Hermitage, Greccio (January 1224)

Leone knelt beside Francesco, prone and ill on a pile of straw in a little cave at Greccio. The illness that sporadically came upon him had descended again after Christmas. Leone would return to the Porziuncula, leaving Francesco here in the care of Angelo di Tancredi. He was Francesco's new guardian now that Riccerio had returned to school to complete his studies for the priesthood.

"I'll pray for you," Leone said, taking Francesco's hands in his own.

"And I for you. But before you leave, take the parchment." Francesco pointed to a flat boulder.

Leone stood and scanned the writing. "You wrote me a letter?"

"Sì. To keep with you so you will always know my feelings."

Leone carried the parchment toward the morning light filtering in through gaps in the hide that covered the cave's entrance. He read the words, written in poor Latin with no capitalization, which was Francesco's style.

> brother leo, health and peace from your brother francis. i speak to you, my son, like the mother, and all the words we spoke on the road i put briefly in this note. so after this you should not come to me for advice, because i advise you thus: whatever seems to you

the best way to please the lord god and follow his footsteps and his poverty, do it with the blessing of the lord god and my obedience.

Now, in a different ink, the words even more shaky,

and if it is necessary for the sake of your soul or for your consolation, and you want to come back to me, come

Francesco was giving him the freedom, if he felt it the best way to follow God, to leave the ordine, and not just leave but to leave with God's blessing and Francesco's obedience. He read again, taking in all the words, allowing the faith, love, and self-emptying behind them to seep into his soul. As he reverently folded the parchment and tucked it into his tunic, he knew that faith, love, and self-emptying were the core of Francesco's vision. No matter what the other brothers did, no matter what the Rule stipulated, Leone could embrace faith, love, and self-emptying.

He turned and knelt at Francesco's side. "Bless me, my father, until I see you again."

NOTES

Fra Leone preserved the letter described in this chapter. It is now kept in a chapel in the Cathedral of Spoleto (*Early Documents I*, pp. 122–123 and footnote 1). Historians have been unable to date the letter, determine where it was written, or decipher the reason behind it.

Various translations have been suggested, including that of Godet-Calogeras ("The Autographs of Brother Francis of Assisi," pp. 86–87): "Brother Leo, your Brother Francis, health and peace. I speak to you like this, my son, like the mother, because all the words that we spoke on the road, briefly in this word, I dispose and advise, and afterward you should not for advice come to me. because I advise you thus: in whatever way it seems better to you to please the Lord God and to follow his footprints and poverty, you may do it with the blessing of the Lord God and my obedience. And if it is necessary for you for your soul for another consolation to you, and you want to come back to me, come." The author of this book has chosen to put the letter in lowercase in keeping with Francesco's lack of capitalization. The Latin "sicut mater," literally "as a mother," is here translated "like the mother" to express the fact that Francis regarded himself as the mother of all the brothers.

116

Fra Antonio

Cell, Bologna (March 1224)

In his cell at the house of the brothers in Bologna, Fra Antonio, quill in hand, was sitting at a desk littered with parchments. As if he were a gray-headed professor of theology instead of a twenty-eight-year-old, fresh-faced Portuguese follower of Francesco, he was outlining tomorrow's theology lesson for his students. Most of them were just a few years younger than he.

The knock at his door startled him. His close-set, dark eyes widened at the cluster of brothers who crowded into his small cell, pressing themselves against the walls, dwarfing Antonio against a mass of taller, towering bodies.

"We have a concern," Fra Marco began. "We think you should be head of the ordine."

Dumbfounded, Antonio stared at them.

"Fra Pietro di Catanio was a cleric, but Fra Elia has had no training in the things of God. You're a priest. You know more than all of us combined."

Antonio immediately understood. Discord. Hatched by Satan between the learned and unlettered brothers.

"Elia may have had no formal religious training," Antonio said, "but neither has Francesco. They've been friends since youth. Surely Francesco knows who can best govern us."

"Francesco is an ill layman," Fra Alfonso said harshly. "You teach us more in one class than Francesco will ever know."

"Francesco has been taught of God. He knows more than I can ever teach you."

"He's too old and weak to hear the voice of God any longer," Marco replied.

Alfonso nodded. "If he could still hear the voice of God, he wouldn't have chosen Elia."

"Maybe he never heard the voice of God. Maybe we're following a merchant who thought he heard God when he really heard himself." Demario's voice was flat with doubt and disdain.

Looking at the students before him, Antonio saw a nest of newly hatched, writhing snakes, crawling over one another as they disentangled and slithered off in all directions to spread their venom.

"Consider the Book of Job," he said, looking from one face to the other and praying that he could remind these men of who they are. "You remember that Job was a righteous and powerful man whose life and livelihood, with the permission of God, were struck by Satan to test Job's faith. Thus, Job lost all that he had and became wretchedly ill. Still, he remained strong in his faith and did not curse God. Now consider this from the Book of Job," he said, quoting from memory, "'If I have despised to abide judgment with my man-servant or my maid-servant, when they had any controversy against me,' Job said, 'for what shall I do when God shall arise to judge? And when he shall examine, what shall I answer him? Did not he that made me in the womb make him also? And did not one and the same form me in the womb?'"

Antonio looked directly at each brother. "Saint Gregory explains this passage. He says, 'He'—that is, the righteous man Job—'comes to judgment with his servants as an equal, because he fears the judgment of the One who is over all. He regards himself as a servant of the true Lord, and so he does not set himself above his servants with a haughty heart.'"

He paused to let the words penetrate. "'He who does not refuse to be judged along with his manservants and maidservants shows that he is not proud in the presence of his neighbor.'"

The room was silent. "Saint Gregory concludes, 'The virtue of humility is a great thing for powerful men, when they consider,'" he paused, "'the equality of their condition.'"

Marco and Alfonso had averted their gaze from his. *They understand*, he thought. Demario was staring defiantly at him.

He lowered his voice so that it became, he hoped, balm for the soul. "My brothers, let's speak no more of Elia or Francesco but only of our Lord Jesus Christ. Haven't we joined this ordine, not to get ahead but to get better?"

NOTES

Beginning some time prior to this, discontented brothers began seeking other leadership (AC, section 17 and 2C, second book, chapters CXVI and CXVII). While we have no proof, it is plausible that some brothers approached Antonio, later known as Anthony of Padua, about leadership. Antonio's words in this chapter are from his sermon notes for the thirteenth Sunday after Pentecost, as translated by Paul Spilsbury (*Sermons*, Vol ii, pp. 351 and 359).

117

Fra Agnello di Pisa

Dover, England (September 10, 1224)

Thirty-year-old Fra Agnello di Pisa sat on the deck of the ship, studying the broad wash of the chalk cliffs of Dover. Thin and distant this morning when the brothers embarked from Calais, the cliffs grew thicker, steeper, and more streaked as they approached. The breeze that had been at their back had shifted direction and was blowing across his sparsely bearded cheeks, even as the smooth waves of the channel grew choppy. On the other side of those white cliffs, friendly contacts awaited them. Agnello had sent letters in advance of the mission to ensure that.

Sitting ahead of him, like so many kegs of wine, were this mission's other Lesser Brothers, each facing the shore, each lost in thought. Agnello had handpicked these men. Their combined gifts would foster the mission's success.

There sat Fra Richard of Ingworth, older and wiser than the others, a powerful preacher of deep faith and humility. Not only could he, being a priest, offer Mass for the brothers, but everyone felt comfortable baring their souls to him. Richard would draw his fellow English to faith. If only Agnello, a deacon in orders, could someday be as holy, compassionate, and insightful as Richard!

Fra Richard of Devon, a very young acolyte in orders, was bright, outgoing, and delightful. His fellow English would find it difficult to resist his winsomeness.

Fra William of Ashby, a novice from England, had been studying in France under the provincial minister Fra Gregorio di Napoli. When Gregorio had asked William if he wanted to return to England as part of the mission, he said that he didn't know. "How could you not know?" Gregorio had asked. William had been a bit flustered, and his broad, thick chin had trembled as he fumbled for words. "I don't know what I wish," he'd stuttered, "because my will is not my own but yours. Whatever you wish for me is my will." William knew the value of obedience, so Agnello had been delighted when Gregorio had told him, "Then your will is to go."

Fra Enrico di Treviso, unlettered by worldly standards, was a sturdy, diligent laborer whose holy example and ready obedience spoke more effectively than words.

Fra Laurent de Beauvais, a capable manual laborer dear to Francesco, whose skill in construction would help establish loci here.

Fra Guglielmo di Firenze, whose knowledge of French language and customs had guided the missionaries as they had traversed that country on their northward trek toward Calais.

Fra Melioratus, short, quiet, quick to obey.

Fra James of England, a new novice who was teaching the brothers the English language.

Nine brothers to conquer a nation.

Two months ago, Francesco and Elia had appointed Agnello as provincial minister of England. "You'll do well," Elia had told him. "You've done exceptionally well as custos of the brothers in Paris."

In the two months since leaving the Porziuncula, these nine men had become family.

Agnello closed his eyes against the breeze coming off the shore. *My Lord,* he prayed, *deepen our faith, guide our steps, keep us safe, and make our mission fruitful. Amen.*

Eight years before, Agnello had been sensing that God was inviting him to serve Him, not as a prominent prelate, but as a poor priest. However, how could the son of the prestigious Angenelli family do such a thing? Then, on their way to France, Francesco and Pacifico had visited Pisa. What preaching! Interspersed with his harangue, Francesco, accompanied by Pacifico, had sung love songs to

God, set to troubadour tunes. Fascinated, Agnello consulted Francesco, who invited him to join the brothers. He and Pacifico were going to France. Agnello could study at the University of Paris to become a poor priest. Agreeing, he had accompanied Francesco and Pacifico, stopping at Florence on the way. There, unexpectedly, Cardinal Ugolino had advised Francesco to remain in Italy. Despite his disappointment, Francesco had sent Pacifico and Agnello on without him.

When he and Pacifico were crossing the Alps, Agnello had been thinking about the troubadour songs about loving God. The French people wouldn't hear Francesco.

THEY CAN HEAR YOU, the thought came.

Me? Fra Pacifico, sì.

BOTH OF YOU.

The thought persisted until Agnello had pinned down a French phrase that was the foundation of Francesco's life.

Le Royaume de Dieu doit conquérir le Royaume de soi.

The phrase had rhythm. He and Pacifico based a song on it and sang it to the French.

With a jolt, the boat struck sand and shivered to a halt. Two sailors heaved an anchor overboard. Agnello leapt to his feet and sprang around to the front of his little band.

"Before we disembark, my brothers," he said, switching the last words to English, "let's pray." His tongue felt a little odd, speaking the new language. He signed himself, and the brothers followed him. Then he prayed in English, "My Lord, use us to glorify Your Name in this land."

SING.

Had Fra James taught him enough English?

TRY.

Agnello began to sing in English what he and Pacifico had sung in French.

"The Kingdom of God must conquer the Kingdom of Self." That was the refrain. He sang a verse about the battle between the two and then the refrain again. Then another verse about how the soul, like a chaste maid, awaited the battle's outcome. The refrain. A third verse about the victory that is never conclusively won because self cannot be killed in this world. By the time he sang the refrain again, not only his brothers but also some of the sailors joined in the singing.

"The Kingdom of God must conquer the Kingdom of Self!"

NOTES

As provincial minister of England, Agnello set out with the brothers mentioned, having prepared the country for their arrival by sending letters in advance. Thomas of Eccleston, in chapter 1 of his *Chronicle* (13CC), records the names of the brothers, apparently selected for their talents, enumerated in this chapter. The author of this work has postulated the talents of Brothers William of Florence, Melioratus, and James.

Francesco and Pacifico quite likely sang love songs about God as part of their preaching. Agnello's song "The Kingdom of God Must Conquer the Kingdom of Self" is the author's imagination.

118

Fra Leone

Monte La Verna, Chiusi (September 14, 1224)

In the early morning light, just before he and Angelo di Tancredi, Rufino, Illuminato, and Masseo would pray the Office of Lauds, Fra Leone filled a jug with rainwater. It came from one of the cisterns that Count Orlando's laborers had constructed for the brothers on Monte La Verna.

If only he could speak to Francesco!

Impossible, because Francesco was in solitude in a forty-day fast from the feast of the Assumption on August 15 until the feast of Saint Michael on September 29. Leone was "Martha" to Francesco's "Maria."

If only he could consult Francesco about his weak faith! He should have confessed it last winter when Francesco shared how God had given him the grace to accept the new Rule.

God had not given Leone that grace.

Why had the years evolved this way?

Why were the clerical brothers unable or unwilling to see the joy of the beginning?

Why was the Lord Pope turning the brotherhood into an ordine of educated men?

Leone had no answers, only a longing for the past. As he carried the jug into the small refectory to select a loaf of bread from the week's supply that Count

Orlando had sent, he thanked God for the count's good graces. Indeed, Francesco would admonish him to thank God for everything.

When he reached the chasm, he was thanking God for the giant trees that thrust above him and for the wildly profuse shrubs and weirdly tumbled boulders that sang of God's exuberance.

"Lord, open my lips!" he called, waiting for Francesco's "And my mouth will proclaim Your praise." Then Leone would cross the chasm, leave Francesco the bread and water, and return to the other brothers.

Nothing.

Maybe he hadn't heard. Leone called louder. "Lord, open my lips!"

Birdsong.

"Lord, open my lips!"

Leone tried to suppress his panic.

"Lord, open my lips!"

No answer.

Oh, my Lord!

Francesco had been emaciated and weak when Leone had last seen him. Was he eating the bread Leone daily brought or was he feeding it to the falcon that nested near his hut? Francesco concealed his penances. Leone dared not ask what happened to the bread.

"Lord, open my lips!"

The panic was crushing.

He's all right. He told me not to come unless he answered. I promised. I must be obedient. He hasn't answered me before. I've left the bread and water before. I'll leave it today. He'll come to get it when he's ready. I'll just leave it.

Lord, is he well?

Leone's faith in God's protection wasn't dispelling the panic. Adding to it was that insistent, persistent push that Leone had come to recognize as the Spirit.

"No! I am not going to see him!" Leone said firmly. "He told me not to come unless he answered."

AND FRANCESCO IS GOD NOW? the inner voice asked.

"No! He's not God," Leone spoke too loudly.

GO TO HIM. HE NEEDS YOU.

"He said . . ."

I SAY.

Leone groaned. Francesco would be angry. Maybe tomorrow Francesco would answer—or even later this morning. Maybe he was sleeping. He had been so weak.

GO TO HIM.

He was going. Now. Leone picked his way across the massive log that the brothers had felled across the chasm. He walked carefully, noiselessly. If only he could sneak up on Francesco, see that he was fine, and move quietly back across the log.

Francesco was not in the hut.

Francesco! Leone shrieked internally.

He's praying somewhere. Sì. Praying somewhere. He's all right. He'll answer tomorrow.

The Spirit wouldn't let him rest. He was to find Francesco. Today.

Where, my Lord? The forest was thick, the rocks massive, the fissures deep. Francesco could have gone far in any direction. *Where, my Lord?*

LEAN NOT ON YOUR OWN UNDERSTANDING.

Leone took a deep breath to calm himself. He looked around. There. The sun was risen. He would go toward the sun. Carefully, attempting to be silent, he moved in the sun's direction.

The sun's light was flooding the forest. How far had he come? Through the trees he saw something dark, the deep gray of a tunic. Francesco, kneeling before a huge boulder, his arms stretched toward the sun whose radiance was swallowing the boulder from behind and above. Never had Leone witnessed such a brilliantly majestic sunrise. He closed his eyes against the blinding light, but the brilliance penetrated. Then, instantly, it was gone.

Leone's eyelids shot open. Francesco was kneeling, his head bent to his knees, his hands on the ground. Francesco was fine. Leone could leave now. Where was the least obstructed exit? As he scanned the forest behind him, he saw the radiant rays of the rising sun pouring into the forest from the east.

The morning sun rises in the east. So he must have been walking toward the west.

Leone stood motionless. What had he seen? Two suns?

How could he retreat from here without Francesco knowing?

He felt the Spirit within, holding him there. He was not to move. He glanced at Francesco, still kneeling. Leone bowed his head, closed his eyes, and felt the morning calm seep into his soul. He waited, listening to birdsong greet the dawn. The Spirit's peace flooded him. He rested in it, adoring, praising, loving.

"Eeeeay!" The stifled shriek roused him. Francesco, erect but not really, collapsing against the boulder, catching himself with his hands. "Eeeay!" Another scream. Sudden. Stifled.

Leone bolted from the trees, caught the frail body as it tried to balance, but couldn't. He eased Francesco to the ground and leaned him against the boulder. Never before had he heard Francesco scream.

Wincing, Francesco pulled his splayed-out legs toward his body and studied the grimy soles of his feet. *Whatever the pain*, Leone thought, *he still has it. But now he knows it. He won't scream again.*

"Why are you here, my little lamb? I didn't answer you. Did I?"

"No, my father."

Francesco nodded. "He sent you, didn't He?"

Leone nodded.

"He sent you because I can't walk."

"Perhaps you cut your feet on a sharp boulder. I'll wash your feet and we can look for wounds."

Francesco shook his head.

"Please. Let me do this for you. Maybe you need bandages."

Francesco shrugged. Leone took that for a yes.

Leone's hands were gentle as he washed away the dirt encrusting Francesco's bony feet. He could feel Francesco stiffening as his fingers lightly swabbed and rinsed. Beneath the dirt were no cuts or wounds but only small, circular red splotches that, when touched, made Francesco catch his breath. Could Francesco have walked over small, sharp rocks that bruised the skin and muscle? How odd! He had been walking barefoot over small, sharp rocks for so many years that the soles of his feet were as tough as leather. Perhaps the sores that dotted Francesco's body were now also erupting on the soles of his feet. If only Leone could ease his suffering!

When Francesco had leaned against the boulder with his hands, he had screamed again. "Let me wash your hands." Francesco obediently opened his grimy palms. Leone tried to be as gentle as if he were washing a newborn. Francesco trembled silently at the touch. No wounds or cuts. Just a circular, tender red splotch on each of Francesco's palms. How very odd!

Leone sighed and leaned against the boulder. He closed his eyes, but peace eluded him. Poor Francesco! He has suffered so much already. Interiorly. Physically. Now this. *Why so much agony, my Lord?*

"My little lamb, you know my soul. Now I must tell you of a vision I have had, but you must tell no one. I can make no sense of it."

Leone nodded.

"You know I've been asking God for two favors before I die."

"To feel in your body the pain our Lord felt at His crucifixion. And to feel in your heart the love He had for all humanity."

Francesco grinned. "I have added 'as much as possible' to this prayer, as you requested."

Leone smiled. No mere human could possibly endure the full measure of Christ's pain or experience the extent of His love.

"As much as possible, Leone. To feel these would help me to love Him as He deserves. My love is so shallow."

You have more love, Leone thought, *than anyone else I know.*

"I was praying this again this morning, right here. In the sky up there behind us, I saw a light like the sun, coming toward me. Then in the light I saw flames of light that looked like wings. Huge wings. Two were pointing straight up." Francesco moved his arms over his head, his palms pointing to the sky. "Two out to the sides." He brought his arms down and stretched them out horizontally. "Two pointing down to the earth. Very brilliant. They were all of one piece, connected at the center."

Leone remembered a passage from Scripture. "You've described a seraph. The prophet Isaiah had a vision of seraphim when God called him to be a prophet." He could recite almost the exact words. "'Seraphs were in attendance above him; each had six wings: with two they covered their faces, and with two they covered their feet, and with two they flew. And one called to another and said: "Holy, holy, holy is the Lord of hosts; the whole earth is full of his glory."'"

"I saw only one, Leone. It didn't speak. But it did look as you describe."

"The seraphs worship God continually. They were sent to Isaiah to purify him for his ministry as prophet." Leone remembered the passage. "Isaiah said he was 'a man of unclean lips' so one of the seraphim took with tongs a burning coal from the altar and touched it to Isaiah's lips, saying, 'Now you are clean, your guilt removed, your sin blotted out.'"

"Nothing touched me, Leone."

"God may, nevertheless, be calling you to be a prophet."

"He didn't ask that."

"Did He ask anything?"

"No. The fiery wings came close. Then I could see among them a figure like a man affixed to a cross. The wings pointing up were above His head, those pointing out were over his arms and those pointing down were covering His body. He seemed to look at me with great love. He came down to this boulder behind us, rested there a moment, and disappeared. I'm filled with such joy that the seraph gave me such a kind and gracious look. But the pain of that seraph's passion, fixed to the cross like that, thoroughly frightens me. Leone, I don't understand the vision. Do you?"

Leone took a deep breath. *Lord, he trusts me.* His mind grappled for meaning. None came.

"Perhaps God wanted to give you a grace . . ." There was one remedy when one had no answer. "Let's pray, Francesco. Perhaps God will grant insight."

Francesco sat back against the boulder and closed his eyes. His body relaxed into a familiar posture of prayer. Leone sat back against the boulder, too. Perhaps if they both prayed . . .

Leone rested, basking in the rising sun's warmth and the morning breeze's caress. The swelling birdsong soothed him. God was here, in the daily miracle of dawn. He would let God speak. But no words came, only the Spirit's gentle peace about him, within him. Wordlessly his spirit praised the Spirit. Time dissolved.

Long after they had begun to pray, the almost inaudible whisper nudged Leone's peace. A murmur he would have missed had the wind arisen or a bird trilled.

"Sì, my Lord."

Not God's voice. Francesco's.

"Sì."

God was speaking to Francesco. Leone peeked. Maybe God was appearing.

No. He saw only Francesco, sitting against the boulder, his head bowed, his eyes closed.

"Grazie." So soft.

Leone closed his eyes, speaking with his heart. *Grazie, my Lord, for speaking to Francesco. Grazie for Francesco. Grazie for You, my Lord.* He would not interrupt Francesco's prayer. They would both know when the Spirit departed.

Sometime later he heard Francesco stirring. Francesco was staring straight ahead, deep in thought. He turned to look at Leone.

"Leone, He spoke to me."

"What did He tell you?"

"He told me that the brothers would continue until the world's end and that evil ones would not remain long in the brotherhood."

Leone breathed a sigh of gratitude. "Grazie, my Lord."

"Those who hate us will not live long and those like you, my little lamb, who love the brotherhood will come to a good end."

"Did He speak my name?"

"No." Francesco smiled. "Nevertheless, He meant you and so many other brothers who are so good."

"What else did He say?"

Francesco smiled. "I cannot speak of that. But He gave me to know something. All along I have known that the brotherhood is God's. But He has given me to know that it must really be HIS from now on. My part in the brotherhood is done."

"No, Francesco!" The brothers needed Francesco. What was he thinking?

"Sì, Leone. I give the brotherhood completely to God. Really give it to Him now. The brothers, the direction, the decisions. All is His. He will take them where He wishes. I am not to worry about His decisions. I must control nothing. I am only to surrender myself to Him totally."

"Francesco, you've already surrendered to Him."

Francesco shook his head. "No, Leone. In the presence of my father and Messer Bishop, I gave God all, yes. And God gave me so much more. The brotherhood, the joy, the way we live. And I have clung to this life like the greedy merchant that I am. Leone, all my grasping must be consumed as if in flames. I am to be like the crucified man, completely helpless, dying, afire only with love of God. Nothing else. There is nothing else."

Francesco looked earnestly at Leone. "He loves us so much. I cannot comprehend it. He gave us everything. Even His Son. Everything given so that we might gain everything. Leone, I give Him my sons. I give Him you and Rufino and Masseo and all the brothers. All of you are His, not mine. He is your Father, not me. So, He always has been, Leone. He has everything. What remains to me is to be a good example to my brothers and to die well so that He will have me fully."

Leone felt panic rising again. "You can't leave us!"

Francesco grinned. "You know that's not for you to say." Francesco's eyes were dancing, his expression more vibrant than Leone had seen in many years. "Leone, I'm in love with Him. The brotherhood will remain, He told me, and this rejoices me. But brothers will fall away, there will be hatred within and without. This He told me, too, and this grieves me. What could happen terrifies me. But it's not my concern. The brothers are His. HIS, not Francesco's. Leone, I'm at peace with this."

"You've had no peace for so long, Francesco."

Francesco nodded. "But I have it now. Peace like I had in the early years when we had only God."

Leone could sense the peace in Francesco's relaxed body. Could the serenity and joy of the early years really have returned? "This is a grace, Francesco."

Francesco smiled. His gaze scanned the forest. Spontaneously he began to sing. "*You are holy Lord God Who does wonderful things. You are strong. You are great. You are the Most High. You are the almighty king. You holy Father, King of heaven and earth."* His smile gleamed. "I will write more, Leone. You must bring me a parchment and quill."

Leone laughed. Francesco singing again! Like in the old days, he was singing!

"Leone, what are these?" Francesco was staring at his open hands, resting in his lap. Where a red bruise had been in the palm of each hand was a dark knob about the size of a hazelnut. Francesco poked the knob in his left palm. He winced. He touched it again. Winced again. Then he lifted his right hand and stared at the back of it on which rose a dark ridge that tapered into a point. Quickly he turned his left hand. Same ridge on the back. Then the right hand. Same knob on the palm. He rubbed the right hand's ridge with his left hand's index finger and gritted his teeth. "I think these are my flesh, Leone." His gaze searched Leone's face.

"Francesco." Leone pointed to Francesco's feet.

Francesco stared at his feet. He pulled his left foot closer, crossing his right leg. Gritting his teeth, he lightly touched the raised knob on the upper part of his foot. Then he turned the sole toward himself. On the bottom, below the knob on the other side, was a raised, dark ridge tapering into a point. Francesco grabbed his right foot and pulled it toward himself. Similar knob. Similar ridge. Francesco smiled weakly. "So. Now I see why I can't stand. What are these, Leone?"

Leone's mind stretched. "I've seen these sometimes in men who had deep puncture wounds. Sometimes a knob of dark skin forms over a puncture wound."

Francesco nodded. "I've seen that, too. Some knights in the prison had this sort of thing develop from wounds. They were unsightly. But not painful."

"Not painful," Leone agreed.

"I've had no puncture wounds, Leone." Francesco struggled to rise again. He gasped and again sank down, breathing hard.

Leone took a deep breath to slow his racing mind. This wasn't the time to make sense of what happened, if any sense could be made. Clearly Francesco needed help. "I'll get Rufino and Angelo. We'll carry you back to your hut where we can care for you until these wounds, whatever they are, heal."

Wincing, Francesco touched Leone's arm. "They mustn't see these. I don't want anyone to see these, Leone."

"Francesco!" Leone pointed to the knobs in the hands and feet. "How can they not see them?"

"Bring bandages, Leone, to bandage them. And bring parchment. And a quill."

Leone hesitated.

"Don't worry, Leone," Francesco smiled. "You'll find me here when you return."

And so he did.

"I've cut some old tunics," Leone said, showing Francesco the lengths of undyed wool.

"Grazie."

Tenderly, Leone bandaged the soles of Francesco's feet and the palms of his hands. Then, intending to help Francesco back into the hermitage, Leone grabbed Francesco about the chest to help him to his feet.

Francesco screeched and blanched.

Immediately, Leone released his grip.

"What?"

Francesco shook his head. Pale and trembling, he pointed to his right side below his armpit.

A red blotch the size of a bird's egg stained the gray tunic.

"You're bleeding."

He had to get Francesco back to the hermitage to stop the blood. Supporting Francesco under his left arm, Leone helped him hobble to the hermitage and lie on his bed of leaves. Gently Leone rolled the tunic up over Francesco's frail frame until he was able to peel the wool from where the blood had plastered it to the skin. A gash in Francesco's side trickled blood. Gently Leone tied a wad of cloth around Francesco's chest.

"I can stay nearby," he offered.

Francesco shook his head. "No. Do as you've always done. But leave the parchment."

He was thinking about parchment? Leone fished into his hood for the goat skin, quill, and ink he had found when he went for the bandages. He placed them on the table next to a small clay cup.

"Grazie. You can go, Leone. I'll be all right."

"I'll bring food and water tomorrow. But perhaps I ought to cross the log and bring them here?"

Francesco smiled. "That would be wise."

For several days, Leone crossed the log, bringing Francesco clean bandages, food and water, and more ink. When the Lent of Saint Michael ended with the feast of that great angel warrior, Leone and Rufino placed two other logs across the chasm next to the first. With lengths of rope, they bound the logs together, creating a bridge over which they carried Francesco, being careful to avoid touching the wounds. When they reached the other side, Francesco gave Leone the parchment.

"Take this paper and guard it diligently until the day of your death," he told him.

After Compline, Leone sat under a tree in the deepening dusk and unrolled the parchment. On the flesh side, in dark-brown ink and in Francesco's own writing were the words:

you are holy, Lord, the only God who does wonders
you are strong you are great you are most high
you are all-powerful, you, holy father, king of heaven and earth
you are three and one, Lord God of gods
you are the good, all good, supreme good, Lord God living and true
you are love / charity you are wisdom you are humility
you are patience you are beauty you are meekness
you are security you are quietude
you are joy and gladness you are our hope you are justice
you are temperance you are all our riches at sufficiency
you are beauty you are meekness
you are protector you are guardian and defender
you are strength you are refuge you are our hope
you are our faith you are our charity
you are all our sweetness you are our eternal life
great and wondrous Lord God almighty merciful savior.

The phrases were beautiful and balanced. He could almost hear Francesco singing them. How many names of God were here? Did Francesco deliberately count them? Leone counted. Thirty-three. One for each year of Jesus' life on earth perhaps?

Francesco had once told him that the Saracens prayed ninety-nine names for God. This was one third of that amount. The parchment wasn't long enough to hold any more names.

Leone turned the parchment over and gasped. On the other side of the goat skin, on the grain side on which people seldom wrote, was a childlike drawing of a small, stubbly bearded head in a hood, reclining as if at rest on a jagged, irregular flat form, with a huge cross growing out of the mouth. It was a cross, shaped like a T—the tau cross, as commonly used by Francesco.

Francesco had sketched Silvestro's vision of himself with the cross coming out of his mouth, spanning the formless, flat earth on which the head reclined. Through the vision, the Lord had confirmed that the brotherhood would continue and span the world. Should Leone ever doubt again, he could pull out the parchment, see the drawing, and remember that God keeps His promises.

Above the tau, in Francesco's handwriting, were the words:

May the Lord bless you
and guard you.
May he show you His face
and have mercy on you.
May He turn His visage to
you and give you peace.

Like all other clerics, Leone had received this blessing from the Book of Numbers, a blessing of the Church, at his ordination. Francesco was reminding him.

Below the right arm of the tau were some other letters. Leone could make out "dms" and then the word "bene." And, underneath, the next line was "Te" and "dicat."

Dms bene
Te dicat

So, perhaps "benedicat"? Yes! And "dms" must be an abbreviation of "Dominus." "Dominus te benedicat," the Lord bless you!

Leone felt the delight of having figured out a puzzle.

On the other side of the tau were a few more letters: "f" and "Le." And, on the right side, a little "o" that he had not noticed before. Ah! His name in Latin: frater Leo. "God bless you, Fra Leone."

Francesco's blessing. The Church's blessing.

Leone could hardly imagine the pain Francesco must have endured to pen these imperfectly shaped letters and to craft this childish, awkward drawing.

Francesco had done it for him.

He folded the parchment and tucked it into the pocket of his tunic, next to the one Francesco had given him last year on the way to Greccio. Sì, the brothers were to have no possessions. But Francesco had given him permission to keep these parchments. When he needed a word from Francesco, he could take these out and read them. He would have Francesco ever next to his heart.

NOTES

We are not sure of the day of the Stigmata. It was sometime around the Feast of the Exaltation of the Cross, which is September 14.

Isaiah 6:1–7 records Isaiah's vision. 1C (second book, chapter III) records Francesco's vision and stigmatization and states that the stigmata "was partly revealed by the Saint to one person." AC (section 118) states that, "while his companion brought him food that day [of the vision of the Seraph], he told him everything that happened to him." Leone, as Francesco's spiritual director and confessor, seems to have been that companion.

Prior to Francesco, there was no one known to have received the stigmata, which explains why he and the brothers did not understand what had happened. Only over time did the brothers come to look upon them as the wounds of Christ.

At this time, Leone was struggling with a temptation that he hesitated to share with Francesco (*Early Documents II*, pp. 801–802). Intuiting the temptation, Francesco addressed it in a parchment that he gave to Leone. In his old age, Leone gave this parchment to the abbess of the Poor Clare sisters. It is preserved in the Basilica of Saint Francis in Assisi (see *Early Documents I*, pp. 108–112 and footnotes).

The text of the Praises of God is spaced as it appears on the parchment and follows the configuration in *Early Documents I* (p. 109), with the translation and lack of punctuation and capitalization as offered by Jean-François Godet-Calogeras (*Autographs,* pp. 69–70). The Blessing for Leone is Godet-Calogeras' translation and layout (*Autographs,* p. 71). Godet-Calogeras (*Autographs*) and Michael Cusato ("Of Snakes and Angels" in *The Stigmata of Francis of Assisi*) discuss the meanings of the Praises, Blessing, and drawing.

Part Eighteen

"We Must Be Servants and Subject to Every Human Creature for God's Sake"

119

Fra Leone

Porziuncola, Assisi (December 26, 1224)

After Lauds, Leone and Masseo were helping Francesco hobble to his cell. Francesco felt stronger today, now that they'd feasted yesterday on a sumptuous Christmas meal of boar. Rufino's family had brought the whole feast to the brothers to celebrate the ending of the fast they'd been observing since All Saints' Day.

"I must go and preach," Francesco was saying. "I need to walk."

Francesco's abruptness was always a bit jarring. "You haven't been able to walk since those things." Leone nodded toward Francesco's bandaged feet.

"We thought they'd be better by now."

"At least they aren't worse."

"Suppose they never heal? I need to preach. My Lord has made it clear that I must preach as long as I can. I need to walk."

"How?" Masseo asked.

"I have an idea. Leone, you can make slippers so that, when I walk, I'm putting pressure on my heels and toes, not on those things. And, Masseo, you can always get what you ask for. Can you beg soft hide to bandage over those things and to put under my toes and heels to raise them and to make shoes big enough to fit? I could put woolen socks over everything. I could walk if I weren't walking on these things."

Masseo laughed. "Every family in Assisi must have pelts from their Christmas feast beasts. I'll beg some for you."

Leone grinned. "I'll sew big slippers from whatever Masseo begs. Soon you'll be preaching again."

NOTES

The opening quotation for Part Eighteen is from Francesco's *Later Admonition and Exhortation to the Brothers and Sisters of Penance (Second Version of the Letter to the Faithful)*, 47.

Feeling compelled to preach, Francesco had slippers made to help him walk. One pair of slippers, believed to have been made by Saint Clare, is kept in the reliquary section of the Basilica of Saint Francis (Vardey, p. 109).

120

Ludmilla

Mercato, Gubbio (January 1225)

Despite the steady snowfall, Ludmilla had walked to the Gubbio mercato to select some cheese and sausage for her household's supper. There she overheard the sausage vendor chatting with the cheese merchant.

"Fra Francesco is back. Armani saw him two streets over." He pointed to the north.

Francesco was two streets over? Her heart leaped as did her feet, and, trying to keep her balance on the slippery pavement, she hurried to find him.

There! Leading a hunched-over, snow-covered friar astride a donkey. Probably an old, sickly brother who could no longer walk. She went straight up to the donkey leader and said, "Fra Francesco?"

The friar turned to her. Young face. Full, black beard. Squarish head. Twinkling eyes. "Fra Francesco," he said, pointing to the donkey rider.

Fra Francesco? Ludmilla remembered him, spry and lively, coming to Gubbio years ago. He had been, she thought, about her age. Could time have done to him what it had done to her?

To the riding friar, she pleaded, "Fra Francesco, please." She extended her hands, red with cold, twisted and stiff, toward him. "Look." She turned her hands from one side to the other while she tried unsuccessfully to gaze into his eyes, shielded by a huge hood.

"Will you touch my hands?" she asked. She asked for a touch. She wanted a miracle. She had heard stories of him healing a child whose legs had been like twisted twigs. Driving out a demon from a possessed lady. Giving sight to a blind woman.

"Please," she begged again.

Wordlessly, the friar's bandaged right hand reached toward her own hands and gently stroked her fingers.

"Grazie," she said.

He nodded.

Then, as the brother led the donkey up the street, Ludmilla returned to the mercato.

Sausages. One for her, her husband, her daughter, her son-in-law, her grandchild.

A hunk of cheese they could divide among themselves for dinner.

As she put the cheese into her basket, her hand stopped in midair.

She had picked up the sausages.

She had picked up the cheese.

For the past months, she hadn't been able to pick up anything. Her fingers had ceased working, so she scooped up things with her two stiff hands and plopped them wherever she wanted them.

She placed the cheese into her basket and tried to wiggle her fingers. They wiggled! Flexed! She could use her hands!

She grabbed the coin pouch slung over her shoulder, but instead of dumping the money onto the counter so that the vendors could pick out the proper payment, her newly nimble fingers counted out the coins.

Grazie, my Lord! Grazie! Grazie!

Her hands could do anything! Clean. Mend. Cook. Bathe. Bake. She had been preparing the simplest, plainest, chunkiest meals because she couldn't dice or slice or chop. But now! She flexed her fingers again. She could make stews! Soups! Omelets! Pies! Cakes! What first? What was her household's favorite?

Cheesecake!

She hadn't made one for years. There, in the cheese vendor's booth sat the soft, mild cheese she needed. At home, she had flour. Eggs from the family's chickens. Honey gathered in the fall. She almost danced home.

Ludmilla's family whooped to see how nimble her fingers had become. She set to work, pounding the cheese and mixing it with flour, eggs, and honey. Then she shaped it on a griddle and cooked it over the hearth. How delicious it smelled!

"Is that for us or for Fra Francesco?" her husband asked.

Goodness, it should really be for Fra Francesco! Why hadn't she thought of that? She could make another for her household.

"Would you mind if I took it to him?" she asked.

Her husband took her hands in his own and kissed them. "I think he deserves it, don't you?"

When her household went to hear Francesco preach the next day at the Cathedral of Santi Mariano and Giacomo Martiri, she carried the cheesecake with her.

She expected what she had seen during his other visits to Gubbio—Francesco, animated and lively, haranguing his audience to serve God. Today he sat, his bandaged hands gesticulating, his voice strong and persuasive.

"Blessed is the servant who loves his brother as much when he is sick and cannot repay him as when he is well and can repay him."

She looked at her husband, her son, her daughter-in-law, her grandson. What patience they'd shown when she couldn't serve them as before! While she'd grumbled about her stiff, twisted fingers, they'd quietly assumed her work. She'd thought only about her own misery. Now she thought about theirs.

"Blessed is the servant who loves and respects his brother as much when he is far away from him,"—Francesco's arms opened wide, as if to push someone away—"as when he is with him,"—he brought his bandaged hands together—"and who would not say anything behind his back,"—he brought his hand to his mouth as if sharing a secret—"that he would not say with charity in his presence."

Oh, dear. She remembered complaining to her friends that her husband was sloppier than she was in feeding the cow. Why, even with her fingers locked, she could scoop up the hay and let fewer straws litter the floor than he could with two good hands! Oh, she had said that. But she never told him. He wasn't trying to be sloppy. He just didn't see neatness. She couldn't rescind her criticism, but she could show her husband love. She took his hand in hers and squeezed it. He looked at her quizzically. She smiled her love back to him.

When Francesco had finished and the crowd began to mill about him, she and her household joined the throng and finally made their way to his side. "I am the woman—" she started to say, but he put his bandaged hand to his lips, and she understood that she was to be quiet. "I made you this cheesecake with my own hands," she said. "Grazie."

She could not see his face, darkened by the hood, but she heard the smile in his voice. "You are kind, my good woman. May I taste it?"

"It's your cheesecake," she said.

His fingers protruded from the bandages, and he delicately dipped one of them into the cheesecake and put the morsel into his mouth. "Delicious!" He dipped again and ate a second morsel, then sighed contentedly. "It's fit even for the Lord. Grazie for this exquisite gift. Since it's mine, I wish to give it away. I give it to you to share with your family who can rejoice with you in the grace God has given you."

NOTES

1C (first book, chapter XXIV) relates the undated incident of Francesco touching and curing the crippled hands of an unnamed woman of Gubbio who thanked him by making him a cheesecake. Francesco's words for his homily are in his *Admonitions* (sections XXIV, XXV).

121

Dom Vignaiolo

Church of San Fabiano, Forest outside Rieti (Late September 1225)

Walking between his damaged vines, Dom Vignaiolo ran his fingers through his thinning hair and moaned. He'd spent years carving his homestead out of the forest and clearing a wide swath of ground to make this little vineyard open to the sun. His year's supply of wine came from this vineyard. Now it was ruined. All because he had given lodging to a man everyone considered a saint.

Why had he consented to have Fra Francesco here? Cardinal Ugolino had summoned Francesco to Rieti for eye treatment. But Francesco wanted to stay outside the city to avoid the throngs who continually came to see him.

What senseless reasoning! The mobs came anyway. Priests. Bishops. Cardinals. Clerics. Everyday someone walked through Dom Vignaiolo's small vineyard to reach the door of the church where Francesco was staying. Every day someone plucked the grapes and ate them or carried them off or trampled them. Every. Single. Day.

This winter, Vignaiolo would have no wine.

Here came someone else. Messer Somebody. There went another cluster of grapes. Why bother saving the few that were left?

"Take some grapes in to the saint," Vignaiolo invited.

"Certainly. Grazie."

Vignaiolo had just returned from blessing a poor farmer's newborn son when Fra Angelo met him as he approached the church. "Fra Francesco asks to see you."

Francesco was kneeling inside a small room off the right side of the church. Vignaiolo tapped lightly. "You asked to see me?"

"Grazie for the grapes." The hooded head turned toward Vignaiolo. Could the saint see him? He was almost totally blind. "Was your harvest good this year?"

"It would have been."

"The brothers tell me that the people have stripped and trampled your vines."

Vignaiolo groaned.

"Do not be disturbed or offended any longer. We can't do anything about it. But trust in the Lord, because for me, His little servant, He can restore your loss. But, tell me, how many measures of wine did you get when your vineyard was at its best?"

"Thirteen measures, Brother."

"Don't be sad over this anymore, and don't say anything offensive to anyone because of it, or argue with anyone about it."

Goodness, Vignaiolo had been complaining, surely, sinning with his tongue.

"Trust the Lord and my words, and if you get less than twenty measures of wine, I will make it up to you."

Vignaiolo shrugged. Maybe he shouldn't despair. Maybe he should harvest the remaining grapes and see how much wine he got. So, he did. By the time the twenty measures were pressed out, Francesco had left for Fonte Colombo.

NOTES

AC (section 67) records this incident of an unnamed priest's trampled vineyard and Francesco's words to him, as recorded in this chapter. The fictional name, Vignaiolo, means "winemaker."

122

Fra Angelo di Tancredi

Cliffs of Fonte Colombo, Outskirts of Rieti (Late October 1225)

Fra Angelo di Tancredi was sitting with his eyes closed, his feet pulled up to his chest, and his back against the wall of a small cave where Francesco lay nearby on a bed of straw.

"Fra Angelo!"

Angelo's eyes popped open. Had he been dozing?

"Sì, Francesco."

"Doctor Nicola is ready to leave. Please give him a good meal."

Angelo was now fully awake. Nicola, a renowned, wealthy physician in Rieti, was packing up his instruments. He had come several times to treat Francesco, often staying a few hours to speak with him. He had always refused a meal, but what if, today, he accepted?

"Brother," Angelo blurted out, "we're ashamed to say that, because we're so poor now we'd be ashamed to invite him and give him anything to eat."

That wry smile that always melted Angelo's heart lit up Francesco's face. "O, you of little faith!" he chided. "Don't make me tell you again!"

Nicola, a big man who had squeezed into this narrow cell, now seemed twice as big as his patient. His deep voice filled the space. "Brother, it is because the brothers are so poor that I am happy to eat with them."

Angelo nodded, squeezed around Nicola's back, and went to the refectory to set out the food on a low table made of rough-hewn planks. The brothers looked in dismay at each other and at the scanty amount of bread, wine, and greens that Rufino had prepared.

"All I could find," Rufino shrugged.

Sitting cross-legged on the floor like the brothers, Nicola tucked his lavender tunic under his backside and around his legs.

"Would you like to offer the blessing?" Angelo asked him.

"Certainly. Grazie, my Lord, for this good food, these good men, and all Your goodness. Amen."

Rufino tore the bread into small pieces and passed them around with the greens. Then he passed the cup of wine, each one taking small sips.

Angelo broke the awkward silence. "Messer, what is the news from Rieti?"

As Nicola proceeded to tell, a crisp knock sounded at the door. Benito, a new brother assigned as porter, rose to answer the knock.

"Grazie!" Angelo heard his astonished thanks. "Grazie!"

In a moment, Benito was unpacking a large basket. The table was filling with food. Huge loaves of bread. Broiled fish. Succulent crab cakes. Honey. Grapes.

"A woman has ridden seven miles to bring these to Francesco," Benito stammered.

"Do you think he prayed for these?" Rufino wondered.

"Even if he did, how would they get here this quickly?" Angelo breathed in the aroma of the food.

"Aren't they here because Fra Francesco trusted in God?" Benito asked, before returning the basket to the woman at the door.

"My brothers," Nicola said, "neither you nor we sufficiently recognize the holiness of this saint."

NOTES

AC (section 68) records this incident without naming the brothers or doctor. However, Octavian Schmucki ("The Illnesses of Francis," 37) mentions that a "Magister Nicolaus medicus" was a municipal doctor of Rieti between 1203 and 1233.

Part Nineteen

"This Is a Remembrance, Admonition, Exhortation, and My Testament"

123

Messer Pasquale

Cliffs of Fonte Colombo, Outskirts of Rieti (Spring 1226)

Messer Pasquale stroked his clean-shaven cheeks as he gaped at the primitive mud-and-stick huts of the Lesser Brothers. He'd heard about Fonte Colombo, the Fountain of the Dove, named—he surmised—after the Holy Spirit and the Fountain of Life. Both life and the Spirit were certainly present here, but not much else.

Fra Riccerio, who was leading Pasquale up the hill, was a blithe, young man with a springy gait. About as tall as Riccerio, Pasquale was certainly not as nimble. Age and weight, not his red tunic and brown cape, made him lag. In contrast, Riccerio was striding swiftly, his threadbare, mud-spattered tunic whipping about his muddy, bare legs.

"Here," said Riccerio as he pulled back a rude, wattle-and-mud-daubed door to one of the huts.

Riccerio shut the door behind them. In the faint light penetrating through pinprick chinks in the wall, Pasquale could make out a prone figure.

When he had caught his breath, Pasquale complained, "Brother, it's too dark in here. How can I examine his eyes if I can't even see him?"

"The light hurts his eyes. We've been keeping everything closed up." Riccerio faltered.

"Can we get him outside?"

"I'll get Fra Rufino to help."

With Riccerio holding Francesco under his arms and Rufino holding his legs, the two brothers carried him outdoors as if he were a sack of flour. They placed him in the deepest shade under a thickly leafed oak.

Pasquale knelt beside the weakened body. *So, this is the saint*, he thought. *A dying beggar in a tattered tunic with bandages on his hands and feet.* "Fra Francesco, my name is Doctor Pasquale. I have come to see what can be done to cure your eyes."

"The famous eye doctor who treats the Lord Pope!" Francesco's voice was weak. "I am sorry that such a famous man had to come out here for me."

He, famous? The popes, who stayed at the papal fortress in this papal city of Rieti, those popes whom Pasquale treated, were famous, but not Pasquale. "Fra Francesco, it is my honor to visit you. But I am afraid this will be painful. I must examine your eyes."

"Sì." Francesco raised his arm to slide back the oversized hood that lay across his eyes. *How thin his arm!* Pasquale noted.

Pasquale gently pulled back the hood. Francesco's eyes began to tear and blink. Tenderly but thoroughly, Pasquale pulled the upper and lower lid from each bloodshot eye. He asked Francesco to move his eyes from side to side. With a soft swab of silk, he sopped up some of the tears and pus and smelled them.

"Francesco, you have an overabundance of bad humors in your eyes. The most effective treatment is to cauterize the veins between the eye and the ear to let the bad humors drain. When the humors drain, you will be able to see again. I will need to heat the iron I have brought."

"No. Not today," Francesco squeaked. "Fra Elia needs to be here."

Pasquale was confused. "Elia?"

"He's our minister," Riccerio explained. "He needs to give his permission."

"Wasn't he the one who sent me to you?"

"Sì, but he needs to be here." Francesco seemed insistent. Riccerio shrugged. Rufino nodded.

"Well, then, send for me when Fra Elia arrives. Continue to keep the eyes covered if that helps."

Several months later, in the heat of the summer, Pasquale received a hand-delivered message from Lord Pope. He was to go to Francesco immediately and treat his eyes. As he came within sight of the wattle huts, Riccerio darted down the hill to meet him.

"Messer Pasquale, you've come to see Fra Francesco? Fra Elia isn't here. He says he's too busy to come."

"I am under orders from the Lord Pope to treat him."

"Lord Pope? Then Fra Francesco will agree."

Rufino and Riccerio carried Francesco's body out of the dark wattle hut and laid it under the leafy oak.

"I need a hot fire."

Rufino and Riccerio scurried about, clearing the woodland floor of leaves and making a circle of rocks as a small fire pit. A third friar volunteered, "I'll bring a flame from the cooking hearth."

"Grazie, Leone!" Rufino called.

"Fra Francesco, I will cauterize the worst eye first. This will hurt, but it will heal you." Pasquale had used this treatment successfully several times.

When the small fire was blazing, Pasquale poked the narrow cauterizing tool into the flames. Francesco weakly raised his hand toward the fire. "My Brother Fire, noble and useful among all the creatures the Most High created, be courtly to me in this hour. For a long time, I have loved you, and I still love you for the love of the Lord who created you. I pray our Creator who made you, to temper your heat now so that I may bear it." As Francesco made the sign of the cross over the fire, Pasquale drew out the blazing red-hot iron. As he brought it toward Francesco, the friars fled. Pasquale shook his head. None of them had the stamina to be doctors.

He drew the iron across Francesco's skin, from his left ear to the corner of his left eyebrow. The pressure had been right. The burn was deep. The smell of scorched flesh seared the air.

"Are you done?" Francesco asked.

"Sì."

Francesco weakly called, "My brothers! Come back! It is done!"

No one returned so Pasquale shouted, "Brothers! Come back! It is done!"

The brothers appeared one by one from among the trees.

"We are here, Francesco," Rufino said softly.

Francesco laughed weakly. "You fainthearted, of little faith, why did you run away? I tell you the truth: I felt no pain or even heat from the fire. In fact, if it is not well-cooked, cook it some more!"

Pasquale was amazed. How was it possible that he felt no pain from such a burn? "Brothers, I tell you, and I speak from experience: I doubt that a strong man with a healthy body could endure such a severe burn, much less this man, who is weak and sick." The only ones who could endure this without feeling it were those whose disease was a punishment for their immoral and sinful lives. Francesco could not be one of those people. He was far too holy to be a leper.

NOTES

The opening quotation for Part Nineteen is from Francesco's *Testament*, 34.

AC (section 86) details the cauterization of Francesco's eyes through the services of the pope's unnamed physician.

124

Fra Riccerio di Muccia

Porziuncula, Assisi (Mid-September 1226)

In the languid morning sun, Fra Riccerio di Muccia was writing Francesco's Testament as he slowly dictated it. Francesco, with his eyes heavily covered, was lying in the shade on soft grass beside him. Francesco had had other Testaments, including a brief one in Siena, dictated to Fra Benedetto di Piratro when Francesco had been vomiting blood and death seemed certain. That was five months ago. Although Francesco had rallied, he had not improved. Now he was hardly eating. Even parsley, which he frequently requested, did not quell the nausea. There were long pauses in his dictation.

"The Lord gave me, Fra Francesco, thus to begin doing penance in this way, for when I was in sin, it seemed too bitter for me to see lepers. And the Lord Himself led me among them and I showed mercy to them."

Not only to them, Riccerio thought as he waited for Francesco to continue. *To me*. Lovingly he glanced at the prone figure and remembered instead a more vibrant man whom he had once feared to approach.

"And our Lord gave me such faith in churches . . ."

Riccerio had heard him preach many times in churches. Francesco continually focused on the Body and Blood of Christ, as if he were gazing directly into the Lord's eyes.

"Afterward the Lord gave me, and gives me still, such faith in priests . . ."

Why did I doubt that you cared for me? Riccerio had left being Francesco's guardian to resume his studies for the priesthood. But after ordination, he had thought that, because he had grown more learned, Francesco might love him less.

Prior to his ordination, when Riccerio had been a novice, Elia had granted his request to beg a psalter. However, before he accepted this extraordinary permission to have a book when the other brothers didn't, Riccerio had asked Francesco, who was clearly dissatisfied. Riccerio had tried to accept the disappointment, but he just couldn't. When he asked a second time, Francesco scolded him, "After you have a psalter, you will desire and want to have a breviary; after you have a breviary, you will sit in a fancy chair like a great prelate telling your brother: 'Bring me the breviary.'" Then Francesco had scooped up a handful of ashes from the hearth and began to rub them into his head as if washing his hair, saying, "I, a breviary! I, a breviary!" Riccerio was ashamed, for Francesco was clearly saying that both he and a breviary would turn to ash.

"Whenever I find the most holy names and written words of our Lord in unbecoming places, I want to gather them up . . ." Riccerio wrote down Francesco's words.

Back then as a novice, Riccerio should have realized that Francesco despised not learning or holy writings, but rather clinging to something. A soul was freed only by being able to relinquish anything for the love of God.

"And we must honor all theologians and those who minister the most holy divine words. . . ."

Back then, as a novice, Riccerio had been focusing on possessions, not on ministry. The third time he had asked about having a psalter, he had met Francesco on the road near the Porziuncula. First Francesco had said, "Go and do as your minister tells you." But as Riccerio was running off to tell Elia, Francesco, who was by then almost blind, had called after him and asked to be taken back to the spot where he'd told Riccerio to follow Elia's directive. At that spot, Francesco knelt.

"Forgive me, Brother, forgive me. Whoever wishes to be a Lesser Brother must have nothing but the tunics, a cord, and short trousers the Rule allows him; and for those forced by necessity or illness, shoes."

Riccerio smiled wryly. Tunic. Cord. Breeches. That was all he had ever had. No psalter. He no longer craved one.

"And after the Lord gave me some brothers, no one showed me what I had to do, but the Most High Himself revealed to me that I should live according to the pattern of the Holy Gospel."

Those years ago, however, Riccerio's insistence on a psalter had brought his cravings into clarity. He had thought that returning to his studies for the priesthood might remove his sinful temptations. That didn't work. Then he thought that finishing his studies and rejoining the ordine would squelch them. Instead, in addition to temptations to possessions, as well as to frivolity and license, Riccerio now battled temptations to laxity in observing the Rule. Despite being ordained, he felt consumed with countless faults, which Francesco surely would intuit. Concealing his fear of rejection, he had increasingly avoided Francesco while growing increasingly despondent. How he had wanted to speak to Francesco, but now he wondered if his being ordained a priest, while Francesco remained a deacon, would affect their relationship.

"And although I may be simple and infirm, I nevertheless want to have a cleric always with me who will celebrate the Office for me as it is prescribed in the Rule."

Whatever had made Riccerio fear that Francesco would feel uncomfortable around him? Why had he feared that a man who tried to follow the Gospel would reject a sinner, even if he were a priest, when Jesus never did? One day, about a year ago, Riccerio had timidly approached the cell where Francesco was praying. As he hesitantly drew near, Francesco called out, "My son, let no fear or temptation disturb you anymore, for you are very dear to me, and among all those who are dearest to me I love you with a special love. Come to me confidently whenever you want and leave me freely whenever you want."

Leave him?

"And the brothers may not say: 'This is another rule.' Because this is a remembrance, admonition, exhortation, and my testament . . ."

With Elia's permission, Riccerio would stay with Francesco until he died.

NOTES

Many historians believe that Riccerio transcribed Francesco's *Testament*. 2C (second book, chapter XV) recounts Riccerio's fears that Francesco no longer loved him. Riccerio was a brilliant, learned man. Historians speculate that he may have been the friar who asked Francesco about having a breviary. AC (sections 103–105) records Francesco's responses to these requests.

125

Madonna Jacopa dei Settesoli

Frangipani Household, Rome (Late September 1226)

Madonna Jacopa dei Settesoli was kneeling in her house chapel, sunlight streaming through the open windows, as she prayed Lauds. From the streets below came the early morning bustle of Rome, but here was peace. She closed her breviary, glanced up at the crucifix on the wall ahead of her, and suddenly knew.

Fra Francesco was dying.

The dialogue within her spirit was quick. Before she could hardly form the question, the answer came.

He is —

DYING.

I need to go.

QUICKLY. NOW.

But . . .

IF YOU DELAY, YOU WILL NOT FIND HIM ALIVE.

What should I—

CLOTH FOR HIS SHROUD.

Like?

SUCH AS CISTERCIANS USE.

What—

Wax. Incense. Great quantities.

She was being told to bring his burial items.

Ingredients for mostaccioli.

Mostaccioli?

Do not delay.

The rapid impressions ceased.

No delay.

Reverently she kissed the floor of the chapel, glanced at the crucifix again. She mouthed the words. "No delay, my Lord."

First, she called two servants. "Hurry to the mercato and bring back great quantities of wax and incense. I need them today. And find Giovanni and Giacomo. Tell them we're going to visit Fra Francesco."

The servants left. She breathed deeply to calm her pounding heart. Now to think.

Cloth such as the Cistercians used. That would be undyed wool. She had a length of it next to Graziano's tunic. Tenderly she lifted it out of the chest in the bedroom. Beneath it lay her fine linen wedding veil, which she had embroidered with repeating patterns of white silk and gold. To cover a corpse's face. Beneath that, a linen that she had embroidered with a red border. What once covered a banquet table could shroud his body. Over here, scraps of soft linen she could use to bathe his body.

From Graziano's chair in the sitting room, she took a red silk cushion embroidered with imperial eagles and lions, which symbolized the Frangipani, to use as a pillow for Francesco's head.

Ingredients for mostaccioli. Almonds. Wine and grape must from the newly harvested grapes. Cinnamon. Cloves. She had best bring her own mixing bowl and bread peel. To keep the raw eggs from breaking, she nestled them in flour in a small chest.

Jacopa's heart was racing.

Calm down. Think, she told herself.

She could think of nothing else to bring for Francesco. She would have to gather her own clothing and belongings and make sure that Giovanni and Giacomo packed sensibly.

Jacopa sat on the edge of her bed, listening to the peace in her room and the bustle outside. Life went on. Life died. Life went on. Tears formed in the corners of her eyes. *Lord, let me see him before he dies.*

Like a regiment moving quickly to secure a position, Jacopa and her retinue rode down upon the Porziuncula. Disheveled and untidy as she felt from her rapid journey, Jacopa leaped down from her steed. She was about to boldly knock at the door of the Porziuncula refectory when it opened in front of her and she almost rapped Fra Elia on the nose.

"What—" he started to say when she interrupted him.

"Is Fra Francesco still alive?"

"Sì."

She felt as if a millstone had been lifted from her heart. "Grazie, my Lord! I brought things he will need." She motioned to her lead servant to begin to unpack the items.

"I'm here to help," she said.

"You can't come in here," Elia said. "Our Rule doesn't permit women in here."

She felt as if she had been slapped. "Can't I at least see him?" She felt the tears welling up. Then she heard Francesco's feeble voice from somewhere within.

"Who's there?"

Elia turned away from her. "Madonna Jacopa. She has brought things—"

"Let her come in. Our proscription does not apply to Fra Jacopa."

She and Elia looked at each other, puzzled. Then he stepped aside, and she entered.

At once she saw that they needed her. Like weeping children, the brothers were clustered around Francesco, lying on straw. The smell of sickness and death was as stifling as the overpowering grief.

Quickly, she went to Francesco and knelt by him, touching one of his bandaged hands. "The Lord sent me, my Father."

"Grazie, my God," he whispered. "Did you bring the mostaccioli?"

Jacopa laughed. "You always ask for those! Let me do a few things first and then I will make the almond cookies. I brought all the ingredients."

"Grazie."

She patted his hand and began.

She introduced him to Giovanni and Giacomo. He marveled how her sons were maturing.

She had her servants light incense to disperse the odors.

She lifted his head, placing the pillow beneath it and countering his objections with, "This will help you to breathe better, my Father."

She asked a brother to bring fresh water and then bathed his face and arms with soft linen scraps. "Use these," she said to the brothers. "More comfortable than your wool."

She took Elia aside and gave him the candles, "for his funeral," she said, and then handed him the undyed cloth for a tunic, adding, "for his burial."

Then she knelt by Francesco again and stroked his forehead. "Tomorrow I will make the cookies."

Leaving the greater portion of her retinue around the Porziuncula like an army, Jacopa took her children and a small contingent and rode into Assisi, where they spent the night at an inn. The following morning, clean, tidy, and refreshed, she made the cookies in the refectory while her boys and the brothers watched.

"We could never beg all those ingredients," Rufino said.

"We would rather beg the cookies from you," Angelo admitted.

The cookies baked well in the brothers' ramshackle oven, and Francesco gratefully nibbled on one after Vespers. "Fra Bernardo," he said, calling the gray-bearded, stately man to his side, "you love mostaccioli, but you have never tasted Fra Jacopa's. Fra Jacopa, give him a large portion."

She scooped up a fistful of cookies and gave them to Bernardo. "Delicious!" Bernardo proclaimed, and they all whooped in agreement.

Jacopa smiled at Francesco. "You used to visit," she teased, "saying that you wished to see how we were doing. But you really wanted cookies. Admit it!"

Francesco's eyes twinkled. "I wanted to see how you were doing. But I also wanted cookies."

So, they laughed and ate cookies and she reminded Francesco of the first time he'd tasted them. It was when he had brought her the lamb. Leone showed Francesco the tunic that the brothers had hastily stitched from the cloth Jacopa had brought, woven from the lamb's wool.

"So, the lamb we saved from death will clothe me in my death," Francesco said with a weak smile. "Our Lord must be grinning!"

That memory caused Fra Masseo to remember other lambs Francesco had rescued on their way to slaughter.

Fra Angelo recalled a *tinca*, a fish that Francesco had tossed back into the Lago di Rieti. "I never saw a benefactor look so dismayed as that man when the fish that he gave you swam away from our boat."

Francesco nodded weakly.

"How about the rabbit you released in Greccio?" Rufino asked.

"I thought that was Perugia," Francesco said.

"It was both places. And probably more places," Leone grinned.

"Probably," Francesco admitted.

"Remember the worms on the roads," Pacifico chuckled.

"The worms!" Elia groaned. "Madonna Jacopa, had you traveled with Francesco on a rainy day, you'd never arrive at your destination. Every worm he saw on the road, he'd pick up and put on the grass."

"It was said of Jesus, 'I am a worm and no man,'" Francesco said.

"So, for Him, you rescued them," Jacopa said.

"Sì."

Now He shall rescue you, she thought, *you who have become as helpless as a worm. He will place you on a throne in His Kingdom.*

NOTES

AC (section 8) records Madonna Jacopa's interior prompting to go to Francesco and bring the burial items mentioned in this chapter. The same source also states that "the brothers" made him the tunic from the cloth she had brought. The pillow is preserved by the Church of San Francesco in Cortona and the veil at the Sacro Convento in Assisi. Grape must is a sweet syrup made from reduced grape juice that contains a degree of pulp, skins, stems, and seeds, set aside from the wine-making process.

This chapter incorporates insights on Jacopa's role at Francesco's death, shared by Darleen Pryds (*Death, Dying, and Mysticism*, pp. 15–34).

The memories of the brothers are recorded in the following sources:

- Francesco remembering that Bernardo liked almond cookies: AC (chapter 12)
- Lambs Francesco rescued from slaughter: 1C (first book, chapter XVIII)
- *Tinca* released into the Lake of Rieti and rabbits released in Greccio and Perugia: 1C (first book, chapter XXI)
- Francesco picking worms off the roads and his words about Christ being a worm and no man: 1C (first book, chapter XXIX)

The quotation, "I am a worm and no man," is from Psalm 22:6.

126

Fra Elia di Bonbarone

Porziuncula, Assisi (Dusk, October 3, 1226)

His back pressed against the wall of the refectory at the Porziuncula, Fra Elia had drawn his knees up to his chest and was sitting as empty as a cask. Francesco's body lay prone on sackcloth. Like an act of sacrilege, Elia's bare feet were next to Francesco's head. Around Francesco were clustered his brothers. Rufino, sobbing. Leone, tears streaming down his cheeks. Angelo di Tancredi, his face cupped in his big hands. "Fra Jacopa" was here too, her capable hands cradling his feet, her head bowed. Her son, Giacomo, leaned asleep against his older brother Giovanni.

Outside above the hut, Francesco's favorite birds, the skylarks, were singing.

The years spun through Elia's mind as they must be spinning through everyone else's. Their own years. Their own memories. He thought of Francesco's carefree youth. Their mock sword fights. Their partying. Francesco training to be a knight. His returning, nearly dead, to Assisi. Elia's visits. The cave and the prayers. Francesco's crazy conversion and Elia's being unable to embrace it until after his wife's death. Francesco sending Elia to Syria amid the wild growth of the brotherhood. Elia returning to assume the role of minister general, which Francesco once held. The tensions brought into the brotherhood with the learned clerical brothers, none of whom were here. Here were those who understood Francesco best.

The last year and a half had been one futile attempt after another to help Francesco.

The failed cauterization of his eyes.

The fearful piercing of his ears that did nothing to heal his tearing, tender eyes.

The useless carting of Francesco to Siena after doctors suggested a milder climate. He'd grown worse and had vomited great quantities of blood. Certain that Francesco had been dying, Elia had rushed to him.

Francesco had wanted to return to Assisi. As he could neither walk nor ride, Elia had taken him by litter from one hermitage to the next.

Arezzo.

Cortona, where he'd dictated a few words as a final testament, then strengthened a little.

Gubbio.

Bagnara, where the fresh air had done no good, but where his legs and feet had begun to swell and the podestà had sent knights to guard him.

Nottiano.

Satriano.

Assisi. The bishop's palace. Francesco had blessed Elia and prayed that a place be reserved for him in heaven. Elia wished he could remember the exact words, but all he could remember were Francesco's intent and the love in Francesco's voice.

Francesco had worsened. He'd asked to be brought here, to his beloved Porziuncula, to die. "After I die, place me naked, on the naked ground," he'd asked, "and let me lie there as long as it takes to walk a leisurely mile. May you grant this."

So, the brothers had done it. Then they had seen the little man, his emaciated body turned almost as dark as earth, his blind eyes tearing. And they had wept.

But Elia had understood. Francesco had once said, "I am greatly ashamed when I find someone poorer than myself." So, he would give away his tunic or mantle or part of it to anyone needier than he. Sometimes days would pass before he would acquire another tunic. "I chose holy poverty as my Lady, my delight and my riches of spirit and body," he would remind the brothers.

How could Elia allow him to die naked? He had sent Leone to bring a tunic, sackcloth hood, and breeches. He had known only one way to have Francesco wear them. "I command you under holy obedience to acknowledge that I am lending you this tunic, underwear, and hood. And so that you know that they in no way belong to you, I take away all your authority to give them to anyone." Francesco had acquiesced.

Francesco! Francesco! You were such an anomaly! Just before this evening's Vespers, the brothers, at Francesco's invitation, had partied while feasting on Madonna Jacopa's almond pastries.

A few days ago, Francesco had dictated a letter to Madonna Jacopa, asking her to bring candles and gray cloth for his burial as well as ingredients to make her almond cookies. Elia had volunteered to take the letter to Rome when Madonna Jacopa appeared at the door with the requested materials. Francesco had weakly blessed them all. Blessed, too, Jacopa's entourage of soldiers positioned around the hut like a phalanx to dispel any relic hunters.

Upon Francesco's asking, Fra Pacifico and Fra Leone had begun to sing *The Praises of the Lord*, for which Francesco had composed then and there a new stanza. "Praised be You, my Lord, through our Sister Bodily Death, from whom no one living can escape. Woe to those who die in mortal sin. Blessed are those whom death will find in Your most holy will, for the second death shall do them no harm."

When the song had faded, the room had grown silent except for weeping. Curled upon himself, Elia had heard Francesco praying, "With a loud voice, I cried to the Lord; with a loud voice I beseeched the Lord."

Why had Elia so inanely interrupted his prayer? "Oh, kind father, your sons will now be without a father, and will be deprived of the true light of their eyes!" he had pleaded, not just for the others but for himself. Francesco had been light in Elia's darkness. Where would he find light without Francesco? He'd spoken as minister general. "Remember the orphans you are leaving behind. Forgive all their faults, and gladden them all, whether present or absent, with your holy blessing."

In his weakness, Francesco had spoken softly, "See, my son, I am being called by God. I forgive all my brothers, present and absent, all their faults and offenses, and I absolve them insofar as I am able. When you give them this message, bless them all for me."

Weakly, Francesco had then asked Elia to read the Gospel of John beginning at "Six days before the Passover . . . ," the very passage Elia had been thinking that he ought to read. Marveling, he'd opened the Scriptures to that very passage. Sensing the Holy Spirit's urgency, he'd read until reaching the verse, "and bowing his head, he gave up his spirit" when Francesco had interrupted. "Cover me with sackcloth and ashes, for soon I am to become dust and ashes."

Quickly the brothers had laid a length of goat's hair cloth on the ground. Rufino sprinkled ashes on it in the shape of a cross. Angelo and Leone had lifted Francesco and laid him on it.

The shallow breaths had grown more shallow. Elia had not been able to tell the exact moment when they had ceased.

In his mind, he'd seen Francesco's soul, bright and fiery as the sun, large as the moon, cradled on a cloud and blowing upward over many waters.

Now as he sat here with his fellow mourners, *The Praises of the Lord* rang in Elia's memory. "Most High, all-powerful, good Lord . . . Praised be You, my Lord, with all Your creatures, especially Sir Brother Sun . . . through Sister Moon . . . through Brother Wind, and through the air, cloudy and serene . . . through Sister Water . . . through Brother Fire . . . through our Sister Mother Earth." All these creatures seemed part of Elia's vision.

As minister general, Elia would have to tell Assisi that Francesco was dead. He would have to tell Chiara and her sisters. He would have to send word to the brothers in distant hermitages. However, they should not see Francesco like this, in a shabby, soiled tunic. This was no way to respect the body of a saint. Now, while the body was still supple, the brothers would remove the filthy bandages that Francesco insisted should cover his wounds. They would bathe the body and clothe it in the new tunic the brothers had just made from Madonna Jacopa's undyed woolen cloth. They would place the plump, red cushion back under Francesco's head and cover his gaunt face with Madonna Jacopa's veil. The length of red embroidered linen that she had brought would serve as a pall to cover his coffin, which the brothers had made weeks ago. When all was ready, Elia would send word.

NOTES

This chapter follows closely accounts given in 1C (first book, chapters VII–IX), AC (sections 12–14), and 2C (second book, chapters CLXII and CLXIII). AC (section 113) records Francesco's words about choosing Lady Poverty. His frequently giving away his tunic is a theme in all the histories. See especially 2C (second book, chapters LII, LIV, LV, LVI, LVII, LIX).

127

Messer Girolamo di Giovanni di Gualterio

Porziuncula, Assisi (Early Morning, October 4, 1226)

Messer Girolamo di Giovanni di Gualterio, along with other knights of Assisi, had been standing watch over Francesco ever since they had brought him by litter from Bagnara to the Porziuncula about a month ago. No matter that the air in Bagnara was supposed to heal ills, Francesco had developed dropsy, and everyone knew that death could follow quickly. So the podestà had sent the knights to escort Francesco back to Assisi to guard him until he died and to secure his relics so that no one could steal them.

Girolamo's job was almost done. The body was bathed and dressed in a fresh tunic. Soon Francesco would be buried high up in a sealed coffin in the Church of San Giorgio, where he had been schooled as a boy. His relics would be safe.

Girolamo had known Francesco as a youth, fellow knight, and then crazed penitent. Four decades of memories and emotions swirled through his mind, but Francesco's recent admonition in Satriano seemed the climax. In escorting Francesco back to Assisi, the cavalcade of knights had passed through tiny Satriano, where a man had welcomed Francesco and his brothers for a meal. However, the host hadn't had enough food to feed the cavalcade, so the knights had attempted unsuccessfully to buy provisions. Disgruntled, they'd returned to Francesco and joked with him. "Brother, you must give us some of your alms, because we can find nothing to buy."

Girolamo had expected Francesco to say, "Of course. Surely our host will have something for you." Instead he'd reprimanded them. "You didn't find anything because you trust in your flies, that is, in your coins, and not in God."

The rebuke had stung.

"But go back to the houses where you went when you were looking for things to buy, and do not be ashamed, and ask them for alms for the love of God."

Beg? Girolamo had never begged in his life.

"The Holy Spirit will inspire them, and you will find abundance."

So, embarrassed to beg but equally embarrassed to disregard a saint's command, the knights had begged. Amazingly, they'd received ample food.

Girolamo looked into the freshly washed face of the corpse. Trust in God, not in money. That summed up Francesco's life. "Seek first the kingdom of God and all these things will be given you besides." So Jesus had said. So Francesco had done. Girolamo was kneeling by the body of a man who had, in some fashion, known Jesus. Boldly he touched the raised bump in Francesco's right hand, moving it with his finger. How like a nail of flesh! The wound in Francesco's right side was beside him, exposed through the cut Fra Elia had made in the tunic. Reverently Girolamo probed the supple wound with his finger. How this must have hurt when Francesco was alive! When, at Francesco's request, the brothers had laid him naked on the ground, he had covered this wound with his left hand and said, "I have done what is mine; may Christ teach you what is yours."

That was the secret of Francesco's life. Learning what God wanted and then doing it, accepting the wounds that it brought. *May You show me my way, my Lord,* Girolamo prayed, *and may You give me the grace to walk it.*

NOTES

AC (section 96) discusses the cavalcade of unnamed knights, their commission to guard Francesco, and Francesco's admonition to them to beg. Assisi annals record

Messer Girolamo di Giovanni as an eyewitness to the stigmata. Fortini (p. 620) states that he was a well-educated city magistrate and knight, so he could have been a knight in the cavalcade.

2C (second book, chapter CLXII) records Francesco's words, "I have done what is mine."

Part Twenty

"He Regards Himself the More Worthless and Esteems Himself Less Than All the Others"

128

Count Orlando di Chiusi

Monte La Verna, Chiusi (Fall 1227)

Before Francesco died, Count Orlando had been to La Verna at least twice yearly to inspect the rude hermitages that his servants had constructed for the brothers. On this unseasonably warm November day, he was making his first visit since Francesco's death. Earlier his grief had been too intense to return.

Francesco. Gone. Why hadn't Orlando appreciated him more? Listened to him more? Talked with him more? Invited him more often to dinner?

Busyness. Orlando's perennial excuse. He'd always be busy. Why had he let busyness distract him from sanctity? Whom else was he too busy for?

Orlando sent his squire to inspect the brothers' hermitages. He wanted to inspect Francesco's hermitage alone. He swallowed, his hard grief clogging his throat like a huge chunk of unchewed cheese. Tethering his steed, Orlando resolutely walked across a bridge of three downed tree trunks spanning a deep crevice to Francesco's hermitage, flush against the trunk of a gigantic fir.

The hermitage was sagging.

Orlando pushed open the rude door of woven branches. It scratched inward, sending up a little cloud of dried leaves from the packed earth floor. Off to one side was a longer, thicker pile of leaves. A bed? And here on a table beside the door, a small clay cup.

The place was desolate. Dead. Like Francesco. A sob pushed past the lump in his throat. He, here, with his wealth, pride, busyness, and sins. He was desecrating a holy house.

Scratch. Rustle.

Instinctively Orlando reached for a dagger that he, as a penitent, no longer wore. Vulnerable without a weapon, he swung open the door. Across the crevice, his palfrey and that of his squire waited lazily. The squire was standing on a log, inspecting the roof of one of the hermitages.

Scratch. Buzz. Rustle.

Something was here. There. The cup.

The cup was filled with honeycomb.

Orlando laughed at his skittishness as a bee emerged from the honeycomb and flew through a crack in the hermitage wall.

He remembered Francesco's plea. "Put out wine and honey to help sustain your bees through winter." Up here, winter was harsh. The bees would die in that cup.

The solution came swiftly. He would send his squire back to Chiusi to build another hive while Orlando remained here. At dusk, when the bees would have returned to the cup and settled down, Orlando would wrap the cup in his mantle and carry it across the fissure. He would tether his steed in a hermitage and build a fire outside to ward off predators. Like the brothers, he'd sleep on leaves, and, when morning came, he'd return home, carrying the wrapped cup with him. His beekeeper would unwrap the cup over a smoking pot to calm the bees, then put the cup into the new hive so that the sweetness of Francesco's honey would remain at Chiusi. The cup, minus the bees, he'd keep in memory of his saintly friend.

NOTES

The opening quotation for Part Twenty is from Francesco *Admonition* XII.

2C (second book, chapter CXXVIII) mentions the finding of bees in a cup, which Francesco used in a cell on a mountain. No other details are given. 1C (first book, chapter XXIX) describes how Francesco wanted wine and honey placed in hives in the winter to sustain the bees.

129

Prassede

Hermitage, Rome (March 1228)

Prassede pushed her aging body up the ladder to the loft of her hermitage where she stored an extra basket. Her old basket was finally beyond mending. She hated to discard anything of utility, but there comes a time . . .

Where was that extra basket? Not here where she kept rushes to repair her broom. Over there was extra grain. Where?

Whoops! Suddenly her left foot slipped over the side of the ledge, and she fell to the floor. She knew at once, by the pain that knifed through her foot and thigh, that her left leg was broken and maybe in more than one place. She needed help. She tried to drag herself to the window. Pain ripped through her left shoulder. Was that broken, too?

Prassede couldn't move. She was trapped. If no one discovered her, she would die.

How many people had insisted that she accept the assistance of some religious women? It was imprudent, they asserted, for her to live alone. She had steadfastly refused even when a cardinal—what was his name?—ordered her to get help.

Now she was forced to admit that she was a prideful, sinful, stubborn old woman. God was entirely justified in letting her die.

She had vowed—how long ago?—to live in solitude for the rest of her life to better communicate with God. Her simple lifestyle freed her to pray and to listen to, counsel, and advise others, to eat what they brought her, to want nothing more.

She wore the habit of penance, given to her by that holy man Francesco from some place up north. Even he had told her to accept some help. And then she was younger. Now he was dead, and she had heard that the new pope, whoever he was, was going to declare Francesco a saint. Francesco was working miracles all over. Why not work one for her? But, if he did, she'd have to change her way of life. She could no longer be alone. If he healed her, she'd lose her solitude.

My holy father, you so kindly respond anywhere to the needs of so many whom you did not know while you were in the flesh, why do you not help me in my misery since I merited your sweet favor while you were alive? As you can see, blessed father, I must either change my promised way of life or submit to a death sentence.

Over and over she prayed and wept until, entirely spent, she could remain awake no longer.

She saw Francesco, clothed in white, looking exactly as he had when he'd spoken with her about the spiritual life and given her a tunic and cord of penance.

"Get up, beloved daughter. Get up and do not fear. Receive the sign of complete healing and keep your promise intact!" Her spiritual father, younger than she, took her hand, the one not attached to her throbbing shoulder, and lifted her up. She turned to look at him, but he was gone.

She was standing. On one foot. But standing. Holding on to her furniture, she hopped to the window, took a length of undyed cloth from the sill and tied it to the iron bars over the opening. It flapped in the wind.

Almost instantaneously a monk from the nearby monastery knocked at her door.

Was she still dreaming?

"Light the fire," she told him. Feeling the warmth of the flames would prove that she was awake. Yet how could she be awake? She could feel no pain.

NOTES

3C (chapter XVII) relates the general outline of Prassede's story. Her prayer and Francesco's words are quoted directly from Celano's account.

130

Fra Elia di Bonbarone

Colle d'Inferno, Assisi (Early Morning, April 1228)

In the early morning half-light, just after praying the Office of Prime, Fra Elia di Bonbarone had mounted his palfrey and started out from the Porziuncula toward Assisi. Now, as the sun was rising, he could see the distant Colle d'Inferno. Ribbons of smoke rose from the burning garbage. Soon he would smell the stench.

In the saddle pouch were his carefully drawn plans for a massive basilica to honor Francesco, to be built on the Colle. Elia had seen similar structures when he was custos of Syria. He had been commissioned by Pope Gregorio IX, the former Cardinal Ugolino dei Conti di Segni, to erect a similar structure to honor Francesco, whose canonization Gregorio planned for July 16, the day before he would lay the first stone for the basilica. The deed to this massive garbage heap, donated by Messer Simone Puzarelli, had just been signed. Today Elia could begin to eradicate the dump.

As Elia drew nearer, he heard the shouts of workmen he'd hired. Stroking his black beard flecked with gray, he imagined Francesco cavorting before him.

Francesco, this basilica will summarize your life. It will be the shape of a tau, your favorite cross, with the shaft pointing to Assisi. The crossbar will point toward the Porziuncula in one direction and, in the other, toward the cave where you and

I prayed. Francesco, you see yourself as a garbage heap, but the world knows you as a saint. Your eternal penance is to accept your fame.

NOTES

Information for this chapter comes from John Moorman, *A History of the Franciscan Order*, pp. 85–86.

Select Bibliography

Over 800 references were consulted in the writing of this book. The primary print sources are as follows, divided into the following categories: translations of Francis' writings, early histories and biographies, biographies, Franciscan studies, articles, and other resources. A few internet sources are listed at the end.

Translations of Francis' Writings and Early Histories and Biographies

Francis of Assisi: Early Documents. Edited by Regis J. Armstrong, OFM Cap., J. A. Wayne Hellmann, OFM Conv., and William J. Short, OFM. Hyde Park, New York: New City Press (The Franciscan Institute of Saint Bonaventure University, Saint Bonaventure, NY). Vol. 1: *The Saint* (1999); Vol. 2: *The Founder* (2000); Vol. 3: *The Prophet* (2001); *Index* (2002). This includes: *The Life of Saint Francis* by Friar Thomas of Celano; *The Anonymous of Perugia* by Friar John of Perugia; *The Legend of the Three Companions* by Friars Leo, Angelo, and Rufino; *The Assisi Compilation* seemingly compiled by Friars Leo, Angelo, and Rufino and possibly others, and *The Remembrance of the Desire of a Soul* by Friar Thomas of Celano.

Early Histories and Biographies

Arnald of Sarrant. *Chronicles of the Twenty-Four Generals of the Order of Friars Minor*. Translated by Noel Muscat, OFM. Malta: TAU Franciscan Communications, 2010.

Dalarun, Jacques. *The Rediscovered Life of Saint Francis of Assisi by Thomas of Celano*. Translated by Timothy J. Johnson. Saint Bonaventure, NY: Franciscan Institute Publications, 2016.

Thirteenth Century Chronicles. Translated by Placid Hermann, OFM. Chicago, IL: Franciscan Herald Press, 1961.

Biographies

Brunette, Pierre, OFM. *Francis of Assisi and His Conversions*. Translated by Paul Lachance, OFM, and Kathryn Krug. Quincy, IL: Franciscan Press, 1997.

Cook, William R. and Ronald B. Herzman. "Francis of Assisi." The Teaching Company: Course no. 615, 2000.

Cunningham, Lawrence S. *Francis of Assisi: Performing the Gospel Life*. Grand Rapids, MI: William B. Eerdmans Publishing Co., 2004.

Dalarun, Jacques. *The Misadventure of Francis of Assisi: Toward a Historical Use of the Franciscan Legends*. Translated by Edward Hagman, OFM Cap. Saint Bonaventure, NY: Franciscan Institute Publications, 2002.

De la Bédoyère, Michael. *Francis of Assisi: The Man Who Found Perfect Joy*. Manchester, NH: Sophia Institute Press, 1962, 1999.

Englebert, Omer. *Saint Francis of Assisi: A Biography*. Ann Arbor, MI: Servant Books, 1965.

Felder, Hilarin, OFM Cap. *The Knight-Errant of Assisi*. Translated by Berchmans Bittle, OFM Cap. Milwaukee, WI: The Bruce Publishing Company, 1948.

Fioretti (*The Little Flowers of Saint Francis* [and other works]). Translated by Raphael Brown. Garden City, NY: 1958.

Fortini, Arnaldo. *Francis of Assisi*. Translation of *Nova Vita di San Francesco* by Helen Moak. New York: Crossroad Publishing Company, 1981.

Frugoni, Chiara. *Francis of Assisi*. New York: Continuum Publishing Company, 1998.

Gobry, Ivan. *Saint Francis of Assisi*. San Francisco: Ignatius Press, 2006.

House, Adrian. *Francis of Assisi: A Revolutionary Life*. London: Random House, 2001.

Jörgensen, Johannes. *Saint Francis of Assisi.* Garden City, NY: Longmans, Green & Company, 1912.

Julian, Helen, CSF. *Francis and Clare: A Gospel Story*. Ijamsville, MD: The Word Among Us Press, 2005.

Le Goff, Jacques. *Saint Francis of Assisi*. Translated by Christine Rhone. New York: Routledge, 2004.

Manselli, Raoul. *Saint Francis of Assisi*. Chicago, IL: Franciscan Herald Press, 1988.

McMichaels, Susan W. *Journey out of the Garden: Saint Francis of Assisi and the Process of Individuation*. New York: Paulist Press, 1997.

Mercuri, Chiara. *Francis of Assisi: The Hidden Story*. Translated by Robert J. Edmonson, C. J. Brewster, MA: San Damiano Books, Paraclete Press, 2019.

Merlo, Grado Giovanni. *In the Name of Saint Francis: History of the Friars Minor and Franciscanism until the Early Sixteenth Century*. Translated by Raphael Bonnano, OFM. Ed. Robert J. Karris, OFM, and Jean-François Godet-Calogeras. Saint Bonaventure, NY: Franciscan Institute Publications, 2009.

Moses, Paul. *The Saint and the Sultan: The Crusades, Islam, and Francis of Assisi's Mission of Peace*. New York: Doubleday, 2009.

Mueller, Joan. *Francis: The Saint of Assisi: A Novel.* Hyde Park, NY: New City Press, 2010.

Nugent, Madeline Pecora. *Chiara: A Story of Saint Clare of Assisi*. Boston, MA: Pauline Books and Media, 2022.

______. *Antonio: A Story of Saint Anthony of Padua*. Boston, MA: Pauline Books and Media, 2022.

Rega, Frank M. *Saint Francis of Assisi and the Conversion of the Muslims*. Rockford, IL: TAN Books and Publishers, 2007.

Saints and Blessed of the Three Orders of Saint Francis. Translated from the *Auréole Sèraphique* of the Very Rev. Father Leon. Taunton, England: The Franciscan Convent, 1885, "Saint Viridiana," vol. 1, pp. 239–249. "Blessed Luchesio, or Lucius," vol. II, pp. 131–137.

Short, William OFM. "Saint Francis of Assisi: A New Way of Being Christian." Now You Know Media, 2007.

Spoto, Donald. *Reluctant Saint: The Life of Francis of Assisi*. New York: Penguin Group, 2002.

Sweeney, Jon M. *The Enthusiast: How the Best Friend of Francis of Assisi Almost Destroyed What He Started*. Notre Dame, IN: Ave Maria Press, 2016.

Tamassia, Nino. *Saint Francis of Assisi and His Legend*. Translated by Lonsdale Ragg. London: T. Fisher Unwin, 1910.

Thoman, Bret, SFO. *The Road to Peace in Assisi: Following Francis and Clare in the Footsteps of the Lesser Christ*. Self-published through lulu.com, 2010.

Thompson, Augustine, OP. *Francis of Assisi: A New Biography*. London: Cornell University Press, 2012.

Timmermans, Felix. *The Perfect Joy of Saint Francis: A Biographical Novel*. Translated by Raphael Brown. Garden City, NY: Image Books, 1955.

Tolan, John. *Saint Francis and the Sultan: The Curious History of a Christian-Muslim Encounter*. Oxford: Oxford University Press, 2009.

Vauchez, André. *Francis of Assisi: The Life and Afterlife of a Medieval Saint*. Translated by Michael F. Cusato. New Haven, CT: Yale University Press, 2012.

Von Matt, Leonard and Hauser, Walter. *Saint Francis of Assisi: A Pictorial Biography*. Translated by Sebastian Bullough, OP. Chicago, IL: Henry Regnery Company, 1956.

Vorreux, Damien. *First Encounter with Francis of Assisi*. Translated by Paul Schwartz and Paul LaChance. Ed. Jean-François Godet-Calogeras. Saint Bonaventure, NY: Franciscan Institute Publications, 2012.

Franciscan Studies

Barone, Giulia. "Brother Elias Revisited." *Greyfriars Review*, vol. 13, Supplement, pp. 1–64. Trans. by Giles Bello, OFM, from "I Compagni di Francisco e la prima generazione Minoritica," Atti del XIX Convegno international, Assisi, 17–19 Ottobre 1991, 61–80.

Blastic, Michael W., OFM. *A Study of the Rule of 1223: History, Exegesis and Reflection.* New York, New York: Ongoing Formation Committee, Franciscan Friars of the Holy Name Province, 2008.

Brooke, Rosalind B. *Early Franciscan Government: Elias to Bonaventure.* Cambridge: University Press, 1959.

Cusato, Michael F. "Of Snakes and Angels: The Mystical Experience Behind the Stigmatization Narrative." *The Stigmata of Francis of Assisi: New Studies, New Perspectives.* Saint Bonaventure, NY: Franciscan Institute Publications, 2006, pp. 29–74.

______. *The Early Franciscan Movement (1205–1239): History, Sources, and Hermeneutics.* Spoleto, Italy: Fondazione Centro italiano di studi sull'alto Medioevo, 2009.

Dalarun, Jacques. *Francis of Assisi and Power.* Saint Bonaventure, NY: Franciscan Institute Publications, 2007.

______. "The Great Secret of Francis." *The Stigmata of Francis of Assisi: New Studies, New Perspectives.* Saint Bonaventure, NY: Franciscan Institute Publications, 2006, pp. 9–26.

Delio, Ilia, OSF. "A Franciscan View of Creation: Learning to Live in a Sacramental World." *Franciscan Heritage Series*, vol. 2. Saint Bonaventure, NY: The Franciscan Institute, 2003.

Desbonnets, Théophile. *From Intuition to Institution: The Franciscans.* Translated by Paul Duggan and Jerry Du Charme. Chicago, IL: Franciscan Herald Press, 1988.

de Zoete, Beryl. *Homes of the First Franciscans in Umbria, the Borders of Tuscany and the Northern Marches.* Original Publication 1906? Reprinted by HardPress Publishing, Miami FL, n.d.

Esser, Cajetan, OFM. *Origins of the Franciscan Order.* Translated by Aedan Daly, OFM, and Dr. Irina Lynch. Chicago, IL: Franciscan Herald Press, 1970.

Felder, Hilarin, OFM Cap. *The Ideals of Saint Francis of Assisi.* Translated by Berchmans Bittle, OFM Cap. New York: Benzinger Brothers, 1925.

Flood, David, OFM. *The Daily Labor of the Early Franciscans.* Saint Bonaventure, NY: The Franciscan Institute, 2010.

———. *Work for Everyone: Francis of Assisi and the Ethic of Service.* Quezon City, Philippines: CCFMC Office for Asia/Oceania, 1997.

Flood, David, OFM and Thaddée Matura, OFM. *The Birth of a Movement: A Study of the First Rule of Saint Francis.* Translated by Paul Lachance, OFM and Paul Schwartz, OFM. Chicago, IL: Franciscan Herald Press, 1975.

Fortini, Gemma. "The Noble Family of Saint Clare of Assisi." Saint Bonaventure, NY: "Franciscan Studies," The Franciscan Institute, vol. 42, Annual XX, pp. 48–65, 1982.

Franciscan Solitude. Ed. André Cirino, OFM and Josef Raischl. Saint Bonaventure, NY: The Franciscan Institute, 1995.

Francis of Assisi: History, Hagiography and Hermeneutics in the Early Documents. Ed. Jay M. Hammond. Hyde Park, NY: New City Press, 2004.

Gatti, Isidoro. *La Tomba di San Francesco nei Secoli.* Assisi: Casa Editrici Francescana, 1983, pp. 397–406.

Goonan, Michael. *The Crucifix That Spoke to Saint Francis.* Strathfield, New South Wales, Australia: Saint Paul's Publications, 2000.

Guinan, Michael D, OFM. *The Franciscan Vision and the Gospel of John.* Franciscan Heritage Series, vol. Four. Saint Bonaventure, NY: The Franciscan Institute, 2006. Hoeberichts, J. *Francis and Islam.* Quincy, IL: Franciscan Press, 1997.

Habig, Marion A., OFM, ed. *Saint Francis of Assisi: Writings and Early Biographies: English Omnibus of the Sources for the Life of Saint Francis.* Quincy, IL: Franciscan Press, 1991.

Hoeberichts, Jan. *Paradise Restored: The Social Ethics of Francis of Assisi. A Commentary on Francis' "Salutation of the Virtues."* Quincy, IL: Franciscan Press, 2004.

Isabell, Lawrence D., OFM. *The Practice and Meaning of Confession in the Primitive Franciscan Community according to the Writings of Saint Francis of Assisi and Thomas of Celano*. Assisi, Italy: Pontificia Universitas Gregoriana, 1973.

Matura, Thaddée, OFM. *Francis of Assisi: The Message in His Writings*. Translated by Paul Barrett, OFM Cap. Saint Bonaventure, NY: Franciscan Institute Publications, 2004.

______. *Francis of Assisi: Writer and Spiritual Master*. Translated by Paul Lachance, OFM. Cincinnati, OH: Saint Anthony Messenger Press, 2005.

Mitchell, Daria, OSF, ed. *Poverty and Prosperity: Franciscans and the Use of Money*. Washington Theological Union Symposium Papers 2009. Saint Bonaventure, NY: The Franciscan Institute, 2009.

Moorman, John. *A History of the Franciscan Order from Its Origins to the Year 1517*. Oxford: Clarendon Press, 1968.

______. *The Sources for the Life of St Francis of Assisi*. Manchester, England: Manchester University Press, 1940.

Muscat, Noel, OFM. *History of the Franciscan Movement: Volume 1: From the Beginnings of the Order to the Year 1517*. Online course in Franciscan History at Washington Theological Union, Washington, DC. Jerusalem: 2008.

Nguyên-Van-Khanh, Norbert, OFM. *The Teacher of His Heart: Jesus Christ in the Thought and Writings of Saint Francis*. Translated by Ed Hagman, OFM Cap. Ed. Louise Hembrecht, OSF, and Bernard R. Creighton, OFM. Saint Bonaventure, NY: The Franciscan Institute, 1994.

Pazzelli, Raffaele. *Saint Francis and the Third Order*. Chicago, IL: Franciscan Herald Press, 1989.

Pellegrini, Luigi. *I luoghi di frate Francesco. Memoria agiografica e realtà storica*. Milano, Italy: Biblioteca Francescana (January 1, 2010).

Picard, Marc, OFM Cap. *The Icon of the Christ of San Damiano*. Assisi, Italy: Casa Editrice Franciscana, 2000.

Pryds, Darleen. *Enduring Presence: Diversity and Authenticity among the First Generations of Franciscan Laity*. Franciscan Heritage Series, vol. 10. Saint Bonaventure, NY: Franciscan Institute Studies, 2018.

Rivi, Prospero. "Francis of Assisi and the Laity of His Time." Translated by Heather Tolfree. Greyfriars Review (Supplement) vol. 15, 2001.

Saggau, Elise, OSF, Ed. "True Followers of Justice: Identity, Insertion, an Itinerancy among the Early Franciscans" (vol. 10, 2000) in Margaret Carney, OSF (Ed), *Spirit and Life: A Journal of Contemporary Franciscanism*. Saint Bonaventure, NY: The Franciscan Institute, 2000.

Salvati, Carla. "The *Camoscio*: Relic of the Side Wound of Francis of Assisi, 'Living Eucharist.'" *The Stigmata of Francis of Assisi: New Studies, New Perspectives.* Saint Bonaventure, NY: Franciscan Institute Publications, 2006, pp. 75–99.

Schmucki, Octavian, OFM Cap. *The Stigmata of Saint Francis of Assisi: A Critical Investigation in the Light of Thirteenth-Century Sources.* Translated by Canisius F. Connors, OFM. Saint Bonaventure, NY: Franciscan Institute Publications, History Series 6, 1991.

Sister Frances Teresa, OSC. *Living the Incarnation: Praying with Francis and Clare of Assisi.* London: Darton, Longman and Todd Ltd, 1993. Reprint Quincy, IL: Franciscan Press, 1996.

Sorrell, Roger D. *Saint Francis of Assisi and Nature: Tradition and Innovation in Western Christian Attitudes toward the Environment*. New York: Oxford University Press, 1988.

Stewart, Robert M. "*De Illis Qui Faciunt Penitentiam*": *The Rule of the Secular Franciscan Order: Origins, Development, Interpretation*. Roma: Istituto Storico dei Cappuccini, 1991.

Todeschini, Giacomo. *Franciscan Wealth: From Voluntary Poverty to Market Society*. Translated by Donatella Melucci. Saint Bonaventure, NY: The Franciscan Institute, 2009.

Trexler, Richard C. *Naked before the Father: The Renunciation of Francis of Assisi.* New York: Peter Lang Publishing, 1989.

Ugolino dei Conti di Segni. "The First Rule of the Third Order: Here begins the Rule of the Continent Brothers and Sisters [1221]." *Saint Francis of Assisi: Writings and Early Biographies: English Omnibus of the Sources for the Life of Saint Francis*. Ed. Marion A. Habig, OFM. Quincy, IL: Franciscan Press, 1991, pp. 168–175.

Warner, Keith Douglass, OFM and Isom, John E. *Journey and Place: An Atlas of Saint Francis*. Quincy, IL: Franciscan Press, 2003.

Articles

Bigaroni, Marino, OFM. "San Damiano--Assisi: The First Church of St. Francis." Translated by Agnes Van Baer, OSC. *Franciscan Studies* 47 (1987): 45-97.

Custo, Michael F. "Of Snakes and Angels: The Mystical Experience behind the Stigmatization Narrative of 1 Celano." *The Stigmata of Francis of Assisi: New Studies, New Perspectives*. Saint Bonaventure, NY: Franciscan Institute Publications (2006): 29–74.

______. "Talking about Ourselves: The Shift in Franciscan Writing from Hagiography to History (1235–1247)." *Franciscan Studies,* vol. 58 (2000): 37–75.

D'Acunto, Nicolangelo. "Il Vescovo Guido Oppure I Vescovi Guido?" *Mélanges de l'Ecole française de Rome. Moyen âge.* vol. 108, no. 2 (1996): 479–524.

Flood, David. "Assisi's Rules and People's Needs: The Initial Determination of the Franciscan Mission." *Franziskanische Studien*, vol. 66, 91–104 (1984): nos. 91–104.

Godet-Calogeras, Jean-François, "Francis of Assisi's Resignation: An Historical and Philological Probe" in *Charisma und religiöse Gemeinshaften im Mittelalter,* edited by G. Andenna, M. Breitenstein and G. Melville (Münster: Lit, 2005), 281–300.

______. "The Autographs of Brother Francis of Assisi," in *Studies in Early Franciscan Sources, Vol. 1: The Writings of Francis of Assisi, Letters and Prayers.* (Saint Bonaventure: Franciscan Institute Publications, 2011): 51–99.

Haines, Von Keith. "The Death of Saint Francis of Assisi." *Franzickanische Studien* 58 (1976): 27–46.

Hinnebusch, William. "Poverty in the Order of Preachers." *The Catholic Historical Review* 45:4 (1960): 436–453.

Lapsanski, Duane. "The Chartula of Saint Francis of Assisi." *Archivum Franciscanum historicum: periodica publicatio trimestris cura pp Collegii D. Bonaventurae* (1974): vol. 67, 18–37.

Lethaby, W.R. "English Primitives—V: Matthew Paris and Friar William." *The Burlington Magazine for Connoisseurs*. London: The Burlington Magazine, Limited, vol. XXXI, no. CLXXII–CLXXVII. July to December 1917.

Manselli, Raoul. "We Who Were with Him: A Contribution to the Franciscan Question." *Greyfriars Review* (2000): Part 1, 5–39, Part II, 43–144.

Perroni, Ludovico. "Angelo Tancredi: il frate discrete e cortese." Basilica di San Francesco: Febbraio (1996).

Riley, Paul V. "Francis' Assisi: Its Political and Social History, 1175–1225." Saint Bonaventure, NY: Franciscan Institute, *Franciscan Studies* (1974): vol. 34, 393–424.

Robson, Michael. "Assisi, Guido II and Saint Francis." *Laurentianum* 34 (1993): 109–138. Reprinted *Greyfriars Review*, vol. 12, no. 1, 255–287.

Schatzlein, Joanne, OSF, RN, MA, and Danial P. Sulmasy, OFM, MD. "The Diagnosis of Saint Francis: Evidence for Leprosy." *Franciscan Studies*, vol. 47 (1987): pp. 181–217.

Schmucki, Octavian, OFM Cap. "Mentis Silentium: Contemplation in the Early Franciscan Order." Translated by Ignatius McCormick, OFM Cap. *Greyfriars Review*, vol. 4 (1990): no. 2, 35–69.

______. "Saint Francis' Level of Education." Translated by Paul Barrett, OFM Cap. *Greyfriars Review*, vol. 10 (1996): no. 2, 153–170.

______. "The Illnesses of Francis During the Last Years of His Life." *Greyfriars Review*, vol. 13 (1999): no. 1, 21–59.

______. "The Illnesses of Saint Francis of Assisi before His Stigmatization." *Greyfriars Review*, vol. 4 (1990): no. 3, 31–61.

______. "The Passion of Christ in the Life of Saint Francis of Assisi: A Comparative Study of the Sources in the Light of Devotion to the Passion Practiced in His Time." Translated by Ignatius McCormick, OFM Cap. *Greyfriars Review*, vol. 4, Supplement (1990).

Short, William J. "Hagiographic Method in Reading Franciscan Sources: Stories of Francis and Creatures in Thomas of Celano's 'Vita Prima' (21:58–61). Spirit and Life, vol. 10 (2000): 462–495.

Other Resources

Anthony of Padua. *Sermons for Sundays and Festivals.* Trans. Paul Spilsbury. Padova, Italia: Messaggero di Sant'Antonio Editrice, 2007.

Bouchard, Constance Brittain, Chief Consultant. *Knights in History and Legend*. Buffalo, NY: Firefly Books, 2009.

Bynum, Caroline Walker. *Holy Feast and Holy Fast: The Religious Significance of Food to Medieval Women.* Berkeley and Los Angeles, CA: University of California Press, 1987.

Capellanus, Andreas. *The Art of Courtly Love.* New York: Columbia University Press, 1960.

Cattoi, Thomas and Christopher M. Moreman, eds. *Death, Dying, and Mysticism: The Ecstasy of the End*. New York: Palgrave Macmillan, 2015.

D'Acunto, Nicolangelo. *Assisi nel Medioevo: Studi di storia ecclesiastica e civile.* Assisi: Accademia Properziana del Subasio, 2002.

Dalby, Andrew. *Geoponika (Farm Work): A Modern Translation of the Roman and Byzantine Farming Handbook*. Devon: Prospect Books, 2011.

Donovan, Joseph P. *Pelagius and the Fifth Crusade*. Philadelphia, PA: University of Pennsylvania Press, 1950.

Favazza, Joseph A. *The Order of Penitents: Historical Roots and Pastoral Future.* Collegeville, MN: The Liturgical Press, 1988.

Frugoni, Chiara. *A Day in a Medieval City*. Translated by William McCuaig. Chicago, IL: University of Chicago Press, 1997.

Gies, Frances and Joseph. *Daily Life in Medieval Times: A vivid, detailed account of birth, marriage and death; food, clothing and housing; love and labor in*

Europe of the Middle Ages. New York: Black Dog & Leventhal Publishers, 1990.

Gordon, Lina Duff. *The Story of Assisi*. London: J. M. Dent & Co., 1902.

Harpur, James. *The Crusades: An Illustrated History*. New York: Thunders Mouth Press, 2005.

Hoge, Charles W., MD, Colonel US Army (Ret). *Once a Warrior, Always a Warrior: Navigating the Transition from Combat to Home including Combat Stress, PTSD, and mTBI*. Guilford, CT: Globe Pequot Press, 2010.

Kaeuper, Richard W. and Elspeth Kennedy, *The Book of Chivalry of Geoffroi de Charny*. Philadelphia, PA: University of Pennsylvania Press, 1996.

Lamb, Susan, and Tom Bean, *The Natural World of Saint Francis of Assisi: Landscapes, Plants, & Animals That Saint Francis Knew & Loved*. Phoenix, AZ: Tau Publishing, 2009.

Lives of the Saints and Blesseds of the Three Orders of Saint Francis. Translated from the *Auréole Séraphique* of the Very Rev. Father Leon. Taunton, England: The Franciscan Convent, 1885.

Magilton, John, Frances Lee, and Anthea Boylston, eds. *"Lepers outside the gate": Excavations at the Cemetery of the Hospital of Saint James and Saint Mary Magdalene, Chichester, 1986–97 and 1993*. Chichester Excavations 10, CBA Research Report 158, Council for British Archaeology, 2008. York, England: Saint Mary's House, 2008.

Malory, Sir Thomas. *Le Morte d'Arthur*. Adapted by Keith Banes. New York: Penguin Books, 2001 (c. 1962).

Manchester, William. *A World Lit Only by Fire: The Medieval Mind and the Renaissance: Portrait of an Age*. Boston, MA: Little, Brown, and Company, 1992.

Richards, Peter. *The Medieval Leper and His Northern Heirs*. New York: Barnes & Noble, 1977.

Rowling, Marjorie. *Life in Medieval Times*. New York: Paragon Books, 1979.

Seton, Walter W. *Blessed Giles of Assisi*. Manchester, England: The University Press, 1918.

Shah, Idries. *The Sufis*. Garden City, NY: Anchor Books (Doubleday & Company), 1971.

Thompson, Augustine, OP. *Cities of God: The Religion of the Italian Communes 1124–1325*. University Park, PA: The Pennsylvania State University Press, 2005.

Tick, Edward, PhD. *War and the Soul: Healing Our Nation's Veterans from Post-traumatic Stress Disorder*. Wheaton, IL: Theosophical Publishing House, 2005.

Toledo, José Sánchez. *Medieval Knights: The Age of Chivalry*. Madrid: Andrea Press, 2008.

Vardey, Lucinda. *Traveling with the Saints in Italy: Contemporary Pilgrimages on Ancient Paths*. Mahwah, NJ: Hidden Springs (an imprint of Paulist Press), 2005.

Vauchez, André. *The Laity in the Middle Ages: Religious Beliefs and Devotional Practices*. Translated by Margery J. Schneider. Edited by Daniel E. Bornstein. Notre Dame, IN: University of Notre Dame Press, 1993.

Veronensis, Bonifacius. "Eulistea." Edited by F. Bonaini A. Fabretti, and F. Polidori, "Archivo Storico Italiano" 16, 1 (1850), pp. 1–52.

Internet Sources

Much information was gleaned from the Internet for various topics such as birds of Umbria, Jacoba dei Settesoli, symptoms of malaria, Francis' Nativity at Greccio, etc.

Google Earth provided invaluable information regarding distances and details of places in the life of Saint Francis including Ottiano, San Leo, Poggibonsi, Rome, Greccio, Assisi, and others.

YouTube has many videos of medieval songs, ballads, dress, and dance of the period.

The few sources listed below are those which the reader may not necessarily discover.

Grotta di Cinicchio:

http://cultura.ilsentierodiarmenzano.it/grotta-di-cinicchio/

Presepe vivente a Greccio, il primo della storia. 14 Dicembre 2013

https://www.buonviaggioitalia.it/c22-eventi/presepe-vivente-a-greccio-il-primo-dela-storia.

A wonderful online resource, which provides in a searchable format many of the writings and early biographies of Saint Francis and Saint Clare:

https://www.franciscantradition.org/early-sources.

Also by Madeline Pecora Nugent

Continue your journey through early Franciscan history with these new editions of Madeline Nugent's accounts of the lives of Saint Clare and Saint Anthony. Available at www.paulinestore.org.

CHIARA

A Story of Saint Clare of Assisi

0-8198-1686-8

384 pages

ANTONIO

A Story of Saint Anthony of Padua

0-8198-0878-4

384 pages

A mission of the Daughters of St. Paul

As apostles of Jesus Christ,
evangelizing today's world:

We are CALLED to holiness
by God's living Word and Eucharist.

We COMMUNICATE the Gospel message
through our lives and through all
available forms of media.

We SERVE the Church
by responding to the hopes and needs
of all people with the Word of God,
in the spirit of St. Paul.

For more information visit us at:
www.pauline.org